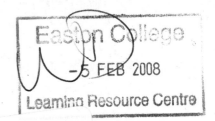

Professional Landscape Management

Second Edition

David L. Hensley
University of Arkansas

ISBN 1-58874-374-8

Published by

STIPES PUBLISHING L.L.C.
204 W. University
Champaign, Illinois 61820

For
Glenda

Acknowledgments

I must thank a number of people for their support, encouragement, and help with the second edition of this book. I can never adequately thank my wife Glenda for her patience, understanding, and support during the development of the first edition and the initial efforts on the revision. She proofread manuscripts many times, always without complaint. Unfortunately, she did not see the final product; she passed away in 2002 from ALS (Lou Gehrig's disease). I dedicate this book to her memory.

I want to thank Kimberly Hensley for her love and support in finishing this project. Her expertise in herbaceous annuals and perennials was invaluable.

I want to thank my children, Erin, Josh, Brooke, Rob, Jessica, and Noah who provided their love and encouragement.

I deeply thank Heather Quinney for her proof reading and editing skills.

Many professional landscape managers, too many to list, provided the expertise that appear in these pages. Many former students contributed information and ideas over the years. Thank you.

Former colleagues and forever friends Roch Gaussoin, Jim Robbins and David Suddarth contributed more than they will ever realize. Thank you.

David L. Hensley

2004

Table of Contents

Introduction

Landscape management has evolved from pick-up truck pseudoscience to a highly sophisticated, fully integrated business that embraces the most sophisticated technology and well trained employees. The 1980's spawned corporate and residential landscapes that demand (dictated) professional landscape management services. The industry grew at a more rapid pace than the educational materials necessary to undergird the art and science. Integrated information is scant and has never been available in a single, holistic reference.

Enter Dr. David Hensley, friend, horticultural colleague, teacher, researcher and contributing editor to *Nursery Manager*. Over the years, I read Dave's lively, entertaining and educational articles with great interest. His pen spoke clearly, with great knowledge and integrity. The Landscape Management field needed a broad encompassing reference, and Dave agreed to the responsibility. He has spent the past five years researching, collating, writing, proofing and rewriting. From my personal experiences with book writing, I told Dave it was a love/hate affair. He crossed the fence many times during the book's development but stayed with the course. His literary journey has resulted in a reference and teaching text that has no parallel in the field.

Dave brought outside experts to bear on the final product, traveled extensively during sabbatical and reviewed thousands of landscape management and maintenance articles. The chapter on *specifications and contracts* provides superb guidance for the preparation of documents that translates to a successful or unsuccessful business. The *fertilization* chapter brings functional, pragmatic information to an area of landscape management that has been treated as voodoo horticulture. *Color in the landscape* is now an integrated part of professional grounds maintenance. Firms have hired full-time color coordinators to manage the design, layout and planting of the displays. Dave brings much needed, up-to-date information to this relatively new area.

Professional Landscape Management was written by a professional for professionals. The book is eminently readable and enjoyable because Dave injects his unique style of humor into the text. This reference will enjoy subsequent fruitful editions and become the standard in the field by which others are judged. Few books withstand the tests of scrutinization and time. Dr. David Hensley has produced such a reference.

Michael A. Dirr

Introduction to the Second Edition

Dave Hensley's wonderful book on landscape management and maintenance is the result of his lifelong passion for the profession. Dave has lived and loved the subject throughout his career from graduate work in the subject under Phil Carpenter at Purdue to a distinguished teaching and research career at Kansas State, the University of Hawaii, and others. I edited Dave's first edition and believed then that he captured the pulse and heartbeat of the industry more thoroughly than anyone who previously addressed the subject. Dave engaged specialists to assist with specific chapters like contracts and turfgrasses. He melded these with his expertise to produce this most holistic and focused reference. This new edition adds invaluable up-to-date information on all facets of landscape management and maintenance. For the student and practitioner, this is the reference of necessity.

Michael A. Dirr
Professor
University of Georgia

Preface

Landscape management is the most challenging field in ornamental horticulture. The true *landscape manager* must be knowledgeable about landscape design, plant materials and turfgrasses, soils, plant nutrition, culture and maintenance, the identification and control of pests, chemical use and misuse, and the ability to use and repair all types of landscape equipment. Additionally, every day the landscape manager faces challenges directing and supervising employees, managing a budget and/or keeping the business afloat, and dealing with owners, managers, sales representatives, customers, and clients. The landscape professional must also wade through the endless mire of taxes, regulations, and government mandates. It is a tough job.

Over the many years I have taught landscape management to horticulture and landscape architecture students, I have tried to expose students to the multifaceted aspects of landscape management as a profession, an art, a science, and a business. I found no text that satisfied my needs. Many excellent books provided the nuts and bolts of maintaining plants or turf. None, however, treated landscape management as a business. This was the motivation for the first edition of this book.

Landscape architects must produce specifications and contracts. They must know something about maintaining plants before producing requirements for others to follow. Landscape managers must efficiently provide the highest quality care for the plants and everything else on and in the landscape. They must also budget and price work for a profit, if they are to remain employed or in business. Too often texts and references deal only with discrete plant-oriented landscape units: turfgrass; trees; shrubs; or flowers. Landscape managers and landscape designers must deal with developing and maintaining the landscape as the sum of all of its parts. Each aspect of maintaining a landscape is interrelated with others.

I have tried to develop a text that provides a survey of business, personnel, and profit-oriented topics, as well as considering techniques and technology for properly managing landscape plants. No single edition, however, could adequately cover the depth and breadth of information that is landscape management.

The motivation for the second edition of this book was to bring it up to date. A great deal has happened in the past 10 years.

During research for both editions of the book I have had the opportunity to meet landscape professionals across the country and to visit many well-maintained landscape sites. I spent a great deal of time reading journals, trade magazines, and books that had accumulated over the past few years. Writing this book the first time was the most time consuming effort I had ever undertaken. Revising it was the second most time consuming project in my professional career.

The information, techniques, and thoughts are the products of a long and satisfying career in landscape horticulture; my hope is that this book will be valuable and thought provoking to students and landscape professionals alike.

About the Author

· Professor and Head, Department of Horticulture, University of Arkansas since 2000.

· Professor and Chair, Department of Landscape Architecture and Horticulture, Temple University, Ambler Campus 1999 to 2000.

· Professor and Extension Landscape Specialist, Department of Horticulture, University of Hawaii 1992 to 1999.

· Associate Professor, Department of Horticulture, Kansas State University;

· Developed and taught undergraduate courses in landscape design, landscape contracting, and landscape management.

· Research programs in landscape installation and management technology and problems.

· Extension experience with the green industry in Missouri, Kentucky, and Hawaii.

· Published more than 40 scientific articles and over 200 trade and popular articles.

· Professional experience in designing, installing, and maintaining landscapes. Superintendent of Purdue Horticulture Park for three years. Consultant for landscape management of Hickam Air Force Base.

· B.S., University of Missouri; M.S. and Ph.D., Purdue University (Dr. Philip Carpenter, major professor).

Chapter 1
Introduction

Landscape management is the art, science, and skill employed by professionals who maintain all or any part of the exterior environment. Most professionals in the field prefer the term *management*, rather than maintenance. Management, in addition to having a more professional appeal, more correctly describes the responsibilities. Landscape managers are involved with much more than maintaining the plants in a landscape. They are responsible for everything within the site: plants, animals, and the inanimate. The true landscape supervisor is a manager of people, time, equipment, and money. He/she certainly does more than merely mow the grass and trim the shrubs. This text, and most in the profession, will use landscape management and landscape maintenance interchangeably. Either is meant to convey the vocation in the highest professional light.

History

The management of landscapes has been conducted for as long as there have been gardens. Adam was the first landscape maintenance contractor to be fired off of a job. During the dim reaches of history, slaves sometimes maintained gardens for the aristocracy. The landscape contractor, I suppose, was the slave driver. According to many, some things have not changed that much.

Private estates were and continue to be maintained by skilled gardeners. In the past, gardeners began as apprentices and, with time and skill, became head gardeners or superintendents. These *men* usually worked for the same estate their entire life. The position was often passed to their sons. The number of elaborate private gar-

Photo 1.1. Good landscape management improves the appearance, environment and quality of public and private grounds. Quality management need not be expensive, but it does require knowledge, care, planning, appropriate design, and a budget appropriate for the needs and desires of the client. Photograph courtesy of James Robbins.

Photo 1.2. Historically, developed landscapes in Europe and America, such as the Vaux le Vicomte, were found only at the estates of the aristocracy and the very rich. Photograph by George Anderson.

1

dens in the United States and Europe declined dramatically during the 1930s due to the Depression and inheritance taxes.

Nurseries and individuals have long offered their services to design, install, and maintain landscapes. Only the wealthy, however, could afford these landscape operations. Public and private grounds, including golf courses, sports fields, college campuses, parks, and others were maintained by their own employees. The landscape management and contracting industry, as we know it, was born in the post-war 1940s. Improved wages and financing opportunities through the GI bill and government agencies made it possible for the number of homeowners to skyrocket.

Major growth in lawn and landscape management began in the 1960s, and the industry came of age in the 1970s and 1980s. This was due to increases in income, leisure time, and recreational activities by the masses. There was enhanced appreciation for the appearance of the home and landscape and for the environment. Add to this the amount of additional expendable income available to the average family. The increase in the number of two wage-earner families in the 1980s and 1990s meant more money and less time to do the lawn chores. By the mid-1990s, surveys estimated there were between 14 and 26 million acres of home lawns. The overall national home lawn is about 0.32 acres, with regional variations.

The importance and growth of television should also be mentioned. Consumers were able to experience gardens and landscapes across the world without leaving home. A well-maintained lawn and landscape became an important status symbol with the growth of the suburbs. In addition to an intangible pride, good landscape and turf maintenance truly added real value to the property. Major TV markets have at least one local and several national weekly gardening programs, and one cable channel is dedicated entirely to home and garden improvement.

These and a multitude of other reasons allowed energetic entrepreneurs to develop service-oriented companies that offered professional lawn and landscape maintenance to the public. They could care for the client's lawn better and often less expensively than he/she could do it alone.

Photo 1.3. Professionally designed and well-groomed residential landscapes are a source of pride and value for their owners. Photograph courtesy of James Robbins.

Franchises and consolidation

Successful and aggressive lawn care companies began franchising nationwide in the 1980s and several companies became national in scope. In the late 1990s, multi-million dollar organizations began an energetic campaign of growth and consolidation of locally and regionally successful firms through purchase. To fuel expansion, some corporations went public with offerings on the New York and NASDAQ stock exchanges. Other service-oriented companies in other economic sectors entered the landscape industry by purchasing existing firms.

The largest firm in the nation, TruGreen-LandCare, operates over 175 local branches in more than 50 metropolitan markets (as of 2003), and expects to continue expansion. The largest lawn/landscape care companies in the nation, based on 2001 revenues, were: TruGreen-ChemLawn ($878 million); TruGreen-LandCare ($830 million); ValleyCrest Companies [Environmental Industries, Inc.] ($521 million); The Davey Tree Expert Co. ($321 million); and The Brickman Group ($290 million).

Procurements and consolidations have produced several firms that are truly national or regional in scope and give a new complexion to the landscape management industry. There are benefits to growth in this manner. Companies are able to leverage a national presence and seek national accounts. Some large corporate clients prefer dealing with a single company who can service their many properties. Consolidation has allowed acquired companies to tackle wider markets and to grow. A local Philadelphia firm, for instance, provides landscape management services to branches of a bank throughout the East. The broader market was impossible before acquisition. Larger clients, in negotiating prices with regional or national consolidated firms, will heighten competition in local markets.

There are certainly cost efficiencies to be realized from increased purchasing power. Consolidated companies can also integrate operations, produce results through a proven system, and reduce overlapping employees and equipment. Management training will be more available and will translocate to other companies as employees change jobs or begin their own firms. Increased capital will be available to invest in the business. Outside funding for medium to large businesses allows for more investment in people, training, equipment, and services. Specialized positions in personnel services and training are being added in many firms.

Consolidation impacts the entire industry; companies are in business to compete. Successful medium-sized companies in the same markets as the corporate giants will feel the competition. Successful companies in cities where the conglomerates have no presence will be approached for acquisition. Small landscape firms will have opportunities in niche markets and can develop a focused plan for growth. Even professional associations will be impacted since large numbers of buyouts mean a reduction in membership.

The pesticide, fertilizer, landscape management equipment, and seed industries have had their share of mergers, acquisitions, and joint ventures. These big business dealings will result in a different complexion of green industry suppliers in the future. The extent and shape of the changes will materialize over time. Consolidation may also benefit the industry because as manufacturers consolidate, the money spent for new product research and development often increases.

A 1998 survey indicated that 40 percent of lawn/landscape companies were concerned about their ability to compete against national giants. However, 58 percent of the respondents felt that development of national landscape maintenance companies was good for the industry. Independent landscape firms felt they would be able to provide quality work at fair prices and that quality work, over such varied markets, would be a weak spot for national companies.

Commercial landscapes

Attractive, functional surroundings for indoor and outdoor activities are highly desirable in the business and corporate world. Those who rent property to others — apartments, condominiums, homes, offices, or retail facilities — find and keep tenants more easily when the property is well landscaped and maintained. Condominium and townhouse developments are significant markets. Attractive shopping centers and malls draw more customers and community approval. Retail managers strive to associate shopping with pleasant experiences: flowers; trees; fountains; and well-groomed landscapes. Motels compete for the traveler with conspicuous exteriors as well as the quality of their services.

Photos 1.4/1.5. Commercial landscapes combine striking vistas, as well as close-in gardens for the enjoyment of employees and visitors. Photographs courtesy of James Robbins.

Private country clubs and golf courses are expected to be manicured, pleasant, and attractive environments for their members and users. There were about 16,000 golf courses serving 26,000,000 golfers in 1998. In 1997, 429 courses were opened for play in the United States alone.

Maintenance of what have been historically internally managed properties is increasingly being contracted or out-sourced (the 90s word). The number of golf courses contracting maintenance services is growing annually. About one-third of all cemeteries contract landscape management. Some sites are co-sourcing, or contracting some maintenance tasks, such as mowing, chemical applications, or tree work, while doing other landscape work with internal employees.

Public landscapes

Governments have promoted landscape opportunities. Public tax dollars spent to beautify parks, playgrounds, schools, and highways contribute to the quality of life. A significant portion of the budget of most progressive cities and governmental organizations is used to maintain and improve the community landscape. Many localities have legislatively required quality landscaping for new developments. Even the military spends millions of dollars per year for landscape development and maintenance by private contractors. Innovative landscape design, plant material, and management have provided an incentive to homeowners.

Photo 1.6. High-quality maintenance of apartment and condominium landscapes is an important marketing tool. The landscape humanizes multiple family residences and makes each unit a home for the residents. Plants provide privacy, brighten public areas, and add quality to the property.

Technology

Growth in professional landscape and lawn management has been enhanced by technology. The introduction of reliable automated equipment has made it possible for one or two people to do the work that previously required a large crew. Development of low-cost and effective herbicides, insecticides, fungicides, and other pesticides has made it possible to realistically reduce biotic factors limiting lawn and landscape quality. Environmental awareness has also opened up new growth and opportunities.

The importance of research and technology must be emphasized. In addition to university research, a significant number of national

Photo 1.7/1.8. Attractive exterior and interior landscapes in shopping malls associate pleasant surroundings with shopping. Photographs courtesy of James Robbins.

Table 1.1.
Budgets (1997) for parks and recreation facility landscape and turf management. *Source of information: Landscape Management. 1998. 37(7).*

Annual budget	Percent of respondents
Greater than $1,000,000	13
$500,000 - 1,000,000	16
$300,000 - 499,999	15
$100,000 - 299,000	23
$50,000 - 99,999	11
Less than $50,000	12
Don't know	amazingly, 10

Photo 1.9. Well-maintained public parks and grounds improve the quality of urban and suburban life. Unfortunately, maintenance is one of the first items to suffer from budget restraints.

landscape management, chemical, and equipment corporations initiated and have continued *bona fide* research facilities. They serve their operators, franchises, and customers. Corporations, as well as professional associations, especially those oriented to the turf industry, have been very generous in their continued support of university research programs. Most of the advances in landscape technology have come from private enterprise or through their financial support. Dr. Chris Starbuck, University of Missouri, wrote that ornamental horticulture represents 13 percent of the nation's agricultural net worth, but receives only one percent of the agricultural research public dollars. There was no indication as to whether landscape service or turfgrass were included in the estimate of the net worth.

Legislative influence

Government interference has caused problems and possibilities for the landscape industry. While

Photo 1.10. Well-designed and managed urban spaces provide inviting, attractive, and functional spaces for residents and day users. Photograph courtesy of James Robbins.

Photo 1.11. Federal, state, and local governments have invested millions of dollars in landscape design and management to make roadways appealing. Some studies indicate that planted roadways and streets may actually help reduce accidents. Photograph courtesy of James Robbins.

legislative activity has removed some of the industry's chemical tools, new, safer, and more effective materials have replaced them. Practitioners have become aware of ecologically friendly best management practices, employed integrated pest management, and made better management decisions. Noise legislation has resulted in banning blowers in some municipalities and also protests and hunger strikes by some landscape workers. Really. The Power Equipment Industry has taken up the challenge to meet future noise and emission requirements.

The Future

The future of lawn and landscape management is, at best, an educated guess. It may be best described by the words of the eminent philosopher, Willard Scott, "The outlook is sunny with a chance of showers." Landscape maintenance has and will continue to have the least capital intensive and simplest requirements for entry in all of horticulture. One must literally have a pickup, some tools, and a few customers. Consolidation of the industry will continue, but there will remain a significant and viable place in the market for new, small, medium, and specialized companies.

The mixture of services offered expands with the length of time in business. Many firms that began as lawn care companies, for instance, have added mowing, woody plant care, annual color, irrigation, seeding, and a host of other maintenance-oriented activities. Non-management operations, including landscape and irrigation design and installation, have become profitable parts of what were once landscape maintenance-only companies. Landscape management firms offer additional services with maturity, experience, increased knowledge, greater sophistication of the owners, expanded customer demand, and the desire to increase market share and profits. Companies will continue to evolve and growth will expand into non-horticultural areas, such as lighting, hard surface management, and janitorial services. One of the hottest areas is Christmas display.

The techniques and materials used, especially by the lawn care industry, have and will continue to change and evolve as concerns for the environment and health grow. The population of chemicals on the market will change in the future. New,

safer, materials have replaced some stand-bys. New products are more specific, have shorter residuals, are more environmentally friendly, and cost more. Research into and introduction of biorational and naturally derived products continues.

Legislative action and reaction

As the largely unfounded media hype increased in the recent past, so did the government's interest in pesticides and their potential effects on people and the environment. There have been legislative pushes from school boards to Capitol Hill to ban or limit pesticide use. Some municipalities have enacted restrictive regulations curtailing or prohibiting selected products and have required additional certification/licensing. These actions are the result of a Supreme Court decision permitting local governments to impose regulations more stringent than those under the Federal Insecticide, Fungicide and Rodenticide Act (FIFRA).

Some products presently used by the lawn/ landscape industry may disappear. The Food Quality Protection Act (FQPA) (1996) resulted in the Environmental Protection Agency (EPA) reassessing the safety of previously registered pesticides by different standards. More than 9,000 pesticides will be evaluated by 2006. The EPA established a *Risk Cup*, which is the exposure over a 70-year period that is determined safe for a particular pesticide mode of action. All products with a particular mode of action are loaded into the risk cup. If the cup runs over, then some of the uses must be eliminated. Higher registration costs are making some suppliers reconsider markets; some products may be withdrawn while others will build

Table 1.2.
Challenges facing the lawn/landscape industry, according to survey respondents.

Challenge	Percentage (%)
Labor	50
Competition	50
Management skills	8
Economy	6
Financing	10
Low ballers	10
Insurance	4
Regulations	4

scape management industry, either in number of companies, number of employees, or in gross sales. Retail expenditures for all floriculture and environmental horticulture products were an estimated $54.8 billion ($203 per capita) by the USDA in 1998.

The federal and state governments collect agricultural farm-gate and nursery production statistics; however, no agency routinely estimates the economic contribution of the landscape service industries. Anil *et al* (2001) reported that the green industry, including nursery, greenhouse, bulb, and turfgrass production, generated the second highest net value-added per dollar of gross income among all agricultural commodities nationwide.

Most public officials do not have a clue that the green industry is as large as it is. Researchers in several states have surveyed the turfgrass and landscape industries. Richard *et al* (1996) estimated that $2.2 billion was spent in 1995 to produce and maintain turfgrass in Mississippi.

Florida consumers spent $5 billion on maintaining four million acres of turf in fiscal year 1991-1992. The market was 75 percent residential and spending averaged $1200/acre. Louisiana and Arizona green industries continue to be leading contributors to the states' agricultural industries and general economies. A 1999 University of Illinois survey placed sales generated by the green industry above corn production in importance to the state's economy. These and other studies could help influence legislative initiatives and bring more research dollars, or be ignored as in the past.

A Gallup Survey estimated that more than 21 million households spent $16.8 billion on professional landscape care in 1998. This was a $2.2 billion increase over 1997. Babyboomers (30- to 49-year olds) made up more than half the market. Another survey estimated more than 50 percent of all landscape maintenance spending came from homeowners over 50.

There are tens of thousands of companies, large and small, providing billions of dollars of

Table 1.7.
California Landscape Industry
Many government agencies and others underestimate the size and economic impact of the landscape industry. The California Green Industry Council (CGIC) estimates that the lawn and landscape industry employs 130,000 people growing plants and maintaining more than 1.5 million acres of landscape and turf, and represents $12 billion (2000) in sales.

Estimated annual landscape and lawn sales and services in California	
Area	**Dollars (million)**
Residential landscapes	3,600
Commercial landscapes	2,500
Cut flowers	1,400
House plants	100
Golf course management	700
Parks	600
Highway landscapes	300
School landscapes	300
Horticultural waste	600
Total	12,100

Estimated acreage under management	
Area	**Acres**
Residential landscapes	680,000
Commercial and public works landscapes	205,000
Golf courses	131,000
Parks	158,000
Highway landscapes	72,000
School yards and landscapes	109,000
Power line areas	158,000
Total	1,530,000

market share. Lobbying to change the rules to incorporate more widely accepted scientific practices continues.

Local, state, federal, and EPA regulations and limitations on landscape management products and techniques (noise limitations, hours of operation, etc.) will force firms to adapt and comply or rethink their future in the business. Many small companies may fall by the way side or consolidate with larger firms.

Landscape and lawn small equipment will be drastically affected by governmental regulation. California Air Resources Board (CARB) and EPA standards dictate allowable emission levels that 2-cycle engines can produce. Many now popular 2-cycle tools will be discontinued and cleaner, quieter, and more costly 4- and 2-cycle engines will be coming on-line.

Other environmental legislation limiting access to public landfills will certainly impact handling and costs for landscape and turf management. Mulching mowers have made a dramatic resurgence and to not bag clippings is stylish. Prices and services offered will certainly be affected. Legislation affecting employment, health care, worker's rights, immigration, and other business factors impacts the landscape industry.

The new generation of clientele, applicators, and managers is very wary of pesticide use. Market research indicates that consumers perceive dry products to be safer than liquids. Injection of materials into tree trunks continues to receive greater interest to avoid environmentally unsound spraying. The number of companies using or attempting *organic* landscape management practices and products continues to increase.

Educators, industry associations, writers, and professionals need to extol the positive, functional,

and environmental considerations of turfgrass and developed landscapes. We have successfully focused on and sold their aesthetics and recreational aspects. Politicians, tree-huggers, and the public need to change their view of the landscape industry as water-wasting, energy consuming, chemically dependent, environmentally polluting, ecologically unsound, lazy, careless, unimaginative, child-killers.

Labor

The landscape industry faced a critical shortage of labor in the late 1990s and early 2000s locally and nationally. On the positive side, the number of trained graduates from two- and four-year schools and universities is increasing. Demand, however, will exceed supply. Contractors expect employment will increase and labor will continue to be in short supply in the near term. Labor shortages mean that some firms will turn away business and not be able to expand to meet new opportunities. Landscape firms compete with other construction trades and other entry-level segments of the economy for employees.

Wages and benefits have increased to attract and retain employees and managers. Benefit packages are competitive with many other employment areas. The industry relies on a large amount of unskilled labor and turn over of field employees is high. Employers have increasingly relied on Hispanic workers and increased mechanization to fill the void. Hispanic workers are now employed by a majority of landscape firms (64 percent), making up more than one-third of all industry employees. Larger companies rely more heavily upon Hispanic labor than smaller firms. The South and West account for the heaviest concentrations. Labor was the primary factor limiting growth of half of the landscape firms responding to 1996 and 2000 surveys.

Table 1.3.
Reasons for difficulty in finding and retaining landscape workers, according to survey respondents.

Reasons	Percent of respondents
Poor work ethic	46
Lack of locally available labor	31
Dissatisfaction with wages and benefits	24
Type of work and hours	23
Substance abuse	8
Other	2

The economy

The economy, recession, price of fuel, and continuing wars in the Middle East, influence the mowing of turf, the caring for trees and shrubs, and the general business climate. Housing starts are a good business indicator for the landscape industry. The lawn and landscape industry has historically been able to track growth on an eight to nine month delay behind the construction industry. Other aspects contributing to industry growth are the aging baby-boomer population, greater time demands on working Americans, more two-income families, and maturation among landscape professions. Some important economic gauges to watch are personal income and general business indicators.

Increasing expansion in the private housing sector also signals increased growth for the landscape industry. Real estate development has helped the growth in golf courses and will continue to do so. The two strongest golf markets in the late 1990s and early 2000s were Florida and Texas.

Water

Concern about the quantity and quality of water used in landscapes and golf courses will increase. Golf courses account for about 1.5 percent and landscapes for about 2.9 percent of the annual fresh-water use in the U.S. An estimated 20 million acres of residential and commercial landscape and turf were irrigated in 1996. More than $800 million of irrigation components and systems are sold for developed landscapes annually.

Irrigation scheduling and technology affect prices, profits, and programs. Will your clients accept dormant turf in midsummer? Some may have to. Low water demand landscape designs and plants have increased and irrigation scheduling and technology has improved. Irrigation withdrawals in 1995 were 2 percent less than in 1990, even though irrigated acreage increased by one percent. We will need to do more. Wastewater is becoming an important source of water for nonfood lands, but not without challenges. The lawn and landscape industry has risen to the responsibility of reducing potential pollution of water resources by pesticides, fertilizers, and other materials. The industry must tell its story and be proactive.

Professionalism

A great deal of the future depends on the actions and reactions of the industry today. The unprecedented growth in the economy resulted in unparalleled growth and success of the industry. Professionalism in the landscape industry will continue to grow; this in itself will ease many problems caused by unknowing and uncaring, anything for a buck, low bid mentality green-bandits. Attitudes, image, and marketing must be positive. The reputation of the industry has and continues to improve as it polices itself. Landscape managers must develop and learn environmentally sound techniques. We will not be able to solve every problem in the landscape or lawn by spraying or fertilizing with something.

Business

Good horticulturists must become good business people. The seasonal nature of the industry, under capitalization, profit margins, people and capital management, and business failure cannot be ignored. A survey of the lawn care industry showed business factors and costs were the greatest concerns facing the respondents.

There will also be hard times for landscape managers. Landscape management is not immune to economic stress. As clients have hard times, they reduce the amount of commercial and residential services they purchase. Many present companies will not be able to weather the storm. Reduction of public landscape maintenance budgets offers opportunities to privatize maintenance service in order to reduce costs by public agencies.

Computers play an ever-growing part of this and most other businesses. Only 11 percent of landscape contractors surveyed in 2000 do not use computers in daily business. Accounting and billing were the most common uses, but more than half of the contractors use the Internet. Most of these (77 percent) used email and the Internet for research. Many large and small firms have web pages and this number grows daily.

The Landscape Management Industry

Landscape management is a vibrant, challenging, and noble profession and industry. Landscape service is an extremely diversified industry and very difficult to characterize. According to the experts, no one truly knows the extent of the land-

Table 1.4.
How do landscape management firms use computers?

Task	Percentage of respondents
Accounting and billing	81
Word processing	70
Inventory control	30
Internet	53
Purchasing	20
Scheduling and routing	32
Estimating	42
Other business functions	4
Do not use computers	11

Table 1.5.
Snapshot of the landscape industry

	1996	1997	1998	1999
Number of firms	~70,000	~70,000	~70,000	~90,000
Revenue (billions)	~$45	~$61	~$60	~$70
Estimated number of employees	630,000	623,000	875,000	1,035,000
Average years in business	16.6	17.5	17.7	15.1
Average number of full-time employees	9	8.7	12.5	7
Average gross sales	$643,000	$875,440	$863,800	$680,000

Source of information: State of the industry. 2000. *Lawn and Landscape* 21(10); State of the industry. 1999. *Lawn and Landscape* 20(10); State of the industry. 1998. *Lawn and Landscape* 19(10); and State of the industry. 1997. *Lawn and Landscape* 18(10).

Table 1.6.
Estimate of the lawn and landscape care markets based on US Department of Commerce, Economic and Statistics Administration and US Bureau of Census data. Source: *Grounds Maintenance* 1996 31(5):10 and *Grounds Maintenance* 1998 33(11):8

Year	Estimated number of firms (rounded)	Estimated number of employees (rounded)
1984	29,500	158,000
1985	31,100	178,000
1986	34,500	199,000
1987	40,500	217,000
1988	39,400	230,000
1989	43,800	249,000
1990	46,900	274,000
1991	51,400	273,000
1992	55,200	304,000
1993	59,500	306,000
1994	62,200	295,000
1995	64,800	326,000

Table 1.8.
How long have lawn and landscape contractors been in business? According to a 2000 industry survey [*Lawn & Landscape* 21(10)] the average landscape contractor has been in business for 17.7 years.

Years in Business	% of Landscape Contractors
2 years or less	4.0
3 or 4 years	9.0
5 to 9 years	17.0
10 to 14 years	21.0
15 to 19 years	15.0
20 to 29 years	20.0
30 to 49 years	9.0
50 or more years	5.0

Photo 1.12. Golf courses and other public or private recreational areas require specialized and intensive landscape management. The Green industry is made up of many site and task specific parts. The overall goal, however, is improving and managing the environment. Photograph courtesy of James Robbins.

services to millions of commercial and residential clients annually. The number of companies and clients grows daily.

The Crystal Ball Committee of the Associated Landscape Contractors of America (ALCA) examined the status of the industry, its growth, and its future in 1975 and again in 1989 [Anonymous, 1990, *Lawn and Landscape Maintenance*, 11(3):20]. Landscape maintenance has become a major profit center and the fastest growing part of the landscape contracting industry. The 1989 report estimated over 23,000 identifiable landscape management/maintenance firms. This did not include landscape contractors and other firms with exterior landscape services as a minor discipline. It also omitted golf courses, athletic fields, parks, schools, universities, and similar organizations. Over 50,000 landscape management firms were considered unidentifiable. These small one-person or part-time companies, and private gardeners operate outside the recognized industry and reporting systems. The contribution of these firms must certainly be considered in the overall economic consideration of the industry. The 1998 US Department of Commerce County Business Matters report indicated that there were 68,157 landscape and horticultural service establishments, a five percent increase over the previous year.

The landscape industry continues to be an industry of small companies. In a 1999 survey, 42 percent of the respondents employed one, two or three people year-round. In 1998, only nine per-cent of survey respondents did less than $50,000 in business. Almost one-half of the firms reported 1998 gross receipts of less than $200,000. The residential market represents the bread and butter for the average entrepreneurial landscape/lawn care company.

Absolute characterization of the industry is impossible. There are many facets to the industry. One must consider the diversification of services and their variations, such as lawn service, liquid-lawn service, chemical lawn service, full-service maintenance, arboriculture, irrigation repair, and so on. There is a myriad of specialized companies concentrating in turf aeration, annual color, chemical application, tree work, and many others. The industry is also segmented by work location: golf courses; resorts; sports fields; public parks; arboretums; cemeteries; and many others. Each separate group, profession, area, or subdivision has different requirements, needs, professional associations, and concerns. Regardless, they are all part of the landscape or green industry.

Educational opportunities and curriculum

The image of custodial groundskeepers is changing, attracting new, sharp, skilled people. Educational support for four-year public and private colleges and universities for landscape management, turfgrass, and the golf course industry has not increased dramatically in the last 20 years. The number of one- and two-year programs of-

Table 1.9
Employment in the lawn/landscape industry by sector.
Occupation outlook data, US Department of Labor

Sector	Percent of employment (%)
Public (Government, parks, hospitals, schools, and others)	50
Lawn/landscape firms	30
Building management companies	8
Recreation sites	7
Hotels/resorts	3
Retail nurseries	2

fering landscape and turf grass management curricula has increased to take up the slack. Their emphasis is on hands-on training, technology, and smart management.

Students in all landscape curricula should receive a basic education in English, math, science, and the humanities. Literature courses may not make mowing a lawn easier, but they may make you a better person. One or more classes in Spanish is advisable.

Basic horticulture and affiliated course topics include, but are not limited to: plant materials; turf management; irrigation; plant science; pest management; equipment repair; soils; landscape design and construction; and many others. A student should become a well-rounded horticulturist.

Plant knowledge must be supplemented with business and management courses. If you make a horticultural mistake, you lose the crop; if you make a business mistake, you lose the farm. Include course work in: computers; marketing and sales; personnel management; production management; business law; and accounting. Too often students neglect business courses or take easy classes to merely fulfill their requirements. Most former students choosing this path of least resistance have expressed regret soon after experiencing the real world.

Many schools offer or require an internship to complete the degree requirements. The internship broadens the student's skills and horizons and exposes him/her to the real work-a-day world. It is a two way street. The firm or agency is exposed to bright young talent, provided some much-needed personnel at a relatively affordable price, and is given the opportunity to try out potential employees.

Photo 1.13. Landscape horticulture attracts many bright students and offers a very rewarding career.

Photo 1.14. Internships provide important hands-on learning for students. Internships are available through many arboreta, public grounds, and private companies. If possible, students should find an internship outside of their home city or state to broaden their technical, horticultural, and geographic horizons.

12

Not all internships are created equal, however. Some employers see it only as a cheap source of seasonal labor. How long does one have to run a line trimmer before grasping the concept? A good professional internship exposes the student to all levels of the operation from field operations, through sales, the shop, to management. Yes, the student will be exposed to the line trimmer, but not for nine hours a day, six days a week for the entire summer.

Employment opportunities

There is tremendous demand for students trained in landscape management and all other areas of the green industry. Growth in recent years has been unprecedented. The requirement has far exceeded the reservoir of students available. High demand will continue for several years as enrollments at two- and four-year institutions stabilize and the number and size of green-oriented service companies continue to expand. Employment in landscape services has grown significantly over the last decade in contrast to the continuing decline in employment in production agriculture.

Twenty-two million U.S. households spent $14.2 billion on professional lawn, tree, and landscape maintenance services. The outlook is for this trend to continue. Employment will increase 10 to 20 percent through 2006, according to the Bureau of Labor Statistics. Rapid expansion and turnover create opportunities in the field.

Landscape management offers the opportunity to work outdoors with plants. Part of the mystique is the opportunity to be creative and to work with people. Job placement after completion of an educational program is excellent. Opportunities are available throughout the country. Students have the latitude of selecting a geographic location they would prefer or like to experience.

Opportunities for women are equal to those of men in the field. Women can be found as crewmembers, supervisors, pesticide or spray technicians, equipment operators, mid- and upper-management, and company owners. Women own and operate multi-million dollar companies. Sexual discrimination still exists, but it is less pronounced in the green industry than in many other phases of the business world. The "Good Ole Boys" will become receptive and accepting once they discover that any person, regardless of gender or ethnic background, can carry their own weight.

Landscape management is hard work and it can also be tedious and detail oriented. It requires developing technical and management skills in preparation for mid- and upper- management positions or for establishment of one's own company. Many things cannot be taught, and come only through experience. Promotions and increased salaries for talented, educated, and motivated employees come with success. Career earnings potential compares favorably with those in allied fields.

Photo 1.15. Landscape management appeals to creative people who like to work with plants, people, and in the outdoors. Opportunities in landscape horticulture for women are equal to those for men.

Photo 1.16. The need and opportunities for well-trained landscape students and professionals to manage prominent sites, to manage entrepreneurial firms, or to start one's own business are never ending. Employment opportunities in landscape horticulture are available throughout the nation and the world.

From my experience in assisting students with employment opportunities, starting salaries in landscape management and other service phases of the green industry are usually higher than in the production and retail ends of the business. Salaries increase with experience, management performance, education, and certification. Starting salaries and benefits have continued to increase as firms compete for a limited pool of trained graduates.

Keeping Up

Landscape management, like every business, operates on information. The landscape professional and student must stay at the forefront. This requires procuring and digesting information on the technical and business aspects of horticulture, turf, machinery, and personnel management. An industry survey of managers and owners found 60 percent thought continuing education was very important and 32 percent thought it to be somewhat important. The remaining eight percent saw little importance in continuing education. Most companies budget for education of full and part-time employees since federal and state regulations mandate safety and right-to-know training. Training becomes even more critical as the business grows into new areas and becomes more complex.

Every manager should develop and update a library for his/her or the firm's use. The size and diversity of the library should grow with the number of people utilizing the resources. The publications should be read and used, not just collected.

There are many books that provide excellent resource and background information. New books constantly enter the market. Some will prove invaluable, while others may not. Since books are expensive, determine if the publication is valuable as a reference before purchasing it. If one must err, I would prefer to buy a book that I may use little, rather than not have one that would be useful. The Internet is a wonderful resource, but it will never replace a good book.

Magazines, periodicals, and newsletters provide a frequent window to the business and technical aspects of landscape maintenance. Publications specializing in certain aspects of the trade as well as general sources of information are avail-

---

Table 1.10.
How many associations should you join?
Many new landscape professionals join local, regional, and several national professional or specialty associations. Dues are ever increasing and members should get value for their money. Reevaluate society or association participation by asking some questions.

Certification and Training
- Does the association provide training or certification programs?
- Do clients in public agencies recognize these programs?
- Are training courses readily accessible?
- Is certification valuable to employees?

Recognition
- Is there a local or regional association chapter so employees and managers can attend meetings and network?
- Do suppliers endorse the association?
- Do you promote the association membership in advertising?

Value
- Does membership help in marketing, recognition, or quality or training?
- Are any discounts available because of membership?
- Can association affect profitability, efficiency or quality of services?

Participation
- Do key employees attend the annual meeting and/or trade shows every year or two?
- Does the association provide publications? Are they valuable to the business or employees?
- Does the association strive to represent business of all sizes?

able. Many magazines are available at no cost to professionals and students, while others charge for an annual subscription. The problem today is not one of too little information available, it is finding the time to read all of the sources available.

Video periodicals and monthly videotapes or CDs covering a variety of subjects, are available on numerous topics from several companies and associations. These offer a source of information that teach or update employees in digestible segments. We have grown up with television as a primary source of information.

Training videos, in English and Spanish, and interactive computer programs are widely available. Videos and computer exercises can train employees on safety, pesticides, equipment operation and care, and many other topics. They are also valuable as library references. Many local associations rent videos to their members.

The Internet is a valuable source of information and communication. Its potential from an educational perspective is tremendous. The world is literally at the fingertips of everyone with a computer and an Internet connection. I am constantly amazed at the amount of information available. Be aware that there are no standards or control on Internet information. Anyone with a computer can have a web page that feeds bad information to the world.

Professional associations, organizations, and societies provide the best means for the professional to stay attuned to business and technical information. A large and growing number of trade organizations serve the green industry. Some are very specialized, while others provide a more ho-

listic approach. ALCA, PGMS, Irrigation Association, and many state associations provide for greater professionalism through certification. Join and participate in the professional organizations.

Do not limit support to only local or only national organizations. Both have value. Local groups allow networking and idea exchange with companies and competitors in the same or similar markets. National and regional groups and meetings allow the manager to meet and learn from people from a wide geographic base.

Most associations also provide publications of news, technical developments, new products, business information, and other topics of interest. Organizations hold annual or more frequent meetings, usually accompanied by a trade show. Trade shows are excellent places to see and compare equipment and material.

Local, regional, and state organizations, as well as university research and extension personnel, also organize educational meetings, trade shows, equipment demonstrations, and field days. Topics are aimed at a narrower geographic or climatic area. A survey of employee training programs indicated that 52 percent used in-house programs, 43 percent used association-sponsored seminars, 36 percent sent employees to university-sponsored programs, and 33 percent used technical/vocational school classes for workers. Take key employees to beneficial meetings. Meetings serve as a reward for work well done, produce a better trained employee, increase morale and let them know the company cares.

Bibliography

1. Anil, S., *et al*. 2001. Factors influencing revenues of the landscape and lawncare companies. *Journal of Environmental Horticulture* 19(3):132.

2. Anonymous. 1990. Landscape contracting today and in the year 2000. *Lawn and Landscape Maintenance* 11(3):20.

3. Anonymous. 1990. Respectable growth predicted this year. *Lawn and Landscape Maintenance* 11(6):15.

4. Anonymous. 1993. The "green" industry. *American Nurseryman* 177(4):17.

5. Anonymous. 1995. State of the industry: residential still outpaces commercial. *Lawn and Landscape* 16(5):6.

6. Anonymous. 1996. Turf acreage. *Grounds Maintenance* 31(5):10.

7. Anonymous. 1996. Reading, writing, arithmetic. *T&O Service Tech,* 1(4):1.

8. Anonymous. 1996. US households invest $14.2 billion in green home improvement. *Indiana Assn. Nurserymen News* (18): June

9. Anonymous. 1998. LandCare USA arrives. *Landscape Management* 37(3):26.

10. Anonymous. 1998. State of the industry. *Landscape Management* 37(7):22.

11. Anonymous. 1998. An industry in transition? *Landscape & Irrigation* 22(4):10.

12. Anonymous. 1998. State of the industry. *Lawn & Landscape* 19(10):s10.

13. Anonymous. 1999. Sports turf industry fact sheet. www.aip.com/STMA/html/facts.html, 8/26/99.

14. Anonymous. 1999. 10 high profile women-run operations. *Landscape Management* 38(9):35.

15. Anonymous. 1999. TruGreen-landscape continues buying. *Lawn & Landscape* 20(8):8.

16. Anonymous. 1999. Pesticide battles heat up. *Lawn & Landscape* 20(9):8.

17. Anonymous. 1999. Industry bests boom. *Lawn & Landscape* 20(10):6.

18. Anonymous. 1999. Spanish training videos available. *Pro* 12(1):8.

19. Anonymous. 2000. California dreamin'. *Lawn & Landscape* 21(12):8.

20. Anonymous. 2000. Getting hooked up. *Lawn & Landscape* 21(6):10.

21. Anonymous. 2001. Inside Illinois' industry. *Lawn & Landscape* 22(3):10.

22. Anonymous. 2002. State of the industry. *Lawn &Landscape* 23(10):s18.

23. Blair, D. 1995. A look at the future. *Tree Care Industry* 6(11):4.

24. Brandenburg, R. 1999. Future of pest management in the landscape. *Landscape & Landscape* 20(10):101.

25. Chazanof, J. 1998. The effects of consolidation on the green industry. *American Nurseryman* 188(1):8.

26. Clancy, D. 1999. What will be left? *Lawn & Landscape*20(8):56.

27. Code, C. 1988. Going full-service? *ALA* 9(10):22.

28. Code, C. 1988. Full service lawn care: The shape of things to come. *ALA/Maintenance* 9(11):24.

29. Code, D. 1990. Will strength in numbers prevail? *Lawn & Landscape Maintenance* 11(11):22.

30. Cox, L., J. Hollyer, and J. Leones. 1994. Landscape services: An urban agricultural sector. *Agribusiness* 10(1):13.

31. Cox, L., J. Leones, and J. Hollyer. 1995. Economic linkages between the U.S. greenhouse and nursery products industry and landscape service. *Journal of Environmental Horticulture* 13(1):1.

32. Dyer, A. 1999. Deck the halls. *Lawn & Landscape* 20(8):40.

33. Fong, H. 1989. The care and science of management. *The Public Garden* 4(3):20.

34. Florkowski, W. *et al.* Economic profile of Atlanta landscape maintenance and lawn care firms. *HortTechnology* 6(4):414.

35. Gibson, S. 1999. Make your peace with change. *Landscape Management* 38(11):7.

36. Goldenberg, N. and C. Marcellino. 1997. Turf chemical applications. *Grounds Maintenance* 32(11):12.

37. Hall, R. 2001. Info to make you turf smart. *Athletic Turf* 4(2):6.

38. Hensley, D. 1993. Are you keeping up with trends in the business? *Nursery Manager* 9(5):70.

39. Hensley, D. 1993. Safety and training videos from LICH. *Hawaii Landscape* 7(6):18.

40. Hensley, D. 1994. The landscape industry council deserves your support. *Building Industry* 39(11):92.

41. Hensley, D. 1994. Join and support LICH. *Hawaii Landscape* 8(2):15.

42. Hodges, A. *et al*. 1994. *Contribution of the turfgrass industry to Florida's economy*. Florida Turfgrass Assn., Orlando, FL.

43. Iwata, R. and D. Hensley. 1996. AGNET Hawaii-Agricultural and horticultural information at your fingertips. *Hawaii Landscape* 10(4):10.

44. Jones, D. 1990. Designing programs to guide your firm's work force. *Lawn & Landscape Maintenance* 11(3):36.

45. Liskey, E. 1999. Consolidation in the green industry. *Grounds Maintenance* 34(10):8.

46. Lied, T. and ALCA Crystal Ball Committee. 1989. *Landscape Contracting Today and in the Year 2000*. ALCA, Hendron, VA.

47. Marcellino, M. 1989. Hiring in the 1990's: Will there be enough workers? *ALA/Maintenance* 10(2):38.

48. Marcellino, M. 1989. Selling, servicing the competitive homeowner market. *Lawn and Landscape Maintenance* 10(9):22.

49. McGary, R. 1990. Service in the 90's. *Landscape Management* 29(11):18.

50. McIver, T. 1990. The water's fine. *Landscape Management* 29(3):54.

51. McIver, T. 1991. Top 50. They can't stand still. *Landscape Management* 30(4):32.

52. Murry, A. 2001. Hispanic workers on the rise. *Grounds Maintenance* 36(5):8.

53. O'Connell, K. 1999. Internships: More than fetching coffee? *Landscape Architecture* 89(9):47.

54. Owings, A., J. Kuehny, and J. McCrimmon, 1996. Louisiana's green industry. *Louisiana Agriculture* 9(3):14.

55. Ratcliff, C. 1999. Water supply and demand. *Grounds Maintenance* 34(6):10.

56. Ratcliff, C. 1999. Update on national emission bans. *Grounds Maintenance* 34(7):10.

57. Ratcliff, C. 2000. U.S. home lawn area. *Grounds Maintenance* 35(5):10.

58. Reaves, R. 1997. Cemetery care smarter, more economical. *Landscape Management* 36(11):6L.

59. Reaves, R. 1998. Parks, grounds pros gain in smarts. *Landscape Management* 37(7):27.

60. Richard, M., *et al*. 1996. *The Impact of the Turfgrass Industry on Mississippi's Economy*. Mississippi State Univ. Coop. Ext. Serv. Bul. 1062.

61. Riggs, N. 2001. Technology guiding turf research. *Turf North* January:B8.

62. Roche, J. 1998. TruGreen/ChemLawn, LandCare USA make overtures of going national. *Landscape & Irrigation* 22(3):28.

63. Roche, J. 1998. What's next for the landscaping industry? *Landscape & Irrigation* 22(12):3.

64. Roche, J. 1999. Christmas/holiday decorations. *Landscape & Irrigation* 23(5):8.

65. Shank, B. 1998. Golf industry booms, supers step up. *Landscape Management* 37(7):32.

66. Stapp, R. 1999. Home grown home value. *Landscape Design* 23(6):s18.

67. Tanzillo, K. 1996. Making enough green in golf course maintenance. *Lawn and Landscape* 17(2):38.

68. Welterlen, M. 1999. Business is booming. *Grounds maintenance* 34(10):6.

69. West, B. 1998. The industry sounds off. *Lawn & Landscape* 19(5):28.

70. West, B. 1999. Money can grow on trees. *Lawn & Landscape* 20(8):29.

71. West, B., 2000. State of the industry report. *Lawn & Landscape* 21(10)S1.

72. West, B., 2000. E-valuating the future. *Lawn & Landscape* 21(10)6.

73. West, B. and P. Schrimpf. 1997. State of the Industry. *Lawn & Landscape* 18(10)insert.

74. West, B. and N. Wisniewski. 1999. State of the Industry. *Lawn & Landscape* 20(10)insert.

75. Westrick, D. 1990. Green industry women are taking on leadership roles. *Lawn and Landscape Maintenance* 11(9):34.

76. Wisniewski, N. 2001. Into the future. *Lawn & Landscape* 22(11):79.

Chapter 2
Marketing Landscape Management Services

The demand for lawn and landscape management services generally reflects the overall economy; business is up during good times and declines during downturns. Successful landscape managers find ways to prosper even during a sluggish economy. Landscape industry surveys reported a 17.6 percent growth in sales (residential and commercial) in 1997 and 23 percent sales growth in 1998. Industry surveys also reported a 15 percent decline in sales revenues for 2001.

Why do people invest in landscape and lawn management? Consumers feel that good landscape and turf management produces a place of beauty and relaxation for the family, employees, visitors, and clients. A nice landscape and lawn reflect positively on the owner. A well-maintained property enhances the neighborhood, improves the customer's experience, and the net real estate market value of the site. Clients are also conscious of the environmental benefits of the landscape and turf, but there is room for additional education in this area. Residential consumers feel that contract maintenance conserves time and improves the appearance of the property. The greatest reluctance to purchasing landscape and turf care is price.

The typical consumer of residential landscape management, according to a 1998 customer survey, lives in a suburban area, has a median income of $30,000, is 30 years of age or older, and college educated. According to a 2001 consumer profile of the average residential lawn service

Photo 2.1. Residential landscapes are the mainstay of most management firms. Management of residential landscapes is a highly competitive and lucrative market. Clientele choose management companies on price and quality. High-end landscapes are obtained by referral from a satisfied customer. Managing residential landscapes requires working closely with the homeowner and understanding their needs.

customer, 71 percent had a household income of more than $75,000, 44 percent were families with children, 33 percent were single and customers had contracted lawn services for an average six and a half years.

DEVELOPING MARKETING STRATEGY

Offering the best landscape service in the world does not guarantee success. Each landscape management firm must first market itself to obtain customers and increase business. Develop-

Table 2.1.

A Well Groomed Grounds from the consumer's perspective, according to a Gallup Survey.

Benefits of well-groomed grounds	Responses
A property that helps beautify the neighborhood	45%
A place of beauty and relaxation for the family, employees or visitors	39%
A property that reflects positively on its owners	38%
A property that has increased real estate value	35%
A comfortable place to entertain, work or visit	33%
A property that provides a safe, high-quality play area	27%
A place that provides an exercise area for pets	13%
A property that helps purify the air	12%
A property that helps cool the air	12%
A property that filters water as it drains into the ground	12%
Other	1%
None of the above 7%	

ing and implementing a marketing strategy is an essential process for every successful business. The process begins as the business is initiated and continues as the business grows, changes, and matures. What works for one company may not work for another, but an astute manager can learn something from every venture, good and bad.

Marketing is neither selling nor advertising, although both may be an important part of a marketing strategy. Advertising and selling vary with the size of the company, scope of services, market niche (residential, commercial, or both), and owner/manager expertise. To develop a market strategy, the owner/manager must pause and answer a series of questions. Developing a true picture of the firm, its potential, its shortcomings, and its goals, takes time, study, and maybe some outside assistance. Actions are developed based on these thoughtful responses.

Identify the services or products the firm sells. What does the company really sell? You are not just mowing a lawn, maintaining the woody plants, and controlling pests. The landscape management firm is providing the science-based, technical services releasing the client's time and improving the appearance and value of the property, with environmental consciousness and biorational decisions to problems.

Photo 2.2. Commercial sites may be maintained by in-house crew or competitively by commercial landscape management firms. Commercial landscapes may allow use of larger, more profitable equipment. Working hours should be coordinated with the client. The market is very price competitive and quality oriented.

Identify and understand potential customers. Who are the potential customers? They are the home or business owners, property managers, or public agencies whose requirements may be filled by the service offered by the landscape management firm. Consumers may be expected to reasonably consider your company as a provider based on price, location, and several other factors. Everyone in the world or even the zip code is not a potential customer. Focus on an attainable and realistic portion of the market.

Table 2.2

Revenue for landscape management contractors came primarily from residential customers in a 2001 survey. Transitioning from a primarily residential customer base to one with larger, commercial clientele can offer many challenges.

Customer category	Average percent of industry revenue
Single-family residential	65
Multi-family residential	9
Commercial or industrial facilities	20
Government or institutional facilities	3
Other sites	3

How does the client make buying decisions? Is purchasing based on studying options or made on the spur of a moment because of an inducement? Typically, purchasers of landscape and lawn services chose a firm based on price, quality, convenience, personal recommendation, or prestige. What is the most efficient and effective method to reach buyers before they make their purchasing decision?

Identify competitors. Competitors are those businesses who fill the same need as your company. They may be small, medium, or large independent or corporate landscape/lawn maintenance firms. Individuals involved in other service industries can be competitors. Custodial enterprises are frequently offering exterior maintenance to clients. Even the high school or college kid down the block competes for mowing during the summer.

Identify advantages and disadvantages. Why should a client choose this firm over another if price, quality, and convenience are equal? What makes this company different or better than others offering the same scope of service? Market analysis helps determine the nature of the firm's competitive advantage.

Some potential clients choose on the basis of price only. If this group represents a significant portion of the identified potential market, are the firm's prices the lowest? If not, how will it compete? If clients desire the highest quality detailed service regardless of price, can the company deliver? Be cautious and realistic in this analysis. Potential clients have established buying patterns that, up to now, do not include your firm. Sufficient reason must be provided to break established patterns and change allegiance if the business is to succeed.

Determine the most efficient methods to reach buyers. The potential customer for services offered by the firm has been identified. The reasoning for his/her choosing this firm over another is established and reasonable. How does this potential patron of the firm's expertise find out about it? Do they typically buy based on an advertisement in the phone book, a flyer received in the mail, a referral from another individual, or something else? Knowing how people will find the firm ensures that the advertising and marketing dollars are spent in the most productive way possible. Forty-six percent of landscape contractors set an annual budget for marketing promotions.

Develop an action plan. Developing a realistic market strategy and market niche helps the firm realize what is needed to accomplish their goal. Develop a sequential, logical plan. Establish market and sales goals and ways to measure success. Determine how the success of advertising will be measured. Once the potential buyer is a client, what proactive approaches are necessary to retain him/her?

Quality Work. Regardless of the variables, every landscape management company claims that their number one advertisement is their quality of work. This is the most effective and inexpensive method of retaining present customers and obtaining new ones. Every landscape management contractor with whom I have talked feels he/she is providing quality service for a fair price. However, quality, like beauty, differs in the eye of the beholder.

Quality, unfortunately, is too frequently equated with price. Quality workmanship need not be expensive. A portion of marketing and selling landscape services is educational. Clients must be shown and taught that price should not be the primary determination for selecting a contractor or management program. Clients have fewer objections to price as long as they understand what goes into it.

Advertising and Promotion. The intensity and scope of promotional activities for landscape managers vary. The greatest amount of advertising occurs in the residential market, with extensive use of flyers, newspaper, Internet, and Yellow pages promotion. Managers supplement paid advertising with good public relations and no-cost promotions designed to keep the company's name before current and potential customers. Studies indicate that some of the techniques that bring in the most business often cost the least.

No-cost advertising

Company image and professionalism. Projecting a strong, professional company image is a powerful method of promotion and advertising. A positive image inspires confidence. It tells the client that these people know what they are doing, they will treat him/her fairly, they are trustworthy, and they are professionals. A negative company image needs no explanation.

The image of the company is exuded in everything it does. Assuming every contractor does or has the potential to do quality work, how is the image of a successful company created and portrayed?

Names and logos. Every company name has a story. The owner chose the name for thoughtful and specific reasons. Names are important. The obvious reason is that it is the initial identification to the customer. A business name is normally, but not always, an indication of the product or services offered.

Research has proven that the name should be memorable. Cutesy names are not always the best designation to use. It may make the company seem too Mom and Pop. I am not sure that the CEO of a Fortune 500 company would feel comfortable recommending the "Starving Surfers Landscape" to one of his/her peers. However, this name may work fine for a residential market along the beach. Be creative, be individual (there are many Dave's Landscape), and remember the market niche. There are lots of enjoyable names in the field that make me smile: Shady Lady; A Cut Above; Better than Good Landscape; Surf and Turf; Mownopoly; Two Nice Guys; and many more.

Use the company's name and logo on all vehicles, correspondence, invoices, advertisements, and uniforms. A *logo* is the visual representation of the company. It is the professional stamp, sign, and signature. The logo is the symbol by which your clients and competitors will recognize the organization. The logo representing the company should be high quality and professionally drawn; it is your trademark.

New companies often spend an inordinate amount of time selecting just the right image for the company logo. Others, however, do not spend enough. New firms should try several logos and symbols before selecting one that justly represents

---

Table 2.3.
What are clients told to look for in a landscape management contractor?

Several professional organizations, cooperative extension services, and even branches of the Federal government have published material and posted web sites telling consumers what to look for in a professional landscape contractor or a lawn care company. The following is a summary of some of this advice. How does your firm stack up?

- Determine the experience level of the prospective company. Look for stable, well-established firms. Key employees should have secondary education in horticulture or several years of experience.
- Ask for references. Examine the style, and quality of similar scale projects.
- Ask for a list of professional affiliations. This helps assure professionalism.
- Select a firm that is licensed and insured. This assures that the contractor is accountable and operating legally. Ask for proof of adequate worker's compensation, liability and vehicle insurance.
- Require a written program, plan and contract.

Photo 2.3 Even pesticide notification signs can help market landscape and lawn management firms. Keep your name in front of customers and potential customers.

Photos 2.4/2.5. Vehicles should be clean and tastefully display the firm's name and phone number. A company hired to bring out the best in a home or commercial site should take pride in its equipment. What better advertising than the vehicle parked in front of a quality landscape being maintained by highly professional employees? Photograph courtesy of James Robbins.

them. Company names and logos can be registered with the Secretary of State in most states to prevent others from inadvertently or intentionally adopting them.

Trucks and equipment. Take a look at the firm's equipment. The trucks should be clean and painted and uniformly lettered with the name, logo and phone number. If the owner and his/her personnel do not take pride in their equipment, then why should the client expect them to take pride in their work or his/her property? The trucks and other equipment do not have to be new, but they do have to be reasonably clean. Few firms, especially new and small companies, can afford to purchase a fleet of shiny, new trucks and equipment. Serviceable used vehicles can be cleaned and painted. Most successful companies re-paint trucks, trailers, mowers, and other equipment during the off-season if needed.

It is the responsibility of the crew to remove debris and clean the vehicle daily, either before or after starting on their appointed routes. The truck should be washed once a week. Some firms have the crews come in early one day per week for washing vehicles; others have designated personnel that come in off-hours to clean vehicles.

Correspondence. Letterhead, invoices, and other correspondence should contain the company logo, complete address, and phone number. Correspondence must be professional and attractive. Perception is important; using recycled paper for

stationery is very appropriate for an environmentally attuned firm. Make correspondence clear, concise, grammatically correct, and typed without corrections. Nothing dampens client enthusiasm or the company's image more than a letter full of spelling errors and poor grammar. Billings must be correct and timely.

Personnel

The client sees the field employees on at least a weekly basis. They are *the company* to the client. What do they say about the firm and how do they say it? The employees should be uniformed, clean, and they should be taught how to respond to questions and deal with clients and complaints. Every employee should feel that he or she is part of a winning team.

Uniforms. Nice uniforms project a professional image. Do employees in ragged beer slogan tank tops and soiled cut offs accurately portray the company? Successful landscape management

Photo 2.6. Employees represent the company to the client. Employees should be neat, uniformed if possible, and communicate professionalism.

companies require uniforms. Uniforms make the landscape crew recognizable and distinguish them from competitors or from others working on-site.

Clients prefer contracted service employees to be uniformed. Surveys of the public indicated an 8:1 preference for uniforms. Uniforms made employees easier to recognize and gave a perception that they were well trained and dependable. Uniformed contract service workers enhance the customer's image and make security easier.

Uniforms should be the company color and should display the employee's name and company logo. Display certification patches earned by the employee. Uniform style and color should relate to equipment and advertising. Loose, poorly fitting clothes are safety hazards around landscape equipment. Tastes differ, but stay conservative. Adopt apparel that is compatibly styled for men and women. The fabric should be comfortable, proper for the season, and clean well. Firms in the tropics and in warm weather areas use uniform shorts. Keep uniforms in good repair and remove worn out uniforms as needed. Collect the uniforms of terminated employees.

Many management companies provide uniforms, but employees are responsible for cleaning or laundering charges. Cleaning is usually through a contract uniform company. Some firms are more generous providing the uniform and cleaning. At a minimum, even the smallest employer can provide employees with Tee shirts and caps in the company color imprinted with the firm's name or logo.

Uniforms are a proven employee benefit and a popular employment perk. Uniforms improve employee morale, loyalty, pride, and team unity. Consider uniforms part of integrated advertising to create awareness.

Appearance and demeanor. Require employees to keep their hair and person neat. Appropriate footwear is essential, including safety boots where imperative or prudent. Some enterprises provide footwear to employees; the cost must be reimbursed if the employee is dismissed or leaves within a given time.

Instruct employees on dealing with client questions or complaints. Every employee running a mower or line trimmer cannot be expected to provide instant problem diagnosis. They can, however, be expected to be polite, understanding, and to refer the questioner to the supervisor. The supervisor or employee should pass any questions, complaints, or comments that cannot be immediately answered to someone within the company who can provide action. Encourage employees to report any damage to the site or equipment, regardless of cause. Consider a finder's fee for employees who produce leads that turn into a new contract or additional work on an existing contract.

Recruitment. Project a professional image when recruiting and hiring employees. Many contractors support and attend career days at colleges and universities and make donations to scholarships and horticulture clubs. Develop a quality recruiting packet for attracting key employees; seek the assistance of a professional designer if necessary. Develop an employee handbook with information on company benefits, insurance programs, policies and procedures, disciplinary rules, and so forth. Have the book available in English and other languages, as necessary.

Certification. Employee certification is an important marketing tool. According to consumers, certification improves their ability to judge a quality company and enhances the ability of the company to diagnose and solve problems. National certification programs are available from Associated Landscape Contractors of America (ALCA), Professional Grounds Management Society (PGMS), and the International Society of Arboriculture (ISA). Many state and local organizations also have certification programs.

Organizations. Joining and actively participating in local, state, and national professional organizations enhances the image and expertise of the company. Do not omit associations of affiliated industries, such as landscape architects and designers, and property managers. Landscape architects and designers frequently recommend landscape management service to clients. Property managers have a very efficient and powerful network. Avail yourself of program and panel discussion opportunities, exhibit at trade shows, and help sponsor social gatherings.

Other things that add up to being professional

Communicate as a professional. Answer any customer questions in a polite manner. Improve communication skills through classes and group speaking experiences. Seek out the customer's opinion and find out what can be done to keep them satisfied. Eliminate small problems before they become big ones.

Explain the service program to the client, including pesticides and equipment that will be used. Take the time to answer the "what-ifs" and the client will be comfortable. Do the homework, but if you do not have the answer, find out and call the client as soon as possible. This builds credibility and reputation.

Point out problem areas, but do not be critical. Tactfully point out to the customer any other areas in the landscape that are or will cause problems, even if they do not fall under the firm's service area. This may lead to additional work, but do not make it seem like a quest for business.

Take pride in the landscape industry, the company, and the work it does. Educate yourself and others about its contributions made locally, nationally, and globally. Take advantage of information from associations, lectures, and seminars. Learn more than just the technical end of the business. Talk to the kids by getting involved in career days.

Refrain from criticizing competitors. There are competitors who do not offer the same level of quality. Communicate the difference through the positive actions of the firm, not by talking stink. Remember that your actions represent the entire industry to the client.

Advertising

Many merchandising and promotional techniques are available to put the company name in front of potential customers. Each has its successes and disappointments, depending upon the market, budget, locality, and quality of the effort. What works for one company may not work equally for another.

Cold Calls. Cold calls, knocking on doors and making contact with a potential client without a referral, introduction, or connection, are something every sales professional learns to do. Cold calls are sometimes easier said than done, especially if the company is new or lacks a reputation for the specific area, for example, commercial work. Develop quality information about the company, its history, and include photographs of various properties currently under management.

Identify and target desired or model clients who fit into the niche the firm has developed or is expanding into. The approach must be professional, avoid gimmicks.

Referrals. Landscape management companies rely heavily upon referrals for increasing commercial and residential accounts, regardless of their market size. Referrals require quality work at a fair price; the customer must feel that he/she has received value for the funds expended. Referrals are especially important with commercial accounts and high dollar residential landscapes. There is a powerful network among commercial and multi-family property managers. Owners of large, expensive residential landscapes will not often consider a firm without suitable references.

Keep in touch with companies that contract for office cleaning, general building maintenance, and so forth. Invite principals of such businesses to breakfast or lunch and get to know them. Build a network of contractors with whom information and job leads can be shared.

Lunches or other entertainment sway few clients. The burden is to provide good service and handle complaints fairly. It is important to do whatever it takes, within reason, to maintain a good relationship with the property managers and persons in charge of the landscape.

Traditional Advertising

Television, radio, newspaper. Few, if any, companies specializing in commercial management accounts use television, radio, or newspaper advertisements. These traditional media do not target commercial markets and are very expensive. Television, radio, and newspaper advertisements are successfully used to attract residential accounts. A recent survey of lawn care and landscape management firms showed 70 percent used Yellow pages, 49 percent used newspaper advertisements, and 41 percent used direct mail solicitations. Lawn service and chemical applicators typically use more mass media than full-service management firms. Before spending lots of money, seek the advice of a competent consultant to develop effective advertisements. I have seen some local, self-produced television spots for lawn service companies that were quite embarrassing.

Business publications. City, area, or regional specialized magazines, newsletters, or other publications are available for the business community. These provide an opportunity to put the company in front of business owners, managers, property managers, and purchasing agents. Again, think quality; seek the assistance of a professional to develop advertisements.

Write articles for business and property management-oriented magazines. Most are anxious for landscape input. Establish professional competence and a willingness to share expertise. A list of published articles enhances the company's résumé.

Yellow pages. According to the Yellow Pages Publishers Association, 38.3 million references are made to the Landscape Contracting heading annually. About 36 million references are made to the Lawn Maintenance heading. Allowing the customers' fingers to do the walking can be an effective, but expensive, form of advertisement for landscape and lawn maintenance companies. Yellow pages charges are based on the dimensions of the ad and the size of the market covered.

Yellow pages advertising is more effective for the residential market. Several commercial market landscape management contractors have told me that they did not feel Yellow pages ads were especially effective. They felt that most people used them to look up the company's phone number, not to select a contractor. All contractors believed that it was important to have an advertisement, however. They felt that since everyone else was listed, they also had to have a listing. A 2003 industry survey of landscape contractors indicated 20 percent found Yellow pages a beneficial marketing tool, 38 percent thought it useful, but did not generate much business, 30 percent thought it did not reach their target audience, and 12 percent had not and would not use it.

Some tips for more successful Yellow pages ads:

- Identify the single most important feature that sets the company apart from the competition.

- Indicate areas of specialization. Listings under various headings (trees, lawns, spraying, etc) may be required to indicate the extent of services provided.

- Give special attention to phone numbers.

- Include the company logo.

- Consider a boldface, humorous, or catchy headline.

- Keep the ad clean and easy to read. Use white space.

- Graphics, illustrations, and color attract attention.

- Borders set the ad apart from surrounding copy.

Direct mail. Many residential and commercial landscape contractors use direct mail advertising. Direct mail can target specific zip codes or segments of the market, depending upon the mailing lists used. Direct mail is a powerful medium, 87 percent of Americans use coupons and more than 10 percent of consumers purchase products and services as a result of direct mail. It reaches customers unavailable through other media and allows the firm to present a great deal of information. The potential client can use a post-paid return card or call a phone number to initiate contact or receive an estimate. Results and success are easily tracked.

Some direct mail companies supply design resources, images, graphics, and advice on wording. Consultants can develop a direct mail campaign, although many contractors formulate their own letter, return cards, and mailing lists. Mailing lists are available from Chambers of Commerce, country clubs, apartment and other management associations, all for a price. Direct mail can be expensive considering the cost of developing, printing, handling, and mailing each piece, even at bulk postal rates.

A typical homeowner within a desirable market area receives several direct mail appeals. Design the solicitation to prevent the campaign from falling into the category of junk mail. A piece of direct mail has only a 20 percent chance of capturing the reader's attention for up to eight seconds. It must attract attention, spark interest, represent quality, and inspire confidence, without having the appeal of a circus barker.

The return on direct mail campaigns is low, usually around two percent or lower per mailing. Most direct letters find a direct route to the trash can. *Bona fide* potential customers return their cards or make contact with the company quickly after receiving the mailing. Contractors sometimes use three to four mailings within a short time span to the same audience. Successive mailings serve as reminders to potential clients who procrastinated in mailing their return card.

According to the Direct Mail Association, each dollar spent on direct mail advertising results in a return of $11.65 (1998) on investment. One lawn care manager indicated that closure rate of direct mail leads was 60-80 percent, second only to referrals.

Direct mail can also introduce the company to new markets or areas and make clients aware of new offerings. It is typically the first advertising effort a new company makes. Direct mail can be successful in the commercial as well as the residential marketplace.

Newsletters. Newsletters are direct mail advertising but are more frequently perceived as information. Recipients are less likely to discard a newsletter as unsolicited junk mail. They are effective in residential and commercial markets, but the content and approach must differ. The newsletter may be elaborate, typeset, illustrated, printed on high quality paper, or it may be simple and photocopied. Desktop publishing has made newsletter development much easier and the results more professional looking.

Residential newsletters discuss almost anything from how-to hints on gardening, to recipes. Commercial newsletters generally take a loftier approach, discussing happenings, changes, and promotions within the company. They may discuss the effect of recent weather (drought or unusual temperatures) on landscape plants. Education is an important function and appeal of newsletters.

Avoid overt self-promotion or advertising in the newsletter. According to the experts, if the recipient perceives the newsletter as strictly advertising, they are less likely to read it.

Newsletters require time from the manager to write, edit, and produce. Many companies begin them as a noble effort but soon lose interest. Professionally written, ready-to-mail newsletters are available. They can be printed with the firm's logo and heading. Some companies will further localize the newsletter by including lead stories from the manager.

Internet. Many landscape and lawn management firms have developed Internet sites to support their marketing and advertising efforts. Consultants are available to help design and maintain web sites. Typically, the website offers information about the firm, its history or profile, and presentations of the services and expertise available. Include samples of the firm's work to show the breadth and quality available. Websites can work well for national-, regional- or local-market companies. Include ways to contact the firm via mail, phone, and email. Many firms also promote employment or career opportunities on their website.

Like all effectual marketing and communication, a website requires thought, and presentation, and must be managed to keep current. Static, unchanging web pages will not effectively promote the company and are probably worse than no Internet presence at all.

Full-time or part-time salespeople. Most landscape management companies eventually grow to the point where the owner or manager is no longer able to keep up with the volume of requests. At this point, dedication of some employees to sales is an option, if not a necessity.

The role of the salesperson varies. Some are involved strictly with calling on property managers and potential clients to present proposals and bids, and to sell contracts. Others provide follow-ups, property and quality inspections, and handle client complaints. Titles such as Contract Representative, Contract Supervisor, or Sales Representative indicate that the duties are expanded beyond simply eating lunch with, and selling the client.

Successful landscape management salespeople are typically paid largely by commission and often make good wages. Good managers realize that the more a salesperson is making on commission, the more work they are providing the company, and the more profit for the owner.

Sales support. The most valuable support for a sales force is quality work. Other important support includes lists of potential clients, referrals, and other sources of leads. High quality, professionally designed brochures, fliers, and sales aids explaining the company's history, philosophy, resources, and services are a necessity. Several firms provide salespeople and clients with brochures to compare the buyer's present contractor with those services and benefits proposed. These client advantages for comparison might include: uniformed employees; number of years in the business; insurance coverage; education and quality of key people; and any other unique, desirable, or vendible attributes of the organization.

Company résumé or profile. Just as job applicants prepare a résumé to give a summary of their experience, education, and talent, so should the landscape management firm. Develop a professional summary of the firm's history, goals, and qualifications. Include the names (photos if possible) and backgrounds of the principals, and the education, critical training, experience, association memberships, certifications, and licenses of key employees. Discuss special equipment or services available from the firm. Other information often contained in company résumés or profiles includes: name of insurance carrier and policy limitations, business licenses, awards and recognitions, and client references. Photos of typical jobs are desirable, as are photos of key employees and a sharp looking staff hard at work. Some firms include information about their pre-employment drug testing, community projects, employee training program, dress code, and other information that sets the firm apart from competitors. Much of the same information is included on web sites.

Consultants and advertising support. Public relations firms, advertising agencies, and advertising consultants can provide real assistance to landscape management contractors in developing marketing strategies, advertisements, and campaigns. The company must be ready to budget sufficient dollars to advertising. The return for dollars invested may not be the equivalent found for other products. I have spoken with landscape contractors who have made it to the big time and hired advertising agency support. Some did not feel the return warranted the investment due to the limited and specialized markets they were approaching. Others felt that outside assistance was critical for specific campaigns.

Advertising education, assistance, and information are available through some trade associations. However, marketing assistance from associations serving the Green Industry is limited. This will improve as markets and budgets tighten in the future. Advertising support and assistance in the residential market is available to companies that are part of a national franchise.

Non-traditional advertising

Many seldom-thought-about, unaccustomed methods of advertising the company and its services are possible. The owner/manager should be amenable to novel ways to place the company's name before potential customers.

Newcomers' assistance groups. In most areas there are newcomers' groups, such as Welcome Wagon®, that meet and greet new families in the community. Newcomer services provide information to people who are new homeowners, who are not familiar with the city, and who may be in the market for landscape services. Several landscape installation and management contractors distribute information, coupons, and other printed material through these groups. This is not a free service. Users can limit exposure to specific zip codes, neighborhoods, or areas.

Lawn and garden shows. Lawn and garden shows are popular in the winter and spring throughout the nation. They provide an opportunity to showcase services and wares to potential residential customers and to conduct public education. They permit direct and personal contact with people.

The effort must be first rate since one never gets a second chance to make a first impression. The booth or display must be attractive and eye-catching so that people will stop. Every firm is vying for the time and interest of the same audience. What makes your display and company different and interesting?

Select the best, most out-going employees to host the booth. They must be able to meet people, inspire confidence and professionalism, answer questions, and politely sell services. Avoid the hard sell; make contact and then follow up. Also remember that people visiting lawn, garden, or home shows like to pick up something to take home. Have key chains, pens, balloons, letter openers, refrigerator magnets, printed information, or anything with the company's name available as souvenirs. Another guise to attract attention is to offer a door prize for a few lucky winners. People will fill out their name and address on the entry forms thus providing contacts.

Community and public relations

Being a good neighbor helps every business. Every landscape management firm must have a sense of community and contribute back to the community. Good community relations also keep the firm's name before potential and present consumers. Environmental projects are popular outreach activities for landscape industries. These are a natural tie-in to the skills and interest of the manager and employees.

A well-organized community activity increases community awareness, educates neighbors, co-workers, and clients, and helps in team building. When selecting a project, make sure the value of the project is obvious and do not be afraid to contact the press.

Consider targeting specific groups such as a school, students, or youth groups. How about

Photo 2.7. Lawn and garden shows are common in the spring in nearly every market. Homeowners and gardeners flock to them for their first breath of spring. These shows provide excellent opportunities to meet potential clients for landscape management. Successful advertising efforts for garden shows require investments of time, money, and effort.

something in a neighborhood where one or more employees live? How about letting the employees chose the project and location?

Various successful public relations projects by landscape management firms have included tree donations and plantings, demonstrations of lawn and tree care to residents or public employees, adopting a park or sports field, helping with field days, and many others. Some firms donate their services to worthy, non-profit, high visibility sites or organizations, such as Ronald McDonald® Houses. Partner with other firms or volunteer groups if the company cannot go it alone.

Be particular on what projects are selected. Landscape managers can sometimes be roped into more than was bargained for. Follow up on the project; a bad project is worse than none at all. Nothing is more uninspiring than seeing a group of dead trees bearing the firm's name as the donor.

Many organizations gladly allow signs or mention the donating firm's name when appropriate. Develop news releases about charitable work or donations and send them to local newspapers and publications. If the releases are well-written and of sufficient news value, they will be printed or a reporter will follow-up for additional details.

Serving on a local board or advisory council, such as the parks board, may be as easy as contacting the city or county department and indicating interest and availability. Pick one that is not too controversial.

Local associations. Membership in local or regional associations of commercial clients is an excellent way to make contacts and become known. Larger market areas have organized groups of apartment managers, property managers, condominium associations, builders, developers, and other trade groups. Be available for programs on landscape management to these groups, as well as to homeowner's associations. This develops and enhances your reputation as a local expert and gets the company name in front of the market.

Joining and attending local service club meetings results in contacts with new people. Service clubs are composed of successful and up-and-coming civic-minded members of the business community. People are more likely to patronize the business when they have met someone associated with it. Contact program chairs of local organizations and offer to speak. Develop a few well-illustrated talks on plant selection, lawn care, water conservation, how to save money, environmental benefits of landscape plants, or other horticultural topics that can be used on short notice.

Awards. Awards for quality landscape design, installation, and management for commercial and residential categories are available from national organizations, including ALCA, as well as some state, regional, and local professional associations. Select the best, not necessarily the largest, properties for entry. Take photographs throughout the seasons. Hire a professional photographer, if necessary, to develop a quality presentation.

Winning an award boosts the firm's professional standing, the client's and employee's morale, your ego, and it is an outstanding advertising point.

Provide a copy of the award or plaque to the client. Awards for management of the site hanging in the reception area dampen the enthusiasm of the competitor's salespeople.

Pass the recognition for the award on to the crew performing the work. Some companies provide trips, bonuses, or other tangible forms of gratitude to crews and supervisors who have accomplished award-winning feats.

News releases. Every business makes news regularly. A company may add a new line of merchandise, expand to new service areas, or hire and promote people. These are potentially newsworthy items. Most business owners are shy about promoting themselves through the news media. One secret of getting the business featured in stories throughout the year is to produce and distribute press releases. News departments are not sufficiently staffed to afford the luxury of sending a reporter to dig up local, small-business news. They are, however, interested in including it. Remember the high school and/or college writing classes and practice.

Local radio stations and cable TV channels are always seeking items of interest for their audiences. Contact show managers or hosts and provide information on gardening or landscape management. Furnish information on the use of annuals that require minimal water, managing home lawns during water restrictions, or other timely topics. Be prepared to explain your qualifications and ideas in a coherent manner. Hemming and hawing on the telephone reduce the chances of getting on the show. Work yourself into the enviable position of the local expert that newspapers and radio and television stations contact for comments on plant or landscape related stories.

In summary, there are many avenues available to present the company's good name to existing and potential clients. Be resourceful and look for opportunities. The bottom line, however, is quality work. If the company provides inferior work, no amount of advertising or high-pressure sales will keep a sinking business afloat.

EXPANDING THE MARKET NICHE

There is no way of knowing what services will be desirable. The client is the best information source on what might be needed or desired. Talk to the client. A new service sometimes starts as a courtesy to a few valued customers. Many firms conduct periodic evaluations to determine the quality of existing services, expanded needs, and to promote new offerings.

When considering an additional service or product, research additional insurance coverage that might be needed. What licenses are needed? Is sales tax necessary? Can existing staff adapt or learn the new techniques or products? What additional equipment, materials, vehicles, or repairs

Table 2.4.
Services performed by lawn and landscape management firms, according to survey respondents. Source of information: *Landscape Management. 1998. 32(7): 22.*

Type of service	Percent of firms offering
Turf fertilization	85
Mowing	84
Seeding & overseeding	82
Weed control	80
Tree & ornamental care	75
Aeration & thatch control	74
Insect control	68
Landscape design	66
Disease control	66
Irrigation installation & maintenance	60
Snow removal	47
Paving, deck, patio installation	38
Lake/pond maintenance	34
Athletic field maintenance	20

are needed? How does the service fit into the existing market niche and image of the company? From the business side, how does the new offering fit into overhead, time commitments, employee or management ability, and profitability? Evaluate all the pros and cons; do not consider just the bottom line.

Add-on services

Landscape renovation. Remedial landscape services and landscape renovations are a significant and profitable part of many market plans. Remedial landscaping by the maintenance contractor makes sense to clients since the employees are already there and the quality of work is good. It is a vote of confidence in the firm.

The life span of a landscape is difficult to determine. According to some, the average life of many residential landscapes is about 15 years, less for commercial landscapes. Renovation of the existing landscape or designing a replacement is an important revenue source. If the maintenance firm is not able to provide the design or other services internally, have a landscape designer or architect and other contractors willing to work through the company. Look for renovation services in communities of older homes and businesses, new owners, and after storm damage.

Seasonal color. Some firms specialize in developing and installing color displays of bulbs and

Photo 2.8. Some companies specialize in landscape color, annuals and other seasonal color for commercial and high-end residential clients. Photograph courtesy of James Robbins.

annuals. For others, it is a substantial profit center. Seasonal color displays are used primarily in commercial, retail, and multi-family residential sites. Some high-end residential sites also look to landscape management firms for seasonal display.

Turf aeration. This vital turfgrass management technique is overlooked by many lawn care and landscape firms. Again, some firms have made a specialty of lawn aeration and others are finding it an essential and profitable service. Aeration can solve some turf problems that lead to call backs. Equipment for residential and commercial properties is reasonable and current employees can easily operate it. Periodic aeration aids trees in compacted sites as well as the turfgrass.

Athletic field maintenance. Maintenance of athletic fields requires large-scale turfgrass equipment and a few specialized skills if baseball infields are involved. The market for athletic field maintenance has grown as the number of facilities provided by parks, municipalities, schools, military bases, and others have increased. The continuing increase in soccer has helped fuel the demand for playing and practice fields. Organizations have found it is often more efficient to contract seasonal maintenance rather than invest in full-time employees and equipment.

In addition to potential growth and profits, athletic field management extends the working season and can provide some good publicity and public relations. Some firms offer special deals for schools and non-profit organizations.

Water features. Again, some firms specialize in design, installation, and management of water features. The ability of a firm to construct water features often helps in marketing management services. Clients are typically unable to properly care for fountains, pools, ponds, and lakes, opening opportunities for contract firms. Water features require understanding of the basic biology of the aquatic system and specialized techniques.

Snow removal. Depending on whom you ask, snow removal can be a necessary evil or a real moneymaker. Snow removal is primarily a commercial and high-end residential market service. Some contractors claim to make 20 to 30 percent profit or more. There are numerous owners of four-wheel drive vehicles anxious to subcontract work. Make sure the subcontractor is reliable, understands the procedures, and insured, because you are the one who receives the complaint calls.

Holiday decorations. Many contractors sell Christmas trees during the holiday season. Decorating commercial and residential properties for the Christmas holiday season has become big business. For some companies it has been a long time moneymaker, but now there are at least three national franchising companies on the scene. Holiday decorations have become the hottest add-on service in recent years. Do the homework and choose quality.

Photo 2.9. Compost and mulch have become profitable additions for some landscape firms. In addition to an environmental disposal method for landscape debris and clippings, composting produces very marketable soil conditioners and organic mulch.

Other add-ons. The breadth of different services offered by landscape maintenance contractors is sometimes amazing. They often reflect the expertise of the principal or employees and differ locally and regionally. Some additional landscape services include: parking lot sweeping; driveway sealing; power washing; small engine repair; brush control and disposal; firewood sales; composting; beach cleaning; stream cleaning and management; equipment rental; and many more.

Franchising

Franchising of lawn care and landscape maintenance by national or regional firms has enjoyed tremendous gain the last 20 years. Recent growth of the industry, much of it because of the impact of franchises, has been unparalleled. The ability to sell new franchises depends on the success of current franchises.

Franchising requires trading operating independence and some profits in order to become part of a larger, proven company. Managers must operate within clearly defined guidelines and there is less room for innovation or system development. However, 64 percent of franchise managers surveyed felt they would have been less successful than they presently were if they had entered the same business independently.

Applicants for lawn and landscape management franchises are heavily screened; acceptance rates of some companies are as low as one percent. Many new lawn care franchisees have little or no experience in the green industry. Some have no administrative experience. This has and will change as competitiveness and regulatory issues increase.

Franchisers typically require an initial fee and a percent of gross revenues. Initial fees are on a sliding scale depending on market, territory, and the package provided by the company (vehicles, product, computers, etc.). A brief survey of franchisers (including Christmas decorating and national lawn care firms) indicated initial fees range from $3,000 to $80,000 or more and royalty payment can range from six to 10 percent of gross. Franchiser revenue comes primarily from royalty fees.

There are some distinct benefits available to franchise managers. They are provided computer technology and marketing resources they could not otherwise afford. They also receive technical, managerial, and administrative training. The proven operating system has been developed through years of field-testing and research. They enjoy the purchasing power of a large firm and have access to technical resources, training, and information that might otherwise be unavailable. Franchising puts a small, new business instantly on a very professional scale with uniforms, vehicles, product consistency, and a strong trade name. Not all franchises, however, offer the same investment potential.

Some franchises eventually convert to independent operations and some employees leave the operation to begin competing firms. Some franchisees maintain separate operations offering other support services (mowing, tree care, snow removal, etc.) not available through the national firm. The lack of independence and the annual reduction in gross are the primary disadvantages according to many managers.

HANDLING CUSTOMER COMPLAINTS

Professionalism is also educating and informing the client. Providing information on all aspects of the services provided including products, techniques, safety precautions, and the customer's role, is a benefit to everyone.

The first step in dealing with customer complaints comes before they occur, during the selling of the program. Educate the client on what to realistically expect. Properties poorly maintained for several years will take some time to bring back. Weeds do not disappear over night.

Return the client's phone calls as soon as possible. No one likes to be ignored or think they are being ignored. How irate did you get when your valid complaint about a product or service was not answered for several days? Train receptionists and secretaries to be pleasant and helpful. Questions and concerns should be routed to the person who can best handle them. Attitude begets attitude. Ninety-six percent of a typical landscape business' clientele do not complain. Fifty to 74 percent of customers who do complain will continue to do business with that company if the complaint is resolved. Retention of customers who complain jumps to 95 percent, if their complaints are resolved quickly.

KEEPING CUSTOMERS

Keeping clients is as important as obtaining them in the first place and more cost efficient. According to a Michigan State University survey, obtaining a new landscape management customer costs the company five times more than servicing an existing one.

A firm should strive to achieve at least 90 percent retention. Sixty-five percent of an average landscape firm's business comes from current satisfied clients. Landscape and lawn management clientele look for reliability, responsiveness, empathy, and tangible benefits. Returning customers allow the company to recapture start-up costs incurred at the initiation of the work. A new job may not come in on budget because of the time required for the crew to become familiar with the site or client, and lots of other reasons. Customer retention opens sales for minor or remedial landscape installation and additional work.

Develop surveys to gauge the client's satisfaction and solve small problems. A survey of clientele is critical to provide immediate feedback on how the firm is doing. Fifty-eight percent of managers responding to a 2003 online study survey their customers by mail or phone at least once a year. New clients should be contacted in person or by mail within 30 to 60 days of initiating the contract. A second survey should be sent before contract renewal. Did the firm meet the customer's exceptions? Identify areas where there may have been miscommunication. Do not expect 100 percent response. Satisfied customers may not respond, but those with problems will almost certainly mail back the survey with comments. Experience with commercial clients has indicated a typical response rate of 30 to 40 percent to mail surveys. Commercial and multi-family residential clients often have a need to meet with the firm's manager/owner and provide feedback.

When negative surveys are returned, someone, usually the manager, should respond as quickly as possible. When dealing with customer concerns, try to see the problem from the client's point of view. Be tactful and provide a full explanation of the solution or lack of solution. Most times the problem will be something minor that the crew or manger was not aware existed. There are also times when the client has unreasonable expectations or requirements. A follow-up should be conducted in two to four weeks after the initial response to make sure the problem is solved.

Also survey returning clients during the season and again before contract renewal. The firm's ability to solve problems, respond to requests, and provide value for the money develops long-term relationships.

Bibliography

1. Anonymous. 1999. Getting the job. *Lawn & Landscape* 20(8):8.

2. Anonymous. 1999. Selecting a professional. *www.malta-inc.org/select.html* 9/19/99.

3. Anonymous. 1999. Selecting the right business name. *www.tfuller.com/600club/fx070014.htm* 11/2/99.

4. Anonymous. 2001. Market value. *Lawn & Landscape* 22(8):8.

5. Anonymous. 2002. Why customers quit. *Lawn & Landscape* 23(11):16.

6. Anonymous. 2003. Survey says. *Lawn & Landscape* 24(5):8.

7. Anonymous. 2003. Follow the yellow brick road. *Lawn & Landscape* 24(7):12.

8. Bruce, F. and M. Lynch. 1990. Customer service. *Florida Foliage* 16(9):7.

9. Capozzi, P. 1990. Uniforms: Helping shape professionalism in the green industry. *Lawn & Landscape Maintenance* 11(10):12.

10. Carnes, B. 1989. Public relations. *Grounds Maintenance* 24(4):90.

11. Clancy, D. 1996. The appeal of a professional. *T&O Service Tech* 1(1):26.

12. Code, C. 1989. Creative marketing targets customer's specialized needs. *ALA/Maintenance* 10(3):22.

13. Code, C. 1996. Professionalism *T&O Service Tech* 1:(2):4.

14. Dyer, A. 1999. Deck the halls. *Lawn & Landscape* 20(8):40.

15. Evans, J. 1993. Keeping in touch. *Lawn & Landscape Maintenance* 14(5):48.

16. Gibson, S. 1997. Take landscape renovation seriously. *Lawn & Landscape* 18(4):52.

17. Hampshire, K. 2000. Uniform appeal. *Lawn & Landscape* 21(10):70.

18. Hampshire, K. 2001. Commercial break. *Lawn & Landscape* 22(10):58.

19. Hampshire, K. 2001. He said, she said. *Lawn & Landscape* 22(11):540.

20. Harrington, W. 1996. Add-on services. *Grounds Maintenance* 31(11):26.

21. Hall, R. 1997. Christmas decorating may offer $$ opportunities. *Landscape Maintenance* 36(11):1.

22. Hensley, D. 1987. Scouting for business. *Nursery Manager* 3(7):60.

23. Hensley, D. 1991. Taking care of your business. *Nursery Manager* 7(7):115.

24. Hensley, D. 1993. Are you keeping up with trends in the business? *Nursery Manager* 9(5):70.

25. Hensley, D. 1997. Professionalism always victor over price cutting. *Hawaii Landscape* 1(1):4.

26. Hensley, D. and J. Rathlef. 1991. Choose the right name, logo for your business. *Nursery Manager* 9(7):97.

27. Krotz, D. 1995. Growing public relations. *Maintenance Executive* 8(4):18.

28. Kujawa, R. 1999. Competing with low-price contractors. *Grounds Maintenance* 34(10):13.

29. Marcellino, M. 1989. Selling, servicing the competitive homeowner market. *Lawn and Landscape Maintenance* 10(9):22.

30. McKeown, M. 2001. Hitting the internet landscape jackpot. *Southwest Trees & Turf* 6(1):12.

31. McNamee, N. 1990. When the customer is dead wrong. *Grounds Maintenance* 25(8):80.

32. McNiel, R. and D. Hensley. 1981. Improving your advertising. *Southern Florist and Nurseryman* 94(41):9.

33. Merrifield, B., Jr. 1993. Perfect Service. *American Nurseryman* 177(7):67.

34. Petree, J. 1988. Direct mail. *American Nurseryman* 168(3)1:91.

35. Petree, J. 1988. The write stuff. *American Nurseryman* 167(8)15:93.

36. Petree, J. 1988. Writing copy right! *American Nurseryman* 168(9)1:97.

37. Pilon, C. 1998. Growing greener with direct mail marketing. *Lawn & Landscape* 19(4):104.

38. Ricciardi, C. 1990. Specialized marketing methods attract and keep clients for interiorscape firms. *Landscape Contractor* 31(5):22.

39. Roche, J. 1999. Christmas/holiday decorations. *Landscape & Irrigation* 23(6):8.

40. Rose, V. 1987. Cracking the commercial market. *ALA* 8(5):30.

41. Schwabe, H. 1999. Water garden, pan, and lake management. *Landscape & Irrigation* 23(5):78.

42. Schrimpf, P. 1995. Necessity is the mother of add-on services. *Lawn & Landscape Maintenance* 16(10):30.

43. Schrimpf, P. 1996. Top add-on services. *Lawn & Landscape* 17(11):36.

44. Schrimpf, P. 1998. More than good looks. *Lawn & Landscape* 19(1):76.

45. Schrimpf, P and B. West. 1997. Adding on adds up fast. *Lawn & Landscape* 18(9):55.

46. Small, L. 1999. How to create a successful yellow pages ad. *Lawn & Landscape* 20(3):39.

47. Spiers, L. 2003. Scratching a niche. *Lawn & Landscape* 23(3):148.

48. Stiles, B. 1990. Promotion ideas to boost your sales. *Landscape Contractor* 31(1):36.

49. Wagner, W. 1990. Avoiding the pitfalls of yellow pages advertising. *Lawn & Landscape Maintenance* 11(9):40.

50. Welterlen, M. 1999. Business is booming. *Grounds Maintenance* 34(10):6.

51. Weller, C. 1997. An image-making marketing too. *Grounds Maintenance* 32(5):58.

52. West, B. 1997. When the call comes in. *Lawn & Landscape* 18(6):75.

53. West, B. 1997. Adding irrigation to the mix. *Lawn & Landscape* 18(6):77.

54. West, B. 1997. Service First. *Lawn & Landscape* 18(12):38.

55. West, B. 1997. Breaking the model. *Lawn & Landscape* 18(12):46.

56. West, B. 1998. Franchising. *Lawn & Landscape* 19(6):28.

57. Westrick, D. 1990. Operators turning to franchising more frequently. *ALA* 11(2):34.

Chapter 3
Specifications and Contracts[1]

Landscapes are sizable investments in the beauty, quality, and value of every developed site. The relationship between the client and the contractor selected to care for the landscape must be established on business and professional terms. Although the integrity of the parties is still important, good business is seldom conducted with a handshake and a smile. Misunderstandings between clients and landscape management contractors can and do develop. Adopting well-written specifications, guidelines, and contracts avoids confusion for both parties.

LANDSCAPE MANAGEMENT SPECIFICATIONS

Mention the word specifications to many contractors and they grimace. Specifications are sometimes viewed as inordinate, unnecessary, and the bane of the contractor. Specifications and guidelines, however, serve to detail the requirements and expectations of the owner and to protect the client and the contractor.

Specifications, guidelines, programs, and/or schedules are simply methods of communication from the client (property owner/manager, condominium board, etc.) or his/her agent (landscape architect, designer, or consultant) to the landscape management contractor or in-house personnel establishing the ground rules of what, how, and when maintenance services are to be performed on the site.

Specifications may be part of the request for bids, the contract documents, or the final contract. Specifications vary widely in their use, complexity, and adherence. They become legally binding when made part of a final, signed contract.

Photo 3.1. Specifications and contracts needlessly strike fear in the hearts and minds of some landscape management contractors. Specifications and contracts are communication instruments that can protect the client and the contractor.

[1] Very special thanks to the late David W. Suddarth, for his input, expertise, and friendship.

Most frequently, specifications are produced by a landscape architect, designer, or consultant at the request of and to protect the owner. Maintenance specifications, programs, or schedules are often part of the client's contractual expectations of the landscape architect. Many landscape architects insist that maintenance instructions are part of their developmental services. They want to be assured that the landscape they have designed will be cared for properly so that it may achieve its design intent.

Specifications protect the owner by ensuring that all necessary care for the landscape and protection for the environment are considered by the contractor. They also establish standards for the work. Specifications provide a uniform format for bids and estimates when several contractors are being considered for a property. The owner can evaluate the various prices for conducting the same work; he/she can compare apples with apples.

Specifications also protect the contractor. By describing the limits of responsibility, the contractor is forestalled from doing work not included in the proposal or bid. Specifications may also establish billing and payment dates and requirements.

Landscape management contractors produce specifications or programs and maintenance schedules. These document details of the program included in the proposal and the obligations of the contractor and owner.

Writing Specifications

The information herein is a *guide*. It is based on research, published recommendations, industry specifications and landscape programs, and the knowledge and experience of many landscape professionals. These guidelines will not necessarily be used in their entirety for every landscape project. The scope and detail for a 5,000 square foot residential property differ from those of a 500-acre commercial site. The specifications or program will also differ, but are no less important to the contractor and client.

The guidelines should be adapted, developed, and revised to meet the needs of the individual property and landscape, quality expectations of the owner and users, and budget. It is impossible to address the care of each individual plant used in landscapes or anticipate every potential problem that may be encountered. Each situation must be evaluated individually. The hope, however, is that these guidelines will serve as a basis for development of individual landscape management specifications and programs.

In this discussion of specifications, we will consider the views of the typical author (landscape architect, designer, or property manager) and the typical reader (the landscape management contractor). The goal of the landscape architect or property manager and maintenance contractor is to provide the property owner the best landscape care possible at a fair price. The communications set forth within specifications should be between members of the same team, not the weapons of adversaries.

Developing meaningful and fair specifications for landscape maintenance is challenging. There are no set standards for their preparation or use. Landscape maintenance specifications vary widely in style, detail, complexity, and scope. Many variables such as climate, plants, soils, and local cultural practices must be considered. Each maintenance operation and manager, landscape site, and client is unique.

Specifications are used to communicate the management requirements, quality expectations, business arrangements, and limitations for a landscape site to the various companies proposing bids for the intended services. Specifications become binding agreements when they are made part of the landscape maintenance contract. Since specifications will usually serve as part of legal documents, the utmost care should be exercised in their crafting.

Several simple one-size-fits-all landscape maintenance specifications and contracts are available from professional societies, consultants, texts, and other publications. While providing a good format and starting point, these universal documents should not be adopted verbatim. Good specifications and contracts use the writer's experience and reflect regional and site variations.

Computers make repeated preparation of contract documents easier. A master outline or template for specifications or contracts is stored, easily recalled and modified to meet the specific needs of the project. This luxury, unfortunately, can result in the specifications becoming stale or not changing with landscape management technology or the site. Landscape architects too frequently use specifications prepared for earlier projects without rewriting them. Each site has unique problems and requirements and, accordingly, specifications must be adjusted.

If the landscape architecture or design firm is developing and implementing projects in various regions of the country, then the landscape architect or project manager should solicit advice and comments from local extension and university personnel, landscape professionals, consultants, or management contractors. If you do not know what is appropriate in a specific situation, find out.

Landscape maintenance specifications developed for a private client, for work let to a limited bid list, or for negotiated contracts, will be simpler than those issued by public agencies. Since most public work requires acceptance of the lowest acceptable bid, public agencies use detailed and stringent specifications to protect against incompetent or unscrupulous contractors. The management procedures are detailed and the selection of materials limited. Specifications for federal and other government work may set the wage rates paid to laborers and the type of equipment used. The qualifications required of the landscape maintenance contractor will also be rigid. The firm's records and performance will likely be audited.

As with any writing, specification crafting begins with an outline. List every management area that will be covered and discussed. Put the meat on the outline by fleshing out the maintenance procedures, quality expectations, and limitations for each management area. Specifications, like contracts, are written in sections. Each section is divided into sub-sections, articles, or paragraphs.

Also communicate the important business, safety, and professional aspects for the project. Consult published specifications, those written for the firm's previous projects, or those received for other projects, for style, guidance, and inspiration. Select a comfortable format and begin writing. A thorough set of instructions requires several drafts; review them for content and clarity. Have the work reviewed and edited by others.

Photo 3.2. Specifications and contracts for large public properties may be detailed and complex. Read them thoroughly and understand what is required before submitting a bid.

The words *shall, will,* and *should* are repeated throughout the specifications and writers and readers alike must understand their definitions. *Shall* and *will* are requirements – the activity or restriction is compulsory. *Should* is a strong suggestion.

A workable format for landscape management specifications might include: *Title, Scope of Work, General Conditions,* and *Technical Specifications.*

I. Title

The *Title* is the subject of the specifications, such as:

- *Specifications for Site Management for _____.*

- *Landscape Management Program for _____.*

- *Specifications for the Maintenance of the Turf and Landscape at _____.*

The title may also include the specific areas of the proposal, such as turf or annual color beds, if it is limited to these sections.

II. Scope of Work

The *Scope of Work* provides a very brief overview of what is expected of the successful landscape management contractor.

- *Scope of Work: Furnish all supervision, labor, material, equipment, and transportation required to maintain the landscape in an attractive condition throughout the year, as specified below.*

- *Scope of Work: Furnish all necessary supervision, labor, material, equipment, and transportation to complete the work described herein.*

- *Scope of Work: Provide supervision, labor, material, equipment, and transportation, necessary to provide complete and continuous maintenance of all trees, shrubs, groundcovers, lawns, seasonal color beds, and all other work connected thereto as specified below.*

Do not get carried away with excessive details in the Scope of Work; that is the purpose of the later sections. Indicate what the company is expected to provide: material; labor; and equipment. Some authors also incorporate supervision, transportation, proper licenses and insurance, and other details into the scope. While these items may be taken for granted, including them in the Scope of Work is worthwhile and recommended.

III. General Conditions

General Conditions address important business, safety, operations, definitions, restrictions, and other non-horticultural items to protect the site, client, and landscape management contractor. General Conditions of specifications, programs, and contracts list the project location, period of expected service, develop and establish the business relationship between the participants, establish or limit responsibilities, and communicate particular requirements. General conditions or requirements are also used to establish qualifications required for the landscape management contractors who may wish to bid on the project.

The term, *"Owner,"* is typically defined early in General Conditions to refer to the client or his/her legally designated official representative. The *"Landscape Management Contractor"* or *"Contractor"* is defined as the individual or firm providing the contract services or his/her official representative.

The following items have been adapted from General Conditions of landscape management specifications, guidelines, and contracts. The particular topics included in General Conditions vary with author, client, and site; not all are required or desirable for every landscape site.

A. Location

The *location* describes exactly where the work will be performed. The location may be simply an address or a legalistic description of the property, such as *...bounded by Elm Avenue to the North and Magnolia Street to the West.* The location where

the work will be conducted is also included in landscape management contracts.

- *"Location of work: JDH Corporate Office Center, 2113 Noah Avenue, Anytown, AR 77777 (a 20-acre commercial site, bounded by Erin Drive on the West, Brooke Avenue on the East and by Jessica Street to the South)."*

Specifications and guidelines sometimes contain maps of the areas to be maintained. Maps are critical if only sections of a site fall under the proposal, or if the areas are scattered within a larger property (such as sections of a campus or military base).

B. Period of service or contract duration

The *period of service*, sometimes called contract duration, is the length of time for the contracted landscape management. The duration is typically from one calendar date to another.

- "The landscape management work described herein will begin September 1, 2006 and end August 31, 2007."

C. Materials

Quality and standards for *material* used in landscape management may be described within a General Conditions section or within the technical specifications section later. Standards and acceptable quality descriptions for landscape plants and construction material are common as a discrete section in landscape installation specifications. Material quality standards are not, however, often used in landscape management specifications or in maintenance contracts.

Material quality and limitations in landscape management are best dealt with in the later technical specifications sections involving their use. Fertilizers are briefly discussed in sections involving fertilization, annuals or other plant size or quality in the color section, and water in the irrigation paragraphs. Presume that the contractor will be reasonable and quality-oriented.

The one material I would be sure to address is water. Concerns can be easily dispatched with a simple sentence, *"All water will be furnished by the owner,"* or similar wording in the irrigation section of the technical specifications. Unnecessary as it may seem, I have read specifications requiring the contractor to furnish the water for the site and heard of one case where the contractor ended up paying the water bill.

D. Schedule

The *schedule* lists the times the landscape contractor's employees will have access to the property for work. Access times are typically selected for the convenience of the client and are usually limited to a normal five or six-day work week. The schedule usually restricts start and end times for work. This is especially important for multi-family residential sites. No one wants to wake to the whine of a leaf blower at 5:30 a.m. It is common for specifications for condominiums, apartments, and other residential communities to restrict the hours that loud equipment can be used. Exceptions are usually made for emergency work, such as repairing storm damage.

Access to the site at times other than those scheduled might be granted with prior permission to make up work lost due to inclement weather or other abnormal circumstances. Seven-day per week access might be required for landscape management of resorts, where maintenance is constant.

It is not uncommon for a client to require the names of employees and an estimated work schedule, especially if the work will be conducted only one or two days per week. This is a matter of security and planning for the client.

Schedule (for condominium site)

- *The contractor shall have access to the property Monday through Friday, between the hours of 7:30 a.m. and 4:30 p.m. The maintenance schedule shall be designed to minimize disruption to residents. Loud motorized equipment should not be operated in close proximity to residential units prior to 8:00 a.m.*

  The contractor will submit the names of all employees and their general work schedule to the resident manager. This information will be updated whenever there is a change in personnel or work schedule for the site.

Schedule (for resort hotel site)

- *The contractor shall have a seven-day per week work schedule. The names of employ-*

Photo 3.3. Resorts may require 7-day a week staffing for services. Work times may also be restricted for the convenience of the guests.

ees and the time of day they will be on the job site performing required maintenance duties will be submitted to the manager. The maintenance schedule shall be designed to minimize disruption to hotel guests and must be approved by the manager prior to implementation or change. Motorized equipment shall not be operated in close proximity of guest rooms prior to 8:30 a.m.

E. Other items included in General Conditions

The number of additional items or sections included in the General Conditions of landscape management specifications varies with author, complexity of the site, and requirements of the client. Some items, such as payment schedule, insurance requirements, dispute resolution, and others may be addressed in the specifications as a point of information for bidders. These important business items and clauses will certainly be addressed within the contract.

Other items that are important to the client such as uniforms, employee appearance, and safety items are included in the General Conditions and are made part of the legally binding requirement upon signing of the contract. The following sections have been used in landscape management specifications to address the concerns, security, safety, and liability of clients.

Licenses and insurance requirements. The client must be assured that the contractor has all required licenses, adequate insurance coverage, and meets all other legal requirements necessary to remain in business. Some states license landscape contractors, but others do not. A pesticide applicator license or certification is required in all states. Any local licenses or certifications necessary to conduct business should also be mandatory.

Adequate insurance coverage is crucial to protect the client and contractor, and high limits are typically required. Demand that the landscape management contractor obtain and maintain necessary insurance coverage: worker's compensation, public or general liability, property damage, and any other insurance as required by federal, state, or local laws. It is essential that the contractor understand what level of insurance might be required over and above that which the company normally maintains. Additional insurance means additional costs that must be factored into the bid. Proof of insurance, and sometimes compliance with worker's compensation and other taxes, may be required for the client's file. Some clients require that they be listed as additional insured on general liability insurance.

Insurance requirements

- *The Landscape Contractor shall carry and maintain at his/her expense the insurance listed below. Insurance coverage will be continuous. The Owner or his/her representative must be notified immediately upon cancellation of any insurance as per the specification requirements.*

  - *Worker's Compensation*

  - *Temporary Disability Insurance (TDI) to the statutory limit*

  - *Comprehensive or General Liability Insurance of ___ ($1,000,000 is a standard minimum)*

  - *Vehicle Insurance including ___ Bodily Injury and ___ Property Damage coverage*

  - *Insurance coverage for damages on all equipment supplied by Owner*

  - *General Liability insurance*

  - *Other insurance as appropriate and required.*

Insurance

- *The Landscape Contractor shall provide proof of insurance (original Certificate of Insurance) throughout the contract term. Without evidence of current insurance, the contract is considered invalid and the Landscape Contractor shall be prohibited from the property. The certificate shall reference the name of the property, name of additional insured as requested by owner, and adhere to the following limits of liability:*

  - *Worker's Compensation: Statutory limit.*

  - *Automobile Collision: $1 Million.*

  - *Comprehensive General Liability: $1 Million.*

Licensing

- *The Landscape Contractor shall maintain a valid Landscape Contractors License from the State of _____. The Landscape Contractor shall maintain valid State of _____ Pest Control Operators (or Commercial Pesticide Applicator or other appropriate) License in the categories necessary to perform work as required herein as per governmental rules and regulations.*

- *The Landscape Contractor must meet all federal and state requirements with regard to the handling of landscape chemicals and assumes all liability for the application of pesticides and chemicals in the maintenance of this site.*

Tax and license requirements

- *The Landscape Contractor shall provide the Owner his/her General Excise Tax License (required in some states) number, Federal Employer Identification Number and copies of any and all other licenses necessary to perform the work herein.*

Protection and safety. Every owner expects the contractor's employees to work safely and to protect the site from damage. Should damage occur because of the actions of landscape employees, the owner has the legal and ethical right to have the damage repaired at the contractor's expense.

The owner should establish safety requirements in the General Conditions of the landscape management specifications or contract to help limit liability due to injury of a resident, customer, or passer-by because of actions by a contractor's employee. Additionally, the contractor should be required to provide proof of insurance.

Protection of existing structures and facilities

- Precautions will be taken to avoid damage to existing structures and all facilities above and below ground. Any and all damage to the Owner's property resulting from actions or neglect of the Landscape Management Contractor or his/her employees shall be corrected and/or paid for by the Landscape Management Contractor at no cost to the Owner.

Protection of property during inclement weather

- The Landscape Management Contractor will report any storm damage to the Owner's representative immediately.

Safety

- All work will be performed in a manner safe to the operators, occupants, landscape users, and pedestrians. Equipment will be operated in a safe manner with all appropriate safety shields and devices in place and operational.

- *Safety gear:* OSHA (and/or equivalent state organization) approved safety protection shall be worn by workers at all time when operating landscape power equipment.

  1. Safety vests shall be worn while performing work in parking lots or on or within __ feet of vehicular streets/roadways.

  2. Safety glasses or face shields are required when eye protection is necessary, including such duties as edging and trimming with power equipment.

  3. Hearing protection is required during operation of power blowers, chain saws, and all other equipment that may damage hearing.

- *Traffic and vehicle safety procedures* are required when work is performed within vehicular traffic areas (median islands, parking lots or garages, streets/roadways, or other).

  1. Safety cones will be used to alert traffic and pedestrians of maintenance operations near walks and traffic ways.

  2. Hazard safety lights will be used when personnel are stopped in a traffic area.

  3. Debris hazardous to pedestrians, residents, or motorists will be removed immediately.

  4. Landscape personnel must adhere to all state and local vehicular laws and regulations.

Employee dress and conduct. Address employee dress and conduct in specifications if it is important to the client. These requirements might include uniforms, uniforms of a specific color, English speaking supervisors to aid communication, restrictions for breaks, lunch, smoking or playing music on site, or prohibit the employees from using resident's hose bibs, furniture, or other items.

Uniforms

- The Landscape Contractor shall provide all employees working on the site with uniforms of the same standard color that display the company logo and employee's name.

Dress Code

- For the purpose of employee identification of all personnel working on the property, the contractor shall provide uniforms and/or other employee identification approved by the Owner.

Employee dress and conduct

- Employees shall wear uniforms (of a particular color or style - with or without names) and carry other employee identification. Employee lunches will be taken in designated areas or off-site. Smoking is prohibited on the site. Foul or abusive language and excessive noise is prohibited.

Supervisory personnel

- Supervisory personnel on site must be able to communicate in English, orally and in writing, with the Owner or his/her representative.

Business items. Many authors include various business items in the General Conditions. The number of sections varies with the style and complexity of the contract. Many of the items such as payment schedule, dispute resolution, and cancellation will appear later in the contract.

Payment schedule

- *The contract for the successful vendor shall be for 12 equally divided payments for the entire amount agreed upon. Payments are due to the Landscape Contractor by the 10th working day of each month, after receipt of an invoice for the work performed for the previous month. Payment for any extra work contracted and approved in writing by the Owner or his/her representative shall be included in the Landscape Contractor's monthly invoice statement.*

Dispute resolution

- *In the event that a dispute may arise with respect to any matters relating to this contract, resolution of the matter will be attempted with the aid of a mediator. Should mediation fail to resolve the dispute, the Owner and Contractor will present their case to a mutually agreed upon arbitrator and decision of the arbitrator will be final.*

- *If at any time a controversy arises between the Landscape Contractor and Owner with respect to any matters relating to this contract, the parties will first attempt to settle the matter through mediation. Upon failure of mediation, the matter will be resolved by arbitration administered by and in accordance with the rules of the American Arbitration Association, unless the parties mutually agree otherwise.*

- *In the event that either party becomes involved in litigation or arbitration arising out of this landscape management contract or the interpretation or performance thereof, the prevailing party shall receive reasonable attorney fees.*

Cancellation of the agreement

- *The Landscape Management Contractor and the Owner have the right to terminate the maintenance contract with a written notification of 30 days.*

- *Either party upon __ (usually 30) days written notice may cancel the landscape management contract. The exception shall be that the Owner may cancel the contract upon ___ days written notice in the event of documented non-performance/neglect/failure to perform as per specifications and contract agreed upon by Landscape Contractor and Owner.*

- *The Owner shall have the right to terminate the maintenance contract with written notification of 30 days, and payment of 10 percent of the annual contract amount within 15 days after receipt of the final billing by the Landscape Contractor. The Landscape Contractor shall be liable for any cost incurred by the Owner for any supplemental landscape maintenance, if needed to fulfill the contract requirements in the event of failure of Landscape Contractor to perform duties up to the point of contract cancellation.*

Communications and reports (condominium project)

- *The Landscape Contractor shall submit monthly status reports and organize monthly walk-throughs with the resident manager to review maintenance progress, discuss problems, and receive additional direction.*

Project inspections

- *The Landscape Contractor or a representative will schedule an inspection with the Owner or his/her representative every ____ (days or weeks) to inspect the project maintenance and to discuss issues. The Owner's representative will submit a written list of items not completed by the Landscape Contractor in compliance with specifications. The Landscape Contractor shall satisfy valid items on the written list prior to the next scheduled inspection.*

Bidder qualifications. The *Basis for Selection* or *bidder qualifications* establish credentials for bidders and for determining the successful landscape contractor. Most common in government work, the basis of selection sets forth requirements for experience, qualifications, previous work of similar scope, required financial disclosure, requisite equipment, quality assurance programs, and others. Qualifying the bidders helps to assure that the successful firm is viable, sufficient in size to handle the work, and understands requirements for working with the government agency.

Government specifications often provide advantages in bidder selection for minority business. Definitions of a minority business vary with state and agency and proof is always required.

Government agency requests for services/specifications require adherence to various mandatory contractual provisions covering nondiscrimination, conflict of interest, drug-free workplaces, buy American requirements, minimum wages, and others.

Some General Conditions request attendance of a formal pre-proposal conference. Typically, any questions asked during the conference and the answers to those questions become part of the government's request for services and eventually the contract. As one might imagine, hard and fast answers to landscape contractor's questions are difficult to come by at these meetings.

Limitations to the Work. Regardless of the author, safeguards and limitations are built into General Conditions of landscape management specifications and will certainly be part of any signed contract. *Limitations to the work* establish that the landscape management contractor will not be required to conduct work not included in the specifications and contract, and that the client will not be charged for work performed beyond the contract without prior approval. Other limitations in landscape management specifications and contracts typically address responsibility for damage due to Acts of God or vandalism, and any other issues necessary for the landscape contractor or client's peace of mind.

The following are examples from landscape management specifications limiting the landscape contractor's responsibility and protecting the client.

- *All items not detailed or listed within these specifications shall be considered extra and will be charged separately according to the nature of the work.*

- *The Owner must authorize additional work identified outside the scope of the resulting agreement in advance.*

IV. Technical specifications

The *Technical Specifications* are the essence of the instructions to bidders. Technical Specifications communicate the chronology, methods, materials, restrictions, standards, grades, and quality that are requested and required.

The Technical Specifications section is organized into *sections*, each covering important elements within the landscape: Trees; Shrubs; Turf or Lawns; Seasonal Color (annuals and/or bulbs); Groundcovers; Walks and Parking Areas; Irrigation System; and others, as necessary. Subsections under each of the sections detail the specific care appropriate for the particular segment of the landscape, such as fertilization, pruning, irrigation, pest management, snow removal, and others.

Care requirements in the subsections should be clear, concise, and as explicit as necessary. Make the subsection instructions results-oriented wherever possible. The client wants more than the shrub beds weeded, he/she wants weed-free beds. Consider what the end result should be and put it in writing when possible.

Avoid generalities such as "good" or "workman-like manner" unless these qualities are defined or details are presented to explain what is meant. What workman-like or acceptable is to one person may not be to another. Hence, everyone is unhappy and a lawsuit may result.

Quantify specifications by providing measurable guidelines when possible.

- *All newly planted trees will be watered weekly (every 7 days) during the first ten (10) weeks after planting by applying water with a hand-set sprinkler and hose. The sprinkler shall cover an area no less than 10 feet and no more than 30 feet in diameter and will run for no less than one (1) hour per setting to ensure wetting of the soil below the establishing root zone (2 feet). No sprinkler shall run for more than two (2) hours.*

Although these requirements to water newly planted trees seem excessive and wordy, they leave few questions to interpretation and are verifiable.

Other factors that can be quantified or verified include: time; distance; volume; weight; area; per unit production; and cost.

In some situations it is impossible to establish quantifiable standards or quality. How does one describe a well-mown lawn? It is difficult, if not impossible, to depict what is expected in measurable terms. In these situations, write the instructions so that if they are followed, then only an acceptable job will result. Include drawings, details, maps, plans, or other documents that will make the requirements clearer.

Photo 3.4. Not every potential problem can be addressed in specifications or contracts. Mowing too soon after a rain or irrigation resulted in unacceptable tracks in the turf. The landscape contractor should be prepared to offer remedy when the call comes.

- *Cool season turf on the site (see attached maps) shall be mown to a height of two inches from the first mowing in the spring until June 15 and at a height of three inches between June 15 and until August 15. The mowing height will be returned to two inches after August 15. Each mowing will be conducted at a frequency so as to not remove more than 1/3 (one-third) of the leaf blade per mowing. A rotary mower with sharp blades will be used so as not to tear the leaf blades. The direction of mowing will be alternated every mowing.*

  All clippings in areas adjacent to the building (marked on attached maps) will be collected by bagging or raking and removed from the site. Clippings in all other areas will be dispersed over the grass so as not to be unsightly. If clippings in these areas remain evident 24 hours after mowing they should be dispersed by blowing, bagging, or raking. All clippings will be removed from walks, curbs, and parking areas.

If accepted and recommended standards for, in this example, mowing cool season turf in the given region, are detailed, an acceptable quality mowing will result.

Do not use references in technical specifications subsections unless they are included in the bid documents. *"Shrubs shall be pruned with a thinning technique as detailed and set forth in the State Extension Pruning Guide."* Unless a copy of this Extension publication is included with the specifications, the statement is worthless.

Even with results-oriented or well-written technical specifications, it may be necessary to address some restrictions or exceptions. Techni-

cal specifications give direction, but they also provide license. If the trees must be pruned but the climber cannot use climbing spurs, then say so. Incorporate major restrictions, but be reasonable. No one can anticipate and provide for everything that can possibly go wrong.

Other explicit restrictions may be listed within the pertinent sections, Technical Specifications. Such as:

- *Pruning of trees greater than 20 feet in height requires the services of a certified arborist and will be covered under a separate contract.*

The above example sets the height of trees that fall under the landscape contractor's responsibility at 20 feet. Trees around this height or shorter can safely be pruned from the ground with pole pruners and standard equipment. Pruning trees that require climbing, lifts, or special equipment is best left to experts for the sake of the contractor and the client. This statement might be found in the tree-pruning segment of the Technical Specifications.

Individual Sections and Subsections of Concern for Landscape Management Specifications. Topics and detail covered under various sections and subsections of landscape management specifications vary with author, complexity of the landscape, geographic region, local customs, and ultimately the budget allotted for landscape management.

46

Appendix 3.1 discusses some areas of concern that specification writers may wish to address in technical sections and subsections.

Contractor Prepared Specifications

Landscape management contractors produce specifications for their program(s) that are included with proposals, bids, and contracts. The contractor's motive for specified provisions is the same as that of the client or his/her agent: that is, to clearly communicate the services to be furnished, establish responsibilities and requirements, list the provisions to be agreed upon by the owner, and to avoid confusion during the implementation of the contract.

Specifications prepared by contractors vary in format and detail. Some refer to schedules listing the exact number of mowings, prunings, and other tasks. Landscape contractor specifications are typically less detailed than those produced by landscape designers. Contractor-produced specifications may also serve an educational function to explain why something is done or not done.

- *Grass clippings will be left to disintegrate and return valuable nutrients to the soil. If clippings are excessive or clumped due to dampness or delay in mowing because of inclement weather, they will either be spread or removed. Clippings in areas where people might track them into the building will also be removed after each mowing.*

The above tells the client why clippings are not bagged or raked and establishes the conditions under which they will be removed. It shows that the company is interested in maintaining quality in the landscape and demonstrates concern for the client's operation by attempting to minimize the tracking of cut grass into the building. It also teaches the client a little about nutrient recycling.

LANDSCAPE MANAGEMENT CONTRACTS

Contracts for landscape management work are not a great mystery and do not require signing in blood. A *contract* is an agreement enforceable by law protecting the client and the contractor. Contracts communicate exactly what is to be done, by whom, for a given compensation, and over what specified period of time.

Contracts provide security and most landscape management is conducted under contract. For some, however, contracts are a needless hassle often too complicated to understand. A nationwide survey of landscape management and lawn care firms indicated that 27 percent had all of their business under contract; however, 31 percent did not use written contracts.

Contracts are always found in government work and usually for work on commercial sites. Residential work is usually under some type of written agreement, especially when conducted by an established, franchised, or larger firm. Some new or small firms still do not use contracts for all of their accounts. Some of this work is likely done on a cash basis and not reported. Regardless, landscape management without a written agreement or contract is a problem waiting to happen.

The basics of a good contract are uniform. The subject of the contract must be legal, there must be just compensation, there must be mutual agreement established and communicated by the parties, and the agreement must be made without duress. Local and state regulations also differ regarding contract language and content. A contract is a legal document; it is defense against consumer ignorance, unreasonable demands, and Acts of God.

Several basic, uniform, or pre-printed contracts are available from landscape professional associations, consultants, and other groups. Most landscape management firms develop their own uniform agreement for bids or estimates that is adapted to each client. When adapting or developing a contract, have an attorney review it before using it or signing it.

Contracts can generally be divided into two sections, the *General Scope* and the *Specifics*.

The General Scope

The *General Scope* of the landscape management contract establishes the overall business terms of an agreement. The General Scope may refer to attached drawings, schedules, specifications, landscape plans, or other contract documents thereby making them part of the legal agreement.

The *Scope of Work* within the General Scope of a landscape management contract is the same as discussed under specifications. The Scope of Work briefly describes the work to be performed.

The exact *dimensions* and *location* of the site found in the contract General Scope might be an address or a more detailed description, as in specifications.

The *duration* included in the General Scope of the management contract is from one specific date to another.

Payment. The *payment schedule* within the General Scope is particularly important to the contractor. The payment schedule stipulates the amount the client agrees to pay and the number of installments. Contractors should make sure payment schedules are practical. Maintenance payments are usually made on a monthly basis based on invoices for the work completed during the previous month, or for a set percentage of the entire contract amount. Invoicing monthly based on work performed minimizes deficit cash flow, reduces interest accumulation on any borrowed money, and makes an all-around better business agreement since landscape management work is heavier in some months than in others.

The contractor typically invoices the client before he/she can receive payment. There may be time limitations on imposed payments, such as,

- *Contractor shall invoice completed work on the 15th day of each month and billings will be payable on or before the 25th day from the date of billing.*

Interest or other penalties may be attached if payment is not received within the specified period only if it is so stated in the contract. The maximum amount of legal interest allowed on past due accounts varies with state. Some clients, such as the federal government, may request a discount if payment is made within a specified time (seven to 10 days after invoice). This may actually be worthwhile for the contractor, given the notorious delay in payment by some public and private entities. There may be requirements for inspections and acceptance of site management procedures detailed in some contracts before payment can be invoiced or received.

Inspections. The number of *site inspections* should also be detailed if they are to be conducted. The language describing inspections may be detailed in the bid specifications and carried into the contract by referral.

Inspections are important to the client and the contractor to forestall problems, provide each party the opportunity to comment on the care of the property and performance within the contract, and the opportunity to communicate. Inspections should be looked forward to, not viewed with dread. If the contractor has done quality work, he/she should be proud to show the owner. If not, he/she should be prepared to receive complaints.

The inspection affords the contractor the chance to answer the client's questions and point out areas where additional work might be conducted. The sole purpose of an inspection should not be a selling mission, but the opportunity for additional work should never be overlooked.

Determine who will inspect the property and when the inspections will be conducted. The contractor's or owner's representative may wish to provide a checklist for the inspection. Always carry a copy of the signed agreement.

Schedule. As in the bid specifications, the *schedule* in the contract General Scope establishes the times the landscape contractor's employees have access to the property. Access days and times are selected for the convenience of the client and are customarily limited to a normal work week.

Some landscape management contracts list the holidays honored by the client or landscape contractor.

- **Holidays:** *The Contractor (or Owner) recognizes the following holidays* (list of holidays observed by the contractor or client that preclude on-site work). *Normally scheduled site visits occurring on a recognized holiday will be re-scheduled to an alternate day.*

Adverse conditions. There will always be days when scheduled work cannot be completed because of the weather or other adverse conditions beyond anyone's control. Work is rescheduled or invoices are prorated to reflect work that cannot be made up due to adverse conditions.

- *The contractor shall not be required to work during adverse conditions including, but not limited to, rainstorms, excessive wind, or fires.*

- *Work delayed due to rain or adverse conditions will be rescheduled the following day.*

Safeguards. One of the most important statements of any landscape management contract usually appears in the General Scope or at the end of the contract document. This statement establishes the limits of what is expected from the contractor and limits the obligation to do work they are not prepared to do, nor paid for under the contract. Such a statement may read,

- *All items not detailed or listed within this contract will be considered extra and shall be charged separately according to the nature of the item.*

- *This contract contains the entire agreement of the parties. Any modification, amendments, or changes shall be in writing and signed by all parties to be effective.*

Requiring additional or extra work to be approved in writing avoids failed memories of verbal agreements on tasks and payments. The written agreement for work outside the contract specifics may be as simple as a signed invoice or letter of agreement.

- **Additional Work**: *The contractor shall undertake no additional work unless agreed to in writing by both parties.*

Damage to the site. The landscape contractor is responsible for any damage to the landscape, turf or facility due to normal work procedures or accidents by his/her employees. The landscape contractor, however, should be exempted from any damage to the landscape or site due to vandalism, storms, or other circumstances beyond his/her control.

- *The contractor shall not be responsible for vandalism, theft, adverse natural conditions, Acts of God, or anything beyond the control of the contractor.*

I have seen contracts that required the landscape contractor to clean up storm damage and replace vandalized plants at no additional cost to the owner. Read and understand all provisions and ramifications of the contract before signing.

The Specifics Section

The second or *Specifics Section* of a landscape management contract establishes a series of articles, sub-sections, or paragraphs stipulating specific responsibilities and standards for maintenance operations. It is within the specifics section of the contract that the *technical specifications* of the bid document are attached and become part of the contractual agreement.

Some preprinted maintenance contracts available from trade associations and publications used by some landscape management contractors list a cafeteria of landscape management tasks. The landscape contractor and owner fill in the blanks to develop a landscape management program and to determine a price. Hopefully, the contract will be retyped to show only the agreed upon program, instead of check marks and handwritten numbers.

Below is a short example of specific sections of such a pre-printed document.

Lawn Maintenance

1. Mow, weather permitting: ( ) _____ times per month or ( ) as needed.

2. Equipment:　　　　　　　　( ) rotary mowers　　　( ) reel mowers

3. Mowing height: Cool season grass _____　　Warm season grass _____

　　　　　　　　　　　　spring _____　　　　　　spring _____

　　　　　　　　　　　　summer _____　　　　　　summer _____

　　　　　　　　　　　　fall _____　　　　　　　fall _____

4. Clippings　　　　　　　　( ) will　( ) will not be collected

5. Edge ( ) and ( ) trim　　( ) each mowing or ( ) _____ times per season.

And so on, for the each lawn or landscape task offered by the contractor.

Regardless of the type of Specifics Section used in the contract, it should provide adequate detail so that the owner understands what he/she is receiving and the standards at which the work will be done.

I spoke with one contractor who signed a landscape management agreement stating that the area would be mown to the owner's satisfaction. This was a poor choice of wording. No height or other guidelines for the turf were included. The property manager insisted that the turf (Tall fescue) be mown at one inch during the summer. A cool season turf in the Midwest mown at one inch in July is placed under inordinate stress. The quality of the turf declined rapidly and the contractor was blamed. He lost the contract in mid-season.

Granted, he was probably better off without this particular property. However, a more detailed specifics section of the landscape management contract detailing mowing operations would have prevented extra work, loss of a contract, hard feelings, and one property manager serving as a less-than-supportive reference.

Breach. *Breach of contract* is a significant and costly problem for the landscape management contractor and the client. Provisions in the contract address remedies if the client or landscape management contractor breaks the contract. The primary breach of the contract is usually non-payment of fees by the client. As a practical matter, failure of the client to make payments results in the contractor's cessation of further work on the project. If substantial work has been performed, the contractor is a financial loser. Losses increase if he/she has to pay additional money for legal fees and collection costs.

Landscape management contracts developed by the landscape firm typically contain clauses requiring the client to pay collection costs, including attorney's fees, in the event the client breaks the payment schedule. The following are ways various landscape management contractors have handled such events.

- *Legal Fees and Court Costs: In the event that either party becomes involved in litigation or arbitration arising out of this contract, its interpretation, or the performance thereof, the prevailing party shall be entitled to reasonable attorney's fees and court costs*

in addition to any other relief that may be awarded.

- *Legal Fees and Venue: In the event of litigation to enforce or interpret this agreement, the prevailing party shall be entitled to reasonable attorney's fees. This agreement is deemed made at the Contractor's place of business and suit may be brought, at the Contractor's option, in the judicial district serving the Contractor's principal place of business.*

- *Work Stoppage: The Contractor shall have the right to stop work if any payments are not made to the contractor as detailed under this agreement. The Contractor may keep the job idle until all payments due have been received. Such action by the Contractor shall not be deemed as a breach of this agreement.*

The client's concern for breach involves the failure of the contractor to perform all of the landscape management services agreed upon, or the contractor's inability to perform them at acceptable standards. Some client-oriented landscape management contracts require that the landscape firm, if it is in breach of the contract for failure to perform, pay the increased cost required for another landscape management firm to take over the contract.

Additionally, the landscape management company can fail, leaving the client in the lurch. Contracts for open bid landscape management developed by the client or his/her representative frequently require substantial financial and experience qualifications of the bidders. Most public work and many private work contracts require substantial bonds to be posted by the landscape management contractor. Bonds protect the client in case the landscape management firm closes or fails to pay its bills.

Mediation and Arbitration. No matter how carefully the landscape management contract is drafted, disputes can occur. As discussed under specifications, mediation and arbitration provide a pre-litigation method to solve serious disputes. Therefore, contracts may contain a clause providing for mediation and/or arbitration of disputes arising from the agreement.

If a contract provides an informal mechanism to settle disputes then costly legal action is averted. *Mediation* is when a third party is used to develop a reasonable compromise between the parties. The third party may be a professional association or someone acceptable to the owner and contractor.

Arbitration is a formal hearing of the dispute that does not require strict courtroom rules of etiquette. Both sides tell their side of the story in plain English in front of a neutral arbitrator. Depending on the rules of the arbitrator, attorneys may be used to represent one or both sides, or may only give advice to their client during the proceeding. Arbitration is not open to the public and the awards are confidential; they are not accessible to the media or a matter of public record. The arbitrator's decision is legally binding and cannot be overturned by the courts on appeal in most states, except where the referee has gone beyond the issues of the dispute.

Arbitration clauses in landscape management contracts cover the types of disputes subject to mediation. The arbitrator is established in the contract or by mutual consent of the contracting parties. The American Arbitration Association, a nonprofit group with offices in 25 cities, is frequently turned to or cited as an arbitrator in many commercial and public agency situations.

The following is an example of an arbitration clause that establishes the actions that may lead to arbitration and the arbitration procedures. The last two sentences of the clause may be void in some states.

- *Arbitration: If, at any time, a controversy develops between the Contractor and Owner with respect to any matters in question arising out of, or relating to this agreement, or the breach of this agreement in which the parties do not promptly adjust and determine, the controversy shall be decided by arbitration administrated by and in accordance with the rules of the (American Arbitration Association or other organization), unless the parties mutually agree otherwise. This agreement to arbitrate shall be specifically enforceable under the prevailing arbitration rules or law. The award rendered by the arbitrators shall be final, and judgment may be entered upon it in any court having jurisdiction thereof.*

Cancellation. Landscape management contracts typically have a clause allowing cancella-tion of the contract by either party upon written notification. Cancellation usually requires an extended notice, such as 30 days. Written notice is typically taken to mean registered mail. Other contracts specifically prohibit cancellation of the contract without a penalty or payment of a portion of the unfulfilled contract as *liquidated damages*.

- *Cancellation of contract: Either party may cancel the contract after 30 days written notice. The final billing must compensate the contractor for the full value of work done up to that time.*

- *Liquidated Damages: It is agreed that the actual damages that might be sustained by the Contractor from breach of this contract by the Owner by terminating the contract prior to its term are uncertain and would be difficult to ascertain. It is further agreed that the sum of _____ percent of the remaining unpaid contract price would be reasonable and just compensation for such breach. The Owner hereby promises to pay and the Contractor agrees to accept such sum as liquidated damages, not as a penalty, in the event of such breach.*

Signature Line. A final small, but powerful, caution occurs at the signature line at the end of the contract document. If you are signing a contract representing the corporation, then include your title when signing the papers. Failure to do so could put you at risk of becoming personally liable should everything go sour.

If a contract does not have your office title typed below the signature line, write it in manually after signing your name. Make sure the name of the organization is stated somewhere in the contract. As an example, the signature line on a contract should read "*by John Doe, President,*" "*John Doe, President of XYZ Corporation,*" or "*John Doe, for the XYZ Corporation.*"

Negotiations. Contracts must be mutually agreed upon. Signatures of both parties indicate that the provisions are agreeable. Contracts written by one party in this accord or their agent are one-sided. The agreement, while fair, may also be one where the author retains advantages in certain situations. Before signing a contract that places the landscape management firm at a severe disadvantage or one that contains unacceptable provisions, ask that they be changed or modified. Few agreements in the business world are not subject to negotiation.

Indicate and substantiate objections to the other party. Provide alternatives that would be fair to both principals. Any changes to a contract must be made in writing. Minor changes can be made on the original document and initialed or signed by both parties. Major changes may require rewriting the contract or attaching amendments. Do not accept verbal agreements to change a contract after signing without something in writing at the time of signing.

If changes in the presented document cannot be made to the mutual satisfaction of both signers, then the alternative is to not accept or sign the instrument. A landscape management contractor is better off without the work if the conditions are not fair or agreeable. Likewise, the owner will be able to find another contractor to do the work according to his/her requirements and wishes. The price, however, may be greater.

Bibliography

1. Arteka Natural Green. 1996. Specifications for site maintenance contracts. In: *Guide to Operating a Successful Landscape Maintenance Business*. ALCA. Hendron, VA.

2. Brown, S. and J. Holsinger. 2001. *Considerations for Developing a Lawn and Landscape Maintenance Contract*. Univ. Florida Coop. Ext. Document SS-ENH-09.

3. Bourne, J. 1984. *Grounds Maintenance Management Guidelines*. 1st ed. Professional Grounds Management Society, Pikeville, MD.

4. Carpenter, P., T. Walker, and F. Lanphear. 1975. *Plants in the Landscape*. W.H. Freeman and Co., San Francisco, CA.

5. City of Anaheim. 1995. *Notice to Bid-Tree Care*. City of Anaheim, Anaheim, CA.

6. Day, S. 1989. Site planning, maintenance specifications pay off. *ALA/Maintenance* 10(6):36.

7. Deshotels-Moore, K. 1998. Personal communication and landscape specifications.

8. Gillman, E. 1999. Writing good pruning specifications. *Hawaii Landscape* 3(3):12.

9. Griffen, J. 1970. *Landscape Management*. California Landscape Contractors Association, Los Angeles, CA.

10. Gross, P. 1997. When in doubt-spec it out. *USGA Green Section Record* 35(2):1.

11. Hall, J. 1978. Guidelines for writing lawn maintenance specifications. In: *Manual of Site Management*. Environmental Design Press, Reston, VA.

12. Hampshire, K. 2001. Get it in writing. *Lawn & Landscape* 22(6):38.

13. Hensley, D., W. McCoskey, and D. Suddarth. 1990. So, what if he doesn't pay. *Nursery Manager* 6(3):108.

14. Hensley, D. 1992. Workshop on landscape lawsuits and liability. *Hawaii Landscape Industry News* 6(5):6.

15. Hensley, D. 1993. Safety important in every firm. *Hawaii Landscape Industry News* 7(2):10.

16. ISA. 1995. *Tree-Pruning Guidelines*. International Society of Arboriculture, Savoy, IL.

17. Kujawa, R. 1997. Put it in writing. *Grounds Maintenance* 32(10):15.

18. Kuroiwa, J. 1998. Personal communication and landscape maintenance specifications.

19. LICH. 1996. *Landscape Management Guidelines*. Landscape Industry Council of Hawaii. Honolulu, HI.

20. Lofgren, D. 1978. General landscape specifications-how to write maintenance specifications. In: *Manual of Sitee Management*. Environmental Design Press, Reston, VA.

21. Lofgren, D. 1986. How to write good specs. *Grounds Maintenance* 21(1):112.

22. Marsh, D. 1985. Specifications for site maintenance and contracts. In: *A Guide to Developing a Landscape Maintenance Business*. Associated Landscape Contractors of America, McLean, VA.

23. Marsh, J. 1978. Practical specifications for contract landscape maintenance. In: *Manual of Site Management*. Environmental Design Press, Reston, VA.

24. Meade, V. and D. Hensley. 1997. *Selecting a Tree Care Professional*. Univ. Hawaii Coop. Ext. Pub. L-1.

25. Milburn, S. 1988. A bad sign. *American Nurseryman* 167(8):67.

26. Mohn, K. 2001. Sign on the dotted line. *Lawn & Landscape* 22(11):66.

27. OperationOutreach. No date. Model landscape maintenance specifications. Irvine Ranch Water District, Irvine, CA.

28. Quinn, R. ASLA. 1998. Personal communication and landscape maintenance specification.

29. Schlueter, S. 2003. Accounting for travel time at outdoors service groups. *Lawn & Landscape* 24(7):114.

30. Smith, L., R. Mann, and B. Roberts. 1989. *Essentials of Business Law*. 3rd edition. West Publishing St. Paul, MN.

31. Stessin, L. 1990. Arbitration: A quick solution to quarrels. *Landscape Contractor* 31(5):36.

32. Suddarth, D. and D. Hensley. 1984. Specific contracts guard maintenance companies against misunderstandings. *American Nurseryman* 159(6):163.

33. Suddarth, D. and D. Hensley. 1988. Know your lien laws. *American Nurseryman* 168(6):91.

34. Suddarth, D. 1990. Muller and Suddarth, Attorneys. Troy, MO. Personal communication.

35. West, B. 2003. The fine print. *Lawn & Landscape* 23(3):53.

Appendix 3.1.

Potential sections and subsections that landscape management technical specifications writers may wish to address.

No two projects are identical and the following is not an exhaustive list of every potential topic that may be included in technical specifications. They are the common landscape management operations that authors may wish to address in landscape management specifications or programs.

SECTION 1.
TURFGRASS MANAGEMENT

Well-managed turf is important to the appearance and overall quality of every landscape. Turfgrass management is covered in detail in Chapter 12. Recommendations for proper turfgrass care vary with type of grass, region, location, use, and maintenance level. Make sure that the care proposed in the turfgrass management section is appropriate for the species and geographic/climatic region. Consider the following cultural and management subsection.

Mowing

- *Debris removal*. Remove all debris, trash, and objects that can be thrown by equipment from the site prior to mowing.

- *Height*. Recommend mowing heights appropriate for the species, maintenance level, and use of the grass.

- *Frequency*. Ideally, mowing frequency is based on growth of the grass. Mowing should be scheduled so as not to remove more than one-third of the leaf per mowing.

For scheduled maintenance operations, however, mowing must be conducted at specific intervals. Intervals between mowings recommended for different situations are based on desired mowing heights and are listed below. Grassed areas mowed infrequently, but where appearance is important, are mowed between three and four inches.

Mowing intervals under managed situations:

Cutting height, inches	Mowing frequency, days
0.25	Daily
0.5	2 to 3
1	4 to 7
2	7 to 14
4	14 to 21

- *Mower type*. Rotary mowers are not used for cutting heights below 1.0 inch. Reel mowers are not used for cutting heights above 1.5 inches. Mulching mowers avoid the need to bag clippings.

- *Blades*. All turfgrass should be mown with sharp blades to prevent damage to the grass leaves.

- *Mowing pattern*. The direction and pattern for mowing landscape turf should be alternated at each mowing to minimize formation of a grain.

- *Clippings*. Returning clippings to the site using mulching or conventional mowers does not increase disease, insect pests, or thatch build-up. Use of mulching mowers requires greater attention to mowing frequency, however.

Large amounts or long clippings should be removed to reduce or prevent shading to the turf. Clippings should be directed away from streets and walks, and removed from walks, streets, parking lots, and curbs after mowing by sweeping or blowing.

Edging and trimming

- *Edging* of hard surfaces (walks, solid bed headers, and curbs) or soft surfaces (plastic, soil, lumber, or other soft material) will typically be accomplished every mowing. High maintenance areas require more frequent edging and trimming than medium or low maintenance sites, but they are also mowed more frequently. In situations where appearance is less critical and budgets are strict, edging can be conducted every other mowing or less frequently. Line trimmers should be used to edge beds and mechanical blade edgers should be used to edge walks and curbs.

- *Trimming* around trees, signs, and other objects in the landscapes should be done at every mowing for appearance.

- *Trim around trees and plants* in turf areas with a reciprocating trimmer rather than a line trimmer. Avoid line trimming around the base of trees to trim turf or groundcovers unless a tree guard is in place.

- *Mowing strips.* Grass around trees and other objects in lawns can be maintained away from the trunks of trees using herbicides or mulched to create a narrow, grass-free mowing strip. Mowing strips reduce the need for trimming and protect plants from line trimmer and lawn mower damage. Grass-free mowing strips can be kept weed and turf free by periodic applications of postemergent herbicides or mulch.

- *Removal of debris*: Debris from the edging operations shall be removed and the areas swept clean. Caution shall be used to avoid flying debris. The operator shall wear safety glasses during edging and trimming operations.

Fertilization

- *Turfgrass fertilization* is discussed in detail in Chapter 12. Higher end of nitrogen recommendations ranges are suggested for sites that are irrigated frequently, those in high rainfall areas, for sandy sites, or if clippings are regularly removed. Lower nitro-

Photo 3.5. Reciprocating trimmers avoid damage to these from standard line trimmers, but require more time for trimming operations.

gen rates are recommended for sites that are not irrigated or irrigated infrequently, heavy soils, and for sites with low maintenance levels and budgets.

- Unless specific ratios or types of fertilizer are required, nitrogen and other nutrient rates should be specified in pounds per 1,000 square feet. If slow-release nitrogen is desired, then request that the total nitrogen contain a certain percentage of slow-release nitrogen.

Dethatching or verticutting

- Lawn areas should be mechanically dethatched when the thatch layer is greater than one-half inch. Aggressive turfs (zoysiagrass, seashore paspalum, and some others) under high levels of management build thatch rapidly and benefit from periodic verticutting or dethatching. Verticutting can be an annual maintenance event. Dethatching or verticutting should be done in the spring and followed by application of a preemergence herbicide.

- *Aeration:* Consider mechanical aeration using a core or spoon aerator for turfgrasses in heavy soils, those receiving significant traffic, or those undergoing intense use. Depending upon these factors, aeration may be required once or twice annually.

55

- *Top-dressing* following core or spoon aeration benefits soils with poor structure. Top dress material should be a finely screened (less than one-half to three-eighths mesh) humus or composted organic material. Top-dressing normal sites with these materials or top-dressing without core aeration has shown little benefit.

Irrigation

- Turfgrass is ideally irrigated to reflect evapotranspiration (ET) losses and site conditions. Apply water in two to four irrigation events per week, depending on site and exposure. Time irrigations to eliminate runoff from the site; however, avoid short, frequent, shallow irrigations.

- When evapotranspiration rates are not available, irrigation must be applied as a timed, scheduled event. Turf should receive one to two inches of water per week (depending upon species, etc.) as precipitation or irrigation. Schedule irrigation to wet the rooting zone of the soil, allow maximum percolation, and yet avoid runoff. Avoid short, daily irrigations, which limit water penetration and encourage shallow rooting. Shallow-rooted turf is more sensitive to water stress than deep-rooted turf and cannot adequately use soil water reserves.

- Owner shall provide all water necessary for irrigation. Contractor will repair any damage to the irrigation system due to mowing or other actions of the contractor; however, any other adjustment or repair to the irrigation system(s) and all accessories will be made on a time plus material basis and charged to the Owner.

- Hand watering of landscape areas not covered by automatic irrigation systems shall be the sole responsibility of the Owner (or Contractor), and the Contractor (or Owner) assumes no responsibility for loss or damage to plant material because of lack or excessive watering by the Owner (or Contractor).

SECTION 2.
SHRUB MANAGEMENT

Pruning is covered in detail in Chapter 8. Differentiate between shearing and pruning in technical specifications and landscape management programs. To the plant the processes are worlds apart. If the plants are to be pruned correctly with a thinning technique, then state it clearly.

Pruning individual shrubs

- Selective pruning of nonflowering shrubs and emergency pruning can be accomplished any time. Use a selective or thinning pruning technique with hand pruners for large-leafed plants or where natural form is desired, yet height control is required. Shearing individual shrubs or masses in a landscape composition destroys the plant's natural form and is not recommended; however, the Owner, manager, or designer may require it.

Remedial pruning for overgrown landscape shrubs

- Some overgrown landscape plants can be pruned to within four to six inches of the ground and they will resprout, producing a thick growth of new shoots. This new growth must be thinned, and proper pruning techniques established. Knowledge of the plant material and its response to pruning is essential.

- Renovation of overgrown plants can be accomplished over several months or seasons by removing a portion (one-third) of the old growth at each of three major prunings. Removing all of the old growth over time restores the natural appearance and retains the use of the plant in the landscape. The time required to renovate older shrubs depends on their size, age, vigor, and the budget.

Hedges

- Shear *formal hedges* so that they are wider at the base than at the top. Frequency and timing depend on species, amount and cycle of growth, desired height and width, and design intent. Upper corners of the sheared hedges can be rounded or square-cut, depending upon preference. Remove visible stubs and branches shattered or split by shears with hand pruners.

- Some *chemical growth regulators* are labeled to retard growth of common hedge plants.

- *Informal hedges and screens* are selectively pruned by hand to control height but retain a natural, softer appearance. Prune screens or informal hedges as necessary to maintain height and appearance.

- *Renovation of overgrown hedges.* If the hedge or screen has outgrown its desired size or becomes unkept, ragged, or open at the base, cut back to one-half of the existing height and width. The height and form redevelop after shearing a few times. Renovation pruning is best accomplished just before a flush of growth so that the hedge is bare for the shortest period of time.

Fertilization

- Uniformly broadcast fertilizer in the shrub beds, or beneath individual shrubs. Fertilizer may be cultivated into beds but incorporation does not necessarily increase its availability where rainfall or irrigation is adequate.

- Nutrient addition, except nitrogen, should be on the basis of soil tests.

- *Chlorosis and nutrient problems.* Soil and tissue tests may be necessary to diagnose the cause of yellow or cholorotic leaves and to formulate corrective measures. *"Diagnostic soil and tissue tests will be conducted for an additional cost and with written permission of the Owner... or as part of the ongoing landscape maintenance program."*

Irrigation

- Shrubs should receive one to two inches of water per week through irrigation or precipitation, depending on site, soil, and species.

- Irrigation timing and frequency depend on soil characteristics, climatic factors, the ir-

rigation system, quality of irrigation water, and budget. Irrigate to wet the soil profile six to 10 inches deep and minimize runoff.

- Schedule irrigation to maintain quality of the least drought-tolerant species in the composition.

Mulch

- Organic and inorganic mulches conserve water, control weeds, moderate soil temperatures, and provide many other positive benefits to the landscape. Organic mulches improve soil structure and reduce compaction.

- Mulches should be applied at a uniform depth of two to three inches. Organic mulches should be replenished at least annually.

- Fresh, uncomposted organic material applied as mulch requires addition of 0.25 pounds of nitrogen per cubic yard to prevent nitrogen drain to landscape plants during the early breakdown of the mulch.

Weed control in shrub beds

- Weeds are controlled in landscape beds using preemergent and postemergent herbicides, mulches, and periodic manual removal. The goal is to maintain the landscape free of weeds. However, no landscape can be maintained "weed free;" therefore, the client should be educated as to what is realistic within the budget.

SECTION 3.
TREE MANAGEMENT

Pruning

- *Tree Pruning Guidelines* (International Society of Arboriculture, 1995) provide realistic professional guidelines and definitions that authors can refer to bidders.

- Some authors include *Pruning Objectives and Criteria* to establish quality guidelines for the pruning.

Pruning Objectives and Criteria

○ All trees should be allowed to grow to their natural form and size, unless specifically exempted by design criteria. Prune to retain the natural growth habit of a tree by removing undesirable growth detracting from the normal shape of each species.

○ Tree pruning should promote the tree's structural strength, accentuate its natural form and features, assure the safety of the landscape users, and enhance the health of the tree by removing dead, damaged, or diseased parts.

○ Prune trees to protect persons and property around and under the tree from injury or damage.

○ Prune trees to select and develop permanent scaffold branches that are smaller in diameter than the trunk or branch to which they are attached.

○ Prune trees to improve the structure of the tree by establishing appropriate scaffolding, and removing crossing or crowded branches, shoots, or suckers that compete with the tree's leaders.

○ Trees with multiple leaders or a branched main trunk system should be pruned to select and develop permanent scaffold branches that have vertical spacing from 18 to 24 inches. Where possible, eliminate V-shaped, narrow branch forks that lack strength. Space branches vertically and radially so as not to overlay one another.

○ Dense crowns may be thinned to enhance the plant's natural wind resistance.

○ Young, developing trees should not have the lower branches stripped (raised up). Lower limbs should be retained and tipped or pinched to retain as much foliage as possible to promote trunk growth and caliper. Lower branches should be removed only after the tree is able to stand erect without support.

○ Remove all suckers (adventitious shoots), water sprouts, root suckers, and crisscrossing, dead, diseased or broken side branches.

○ Remove branches by pruning to, but not through, the branch collar. Do not leave stubs.

○ Large limbs should be removed with a three-cut method. Smaller limbs removed with a saw should be undercut to reduce tears and bark rips.

○ All debris should be removed from the site and disposed of properly.

Topping of trees

Topping, instead of proper pruning, is a tremendous fear for specifications authors and clients.

• All trees shall be encouraged to grow to their mature heights and sizes according to their species. Topping ruins the natural form of the tree and increases the hazard potential of the plant. At no time shall any tree be "topped," "stubbed," or "hat racked" (pruning of all major branches to a uniform height or removal of all lateral or side branches) without the written consent of the Owner or site manager. Special pruning techniques such as *heading back* (drastic shortening of major branches to a uniform level) or *elevating* (removal of significant portion of the lower branches to a uniform height) should be considered only when no other alternative is available.

Timing of tree pruning

• Temperate trees are usually pruned in fall or winter.

• Seasonal differences have not been observed for pruning of most tropical landscape trees.

• Storm damaged and diseased or hazardous growth should be removed as soon as possible after discovery.

Pruning frequency

• New plantings often require more training and pruning during the first three to seven years after planting.

- Most trees may require some pruning annually.

Treatment of pruning cuts

- Pruning wounds should not be covered with a pruning sealer or paint. These materials do not prevent entry of diseases or insects and may reduce wound closure.

Fertilization

Fertilization is discussed in detail in Chapter 10.

- Nitrogen is required by the plant in the greatest quantity, but is transient in the soil so it must be supplied periodically.

- Trees located in lawn areas where the turfgrass receives regular and adequate fertilization do not typically require additional nitrogen fertilization. Additional nitrogen is not necessary unless deficiency symptoms are observed or in special situations.

- Apply phosphorus, potassium, calcium, magnesium, and iron on the basis of a soil test. Soil tests should be taken every three years under normal circumstances and more frequently if the site has a history of nutrient problems or deficiencies.

- Recommendations for fertilizing of street trees, trees in planters, or in specialized situations, should be determined with the assistance of a qualified and certified arborist.

Irrigation

Water is critical for growth and development of landscape and street trees. Select trees to accommodate the microclimate of the site and the water budget and water quality available.

- Newly established trees require careful monitoring for water needs and frequent irrigation during establishment. Watering frequency is determined by the weather and the water-holding capacity of the soil. Drip irrigation is useful and efficient for irrigating newly planted trees.

- Constant over-watering results in shallow rooting, making the trees more prone to wind-throw.

- Older trees have more expansive root systems and are able to obtain adequate water from irrigations of turfgrass, shrubs, groundcovers, and other associated plantings.

Shallow and aggressive roots

- Aggressive, shallow, or surface roots of some trees pose trip hazards, raise sidewalk and curbs, or enter into storm drains and sewer line. Corrective action may be necessary to prevent or eliminate such hazards or damage. Consult a qualified arborist for appropriate corrective measures.

Removing stakes and guys

- Stakes and guys should be removed within one year of planting unless they are required to keep the tree upright. Guy wires and ties to stakes around the trunk of a tree should be loosened as necessary to avoid girdling.

SECTION 4.
PALMS

Pruning

- The only pruning most palms need is the removal of dead, damaged, or diseased leaves.

- Remove the older fronds, flower stalks, and any fruits from Coconut palms (*Cocos nucifera*) a minimum of twice per year in areas used by people.

- Climbing spikes should not be used to climb coconut or other palms. (Use of spikes varies with site and manager. Other climbing mechanisms that do not mar the trunk are available, but their use increases the time and cost required to prune each tree.) Spikes should never be used to climb Royal palms (*Roystonea* spp.).

Fertilization

- Palms should be fertilized with a material formulated for palms according to manufacturer's recommendations. See details in Chapter 10.

Protection

- Keep turfgrass away from the trunks of palms with mowing strips to reduce injury from line trimmers and lawn care equipment.

SECTION 5.
GROUNDCOVER MANAGEMENT

- Encourage groundcover plantings to grow and cover the area in a full and solid mat kept neat in appearance.

- Edge groundcovers with a line-trimmer or power edger to control encroachment into lawns and other plantings, curbs, and walks, and to define borders. Some groundcovers require little trimming to maintain a desirable height, while others require significant work.

Fertilization

- Fertilize groundcover plantings to maintain color and appearance, but not to result in excessive growth. This will usually require application of a 2:1:1 fertilizer applied periodically during the growing season. Fifty percent of the nitrogen in the fertilizer should be a slow- or controlled-release form. Rates depend on species, site, and management.

- Compost and organic fertilizers are useful in fertilizing some groundcovers. Compost and composted organic materials do not contain large amounts of nutrients (usually compost is 1-1-1) and this nitrogen becomes available to plants very slowly. Consider the cost of the nutrients and application carefully.

Pruning

- Groundcovers will be pruned to maintain a height between ____ and ____ inches.

- Groundcovers should be thinned or renovated as necessary to ensure a healthy stand.

Weed control

- Groundcovers will be maintained weed-free by hand removal or selective postemergent herbicide. Preemergent herbicides should be used during establishment and after renovation or thinning.

SECTION 6.
PEST MANAGEMENT
AND PESTICIDES

Specifying particular chemicals for insect, disease, and weed control is difficult for design firms. Pesticides constantly enter and leave the market due to research and development, government intervention, and market forces. Landscape architects do not have the background or time to remain up-to-date on the latest recommendations. It is generally in the purview of the contractor or landscape supervisor to know what material will provide the most effective control with the least environmental risk and cost.

- Specification, recommendation, and use of pesticides should be left to those who are appropriately trained and knowledgeable. When pest control is indicated, use a generic statement, such as "...*shall be controlled with currently recommended and approved (pest)icide.*" This allows the contractor to select the appropriate material for the task and reduces the writer's liability in recommending something inappropriate or illegal.

- All chemical applications must be performed in accordance with current federal, state, and/or local regulations, using Environmental Protection Agency (EPA) and State of _____ registered material and methods of applications. Chemical applications to the landscape and turfgrass shall be performed under the supervision of a Licensed (Category ___) Pesticide Applicator.

- Encourage integrated pest management.

- The Landscape Maintenance Contractor shall have the responsibility for regularly monitoring the lawn and landscape. Integrated Pest Management (IPM) is recommended for controlling pests of trees, shrubs, groundcovers, turf, and other landscape plants.

- IPM does not prohibit the use of chemical controls. IPM monitors the site for insects, diseases, weeds, and other pests, and establishes levels of acceptable damage before controls are implemented. IPM uses all available control mechanisms (biological, cultural, mechanical, sanitation, and chemical) when necessary and as appropriate for the site, pests, use, management practices, and budget. Care is taken to protect site users, employees, and the environment.

- When pesticides are used, select only materials that are recommended and labeled for the intended use. Observe and follow all label restrictions and instructions. All pesticides shall be used in strict accordance with federal, state, and county laws.

SECTION 7.
NON-HORTICULTURAL ITEMS

Non-horticultural items in the landscape often fall under landscape management contracts.

- **Surface drains**. The Landscape Maintenance Contractor shall inspect surface drains located within (or adjacent to) the property __ time period (weekly, monthly) and clear all debris and/or vegetation that would impede the flow of water.

- **Removal of weeds from hardscape areas**. The Landscape Maintenance Contractor shall be responsible for removing (or preventing) all annual and perennial weeds in hardscape areas (walks, parking lots, road ways, and other paved areas).

- Establish an acceptable time period and methods (chemical [postemergent and/or long-term herbicides], physical removal, or both) for the site.

- **Removal of stakes and guys**. Stakes and guy wires installed during installation should be removed within six months to one year of planting except in very unusual circumstances. In many cases, no arrangement has been made with the installation contractor for removal of stakes and guys. Their removal is critical to proper development and health of the trees.

- **Soil and plant analysis**. Soil analysis is a method of monitoring the nutrient status of the soil and fertilizer needs. Soil samples from the site should be collected and analyzed every two years. Sample distinctly different soil types separately. Problem areas may require annual evaluation. The cost of soil analysis and interpretation is normally an additional charge.

SECTION 8.
IRRIGATION SYSTEM REPAIR AND MANAGEMENT

- **System operation.** Water is the most critical factor in determining the growth and quality of a landscape. Operational decisions about irrigation scheduling shall reside with the Landscape Maintenance Contractor, with the knowledge and approval of the Owner.

- The irrigation system shall be kept in good working order and operated to meet the water needs of the landscape while conserving water whenever and wherever possible.

Irrigation practices

- Apply water so as to avoid run-off.

- Ponding and puddling of water on the surface or run-off indicate that the scheduled irrigation time has exceeded the infiltration rate of the soil and adjustments are necessary. The volume of water applied to the area can be increased by additional irrigation times or repeated cycles as necessary.

- Adjust heads to minimize over spray onto paved areas.

- Program clocks of automatic systems to irrigate sometime between midnight and 7:00 a.m. Under extreme environmental stress, additional operating times may be necessary. Drip irrigation systems may be programmed to operate at any time.

- Seasonal changes will require adjustment of frequency and duration of irrigations. Adjustments may also be necessary to reflect prolonged hot/dry periods, system repairs, extended holidays, or other factors affecting plant or site needs.

- Adjust irrigation controllers weekly to reflect environmental and plant needs.

- Irrigation will not be scheduled during periods of high rainfall and other times when suspension of irrigation would conserve water and not impact growth and quality of the landscape.

Manual systems

- Manual systems should only be operated by an employee of the Landscape Management Contractor and operated at times that do not interfere with activities of the clients or of the maintenance crews.

- Seasonal changes require adjustment to irrigation frequency and duration. Additional personnel and materials may be required to assure adequate irrigation during extreme hot and/or dry periods, over extended holidays, or during or following system repairs.

System repairs

- Specifications and contracts must define *minor* or contracted adjustments, replacements, and repairs that are the responsibility of the landscape management contractor and define *major* repairs or replacements that are made at an additional charge to the client.

- During breakdowns or malfunctions of the irrigation system, manual watering of the turfgrass and landscape may be necessary and will be performed at an additional cost to the Owner, unless the malfunction is a result of action by the Landscape Maintenance Contractor or his/her employees. The need for manual watering will be determined by the written approval from the Owner and the Landscape Contractor.

- Keep controller and valve boxes free of soil and debris. Irrigation systems should be operated and evaluated for damage, effectiveness, coverage, and the heads and controller should be adjusted as necessary weekly.

- Repairs will be made only with original brand equipment and parts unless approved in writing by the Owner. All repairs should be made according to installation specifications unless approved in writing by the property manager.

- Repair of damage resulting from vandalism, accidental breakage by others, "Acts of God," or other damage beyond the control of the Landscape Contractor or his/her employees is extra. Damage resulting from actions of the Landscape Contractor or his/her employees is the responsibility of the Landscape Contractor.

Drip irrigation

- Drip irrigation systems should be flushed ___ (time period).

Appendix 3.2.
Sample Landscape Management Contracts

The following sample landscape management contracts serve only as examples and not as the exact construction required for a valid landscape management contract. Many different contracts are used by the landscape industry and the contract laws of each state differ.

The first example is a *simple* document adapted from one used by a landscape management contractor. It is little more that a Gentlemen's Agreement, stating simply that the contractor agrees to perform the work indicated for the amounts listed. The agreement constitutes a legal and binding contract when signed, but it is extremely limited in its scope or protection. Quality standards, limitation of responsibilities, and remedies for breach or other problems are omitted. The contractor's only recourse to non-payment by the client is to charge interest. The contractor must perform work for an additional 30 days beyond written notification, even if no payment has been forthcoming. The agreement also negates starting dates, name of the owner or representative, and other important aspects found in more complete and tighter instruments.

Many landscape management contractors prefer to operate with simple, loose agreements. They feel that their word is enough. Some contractors feel that the client may be turned-off or on-guard if the agreement contains too many contingencies and too much legalese. I am aware of at least one case where a contractor lost a job that he had maintained for several years because he presented an unnecessarily detailed and protective contract to a client.

Other landscape management contractors, however, feel they would rather have the client be wary as opposed to performing work for which they are not paid. Disputes develop because no one really understands the details or limits of the agreement.

The second example refers to specifications or a landscape program for the particulars of what is to be done, the frequency of the tasks, and quality standards. The instrument presents remedies for various contingencies. It explains a number of the duties of the owner and the contractor. Since the contract is written by a landscape management contractor for signature by the property owner or manager, it reflects various protection mechanisms in favor of the contractor. These include liquidated damages, penalties for the owner's breach, holiday exclusions, and others. The instrument also provides solution to future disagreements via arbitration. A contract constructed by the property owner's representative would provide stringent protective clauses in favor of the owner.

Most landscape management contractors use contracts somewhere between these examples in wording and protection. Remember, the more that can be written down and agreed upon, the fewer disputes will erupt in the future.

SAMPLE CONTRACT 1

DAVE'S LANDSCAPES-AR-US

P.O. Box 123, Anytown, AR

AUTHORIZATION

I hereby authorize DAVE'S LANDSCAPES-AR-US to perform the landscape maintenance at _____ as listed on the reverse side of this page. (Applicable taxes will be added.) DAVE'S LANDSCAPES-AR-US will invoice for each service, as performed. Terms are net 30 days. A service charge of 18% per year (or 1.5% per month) will be assessed on any delinquent balance.

Either party may terminate this contract by giving 30 (thirty) days notice with agreement between both parties on charges due.

_____

DAVE'S LANDSCAPES-AR-US

_____

AGENT FOR THE OWNER

_____

DATE

DATE

MAINTENANCE SCHEDULE

STANDARD OPERATIONS	COST PER	# TIMES	TOTAL
Mow, Trim, Sweep, and Bag as needed	$280	22	$6,160
Edge Walks and Curbs	120	8	960
Turf Fertilizer, Weed and Insect Control	375	4	1,500
Grub Control	425	1	425
Pruning	50	2	100
Shrub and Tree Insect Control	90	2	180
Irrigation Service - Timer Adjustments Only			no charge
		TOTAL	$9,325

OPTIONAL OPERATIONS	COST PER	# TIMES	TOTAL
Aeration	$600	1	$600
Mulching beds	0.50/sq. ft.		
Turf Fungicide	$15.00/1,000 sq. ft.		
Grassy Weed Spot Spray	$12.00/1,000 sq. ft.		
	OPTIONAL OPERATIONS TOTAL		$600

SAMPLE CONTRACT 2

LANDSCAPE MANAGEMENT CONTRACT

Agreement made on _____, 20__ by and between **DAVE'S LANDSCAPES-AR-US**, 123 Oak, Anytown, Arkansas, hereafter referred to as "DAVE'S" or the "contractor" and **NOAH'S PROPERTY MANAGEMENT**, hereafter called "OWNER," 1220 W. Palm, Suite 12, Anytown, Arkansas (501-555-1234).

Purpose of Agreement

The purpose of this agreement is to state the terms and conditions under which DAVE'S will provide landscape management for the property of the Owner. This property is located at 1220 W. Palm, Anytown, AR, a (5) five acre commercial office site, bounded by Elm Blvd. to the North, W. Palm to the East, Cercis Ave. to the South and by Broadway to the West, and is hereafter referred to as "property." The name of the property (if any): **Joshua Place Corporate Park**.

Upon acceptance by duly authorized representatives of DAVE'S and the Owner, this contract becomes a legally enforceable, binding contract. If the Owner has any questions concerning this contract, legal advice should be obtained.

In consideration of the mutual promises herein, the parties agree as follows:

1. **Scope of Work**: DAVE'S agrees to furnish all materials, equipment, labor, supervision, transportation, insurance, and licenses necessary to perform the management services set forth in the attached specifications (landscape management program) for the property.

2. **Payment**: Owner agrees to pay DAVE'S the Contract Price of $16,404.00 for performance of the services set forth in the attached specifications. The contract price is to be paid in 12 equal monthly installments of $1367.00, the first installment being due and payable upon execution of this agreement. Each additional installment is due and payable on the 15th day of each succeeding month thereafter until the contract price is fully paid. All accounts not paid within ten (10) days of the date due shall accrue interest on the unpaid balance at 18% per year (1.5% per month).

    a. **Breach**: Failure of the Owner to pay any or all of any accrued portion of the contract price as provided above within fifteen (15) days from the date due shall constitute a breach of this contract and shall entitle DAVE'S to recover damages for this breach as provided herein at the sole election of DAVE'S.

    b. **Work Stoppage**: DAVE'S has the right to stop work if any payments are not made to the contractor as detailed under this agreement. DAVE'S may keep the job idle until all payments due have been received. Such action by the Contractor shall not be deemed as a breach of this agreement.

3. **Term of the Contract**: The term of this agreement is for 12 months, beginning August 1, _____ and ending July 31, _____. This agreement may not be terminated during this period without the prior written consent of the other party.

4. **Owner's Duty to Inspect the Work**. The Owner has the duty to inspect the property within three (3) days after DAVE'S has completed any service described in the attached specifications. If the Owner is dissatisfied with any of the work performed, notice of such dissatisfaction must be given to DAVE'S within five (5) days from the completion of the services. DAVE'S shall then have ten (10) days to repair or correct such work at no additional cost to Owner. Owner's failure to properly notify DAVE'S of dissatisfaction in any services called for under the terms of this agreement constitutes a waiver of any claim or offset the Owner may be due in regard to work rendered under this contract.

5. **Insurance and licenses**: DAVE'S will carry complete workers' compensation, public liability, and property damage insurance, as well as all federal, state, and local licenses appropriate and necessary to conduct the work described in the attached specifications.

6. **Water and/or irrigation**: Owner shall provide all water necessary for irrigation as described in the attached specifications. DAVE'S will repair any damage to the irrigation system due to mowing or other actions of the contractor, however, any other adjustment or repair to the irrigation system(s) and all accessories will be made on a time plus material basis and charged to the Owner.

7. **Adverse conditions and holidays**: DAVE'S will not be required to work during adverse conditions, including but not limited to rainstorms, excessive wind, public insurrection, or fires. DAVE'S recognizes the following holidays: Labor Day, Memorial Day, and DAVE'S Birthday (October 27). If a regularly scheduled workday coincides with one of these, or if it rains on three or more consecutive visit days, DAVE'S will work an alternate day or prorate the monthly bill by 15 percent.

8. **Exclusions**: DAVE'S shall not be responsible for damage or interruption of services due to vandalism, theft, adverse natural conditions, Acts of God, or anything beyond the control of the Contractor.

9. **Liquidated Damages**: It is agreed that the actual damages that might be sustained by DAVE'S from breach of this agreement by Owner terminating the contract prior to its term are uncertain. These damages would be difficult to ascertain. It is further agreed that the sum of 30 percent of the remaining unpaid contract price would be reasonable and equitable compensation for such breach. The Owner hereby promises to pay, and DAVE'S agrees to accept, this sum as liquidated damages, not as a penalty, in the event of breach by the Owner.

10. **Arbitration**: If, at any time, a controversy develops between DAVE'S and Owner with respect to any matters in question arising out of, or relating to this agreement, or the breach of this contract in which the parties do not promptly adjust and determine, the controversy will be decided by arbitration, unless both parties agree otherwise. This agreement to arbitrate shall be specifically enforceable under the prevailing arbitration rules or law. The award rendered by the arbitrator shall be final, and judgment may be entered upon it in any court having jurisdiction thereof.

11. **Legal Fees and Court Costs**: In the event that either party becomes involved in litigation or arbitration arising out of this contract or the interpretation or performance thereof, the prevailing party shall be entitled to reasonable attorney's fees and court costs in addition to any other relief that might be awarded.

12. **Entire agreement**: This contract contains the entire agreement of the parties. Any modification, amendments, or changes must be in writing and signed by all parties to be effective. Any work in addition to that contained within the attached schedule will be charged separately and additionally according to the nature of the work.

Upon acceptance by DAVE'S and the Owner, the parties shall be contractually bound and shall be entitled to and responsible for any and all rights and obligations created herein.

Accepted

OWNER

By: _____

     Name   Title   Date

Address. _____

DAVE'S LANDSCAPES-AR-US

By: _____

     Name   Title   Date

Chapter 4
Estimating and Pricing

Landscape managers in the contractual arena must determine the amount of material, labor, and equipment necessary to perform a task or maintain a given property at a profit. Supervisors of in-house landscape management must develop, justify, and adhere to meaningful budgets. Accuracy in estimating costs determines whether the operation will obtain a contract, make a profit, or stay within a budget. Accurate estimating determines if the operation or manager will succeed or fail.

Job costing landscape management is different in many ways from estimating landscape installation. Materials often constitute a large portion of landscape installation estimates. Labor represents the single largest segment of landscape management estimates; materials are typically a minor item. It is also a misconception that installation is more profitable than maintenance work.

Project Evaluation

Contract landscape management companies are in business to make a profit and expand. However, the firm does not want *every* job that may be available or offered. The company must maintain quality workmanship, respect, and a good reputation. New work should fit into established goals. Consider the following when competitive or non-competitive bid projects are offered to the company:

1. *Size*. Can the firm handle the job? If the job is too small, the firm may not be able to do the work efficiently. Many landscape management contractors, especially those targeting commercial properties, establish a minimum size for maintained sites. Residential oriented companies also operate on a minimum site size, or more likely, a minimum charge sufficient to pay for the inconvenience of a small site.

If the job is too large, the company may not have the capability or equipment to handle it. If the firm obtains the contract, can it mobilize the personnel and equipment to do the work efficiently and for a profit?

2. *Work schedule and current commitments*. Will the job fit into the existing work schedule? Will it require a different route or new crew(s)? If new crews are added, can additional work be found to fill their schedule? Does the company have the equipment, personnel, and supervisory staff to add the work efficiently?

3. *Procedures*. Are special equipment, techniques, or crews required? Does the company have or can it obtain the expertise, equipment, or personnel to do the work? Are subcontractors available for specialized work beyond the firm's capabilities?

4. *Examine the specifications and contract carefully*, especially if it is a public property. Do the owners require techniques or requirements different from those usually conducted? If so, are these requirements reasonable? If the specifications will be time consuming, then adjust the bid. Will the landscape management firm be held responsible for the actions of others, such as vandalism? In some instances, the landscape manager may be asked to anticipate and estimate the cost of replacement and repair of the landscape due to damage of tenants or others in the bid. A difficult task, at best.

5. *Does the project fit the image of the company?* Is it the type of work for which the firm is known?

6. *Geographic area of the work.* Can the additional travel cost be turned into a profit? If the work is out of town, are there reasonable places for the crew to stay overnight? Can local crews and supervisors be obtained?

7. *Who is responsible for inspection of the work and determination of payment?* The property manager, the designer, or a consultant may conduct inspections and arrange for payments. The consultant may be a landscape architect or designer or an independent consulting company. Know who will judge the work against the specifications set forth.

Is the evaluator competent and fair? The manager may wish to increase the bid if there are indications that a percentage of the work will regularly have to be redone, if there are likely to be requests for *gratis* work in addition to the contract, or if there has been a history of withholding partial payment. Some landscape management contractors have an unlabeled Ding Dong factor that is included when they are dealing with notorious property managers or contract representatives.

8. *Payment: when and how?* Does the payment schedule fit cash flow needs? Is payment dependent upon passing inspections? Potential problems in this area have been discussed.

How much time will be required for payment for extra work beyond the contract? Some companies and public entities must go through many layers of approvals and paperwork to obtain payment for additional work. Some owners delay payment as long as possible. Remember, your company is not a bank. Do not allow the client to use the firm's money without interest added or an adjustment to the bill up front.

9. *Are there potential problems that might prevent the efficient completion of the contract?* Labor problems on the site, contract disputes between the owner and installation contractor, and water rationing affect landscape management performance. Be aware of business or financial difficulties that may result in failure of the client's business.

If the bid is for management of a new landscape, will it be completed on time? Also, remember that the site will change drastically during the construction phase. If possible, wait until installation is complete before submitting a final price.

10. *Will design and installation factors affect maintenance efficiency or price?* Items to consider, especially with newer landscapes, are plant selection and location. Have microclimates been addressed? Has the designer selected plants tolerant to the site and conditions? Will the management firm be required to do the impossible? How much winter (or summer) damage can be anticipated? Was the landscape properly installed, how much loss is anticipated, and who is responsible? Excellent landscape management cannot overcome bad design and poor plant selection or quality.

11. *Was the irrigation system installed properly and is it functional?* Irrigation, more than any other factor, determines the summer quality of the turfgrass and landscape. Who controls the operation, scheduling, and repair of the system? Does someone else determine the quality of the maintenance program without the firm's input or control?

Evaluating the Site

A fundamental rule of landscape management contracting is to visit the site before submitting a bid or estimate. Elementary as this may seem, too many contractors rely on windshield or drive-by estimates.

One young would-be contractor successfully bid and signed a contract for maintaining a motel landscape, but did not realize that there was a large courtyard with extensive plantings when he submitted the price. He could not see it from his pick-up, so all that was bid was the mowing and snow removal from the parking lot. This was an expensive lesson.

Walk and evaluate the site. Measure the turf areas and shrub beds, count the trees, and determine problems that must be corrected or that will affect performance and price. Develop the habit of taking thorough field notes for potential sites. Look for evidence of pests, compaction, poor plant selection, etc. Avoid being liable for a landscape that is destined to fail anyway.

Estimating is a sales and management responsibility. Make sure the evaluator is responsible and trained. Some companies have site evaluations or estimates checked by someone in production to make sure they are reasonable and accurate. The manager/owner is responsible for checking all estimates for large or prestigious properties.

Checklist

Most firms use a *checklist* or form that is filled out during on-site inspection. Written reminders assure that valuable information necessary for pricing and program development are not neglected. Checklists also record site conditions that can be used in later evaluations of bid and pricing performance. Consider the following:

1. If history or company procedures warrant, obtain a soil sample for analysis to determine nutrient status, soil pH, bulk density, and possibly cation exchange capacity.

2. Note the surface and subsurface drainage. Look for drainage problems and wet areas.

3. Examine entrances and determine if there is access for equipment. Roof gardens and courtyards often present problems.

4. If the site does not have an automated, underground irrigation system, is there access to water? Are there sufficient numbers and size of outlets? Will water have to be hauled to the site? Look for dry areas.

5. Who determines and controls the schedule for the irrigation system?

6. It is also a good idea to take some photographs or digital images of the site. These can serve as reminders and as persuasive "before" pictures during contract renewal.

Records

Records are critical for determining business costs and developing budgets, estimates, and bids.

Good records allow determination of actual costs and provide accurate information for production times and rates. Historical records are used to determine the effect that changes in equipment and supplies have on costs and profits. Records also identify profitable and unprofitable service areas. The lack of accurate performance records and comparisons of actual and estimated costs are the greatest hindrance to effective bidding and pricing for new firms.

Many different record forms have been developed and are used in the landscape management industry. The specific forms needed and used vary with each operation; there are no industry standards. Record forms must generate the information necessary for the particular operation.

Business record forms must be sufficiently complete and accurate to generate the necessary information, yet simple enough that the employees can fill them out correctly. Several different forms will be illustrated in the following discussions; these are by no means the best, most efficient or only records that will be needed or adopted.

Specialized computer programs simplify record keeping and tabulation. Today, the manager has more and better information at his/her fingertips than anytime in the past. The accumulation of business data, however, does not ensure success. *People* still must interpret and respond to this information.

Developing an Estimate

When developing a bid or budget, the manager or estimator must determine: 1) the work to be accomplished; 2) the area involved; and 3) the time and materials required. We will talk about overhead and profit later. Less simplistically, an estimate or budget considers:

1. The individual jobs or tasks included in the total project.

2. The size of the area for each activity.

3. The frequency with which each task will be performed.

4. The quality level required for each task.

5. The personnel and equipment needs for those jobs.

6. The supplies and material required.

Table 4.1 illustrates the basic inputs that must be brought together to formulate estimates and budgets.

Landscape programs and schedules. A great number of the "what, when, and how" questions are answered by clearly written specifications or schedules supplied by the prospective client. In most instances, however, the landscape contractor bears the responsibility of determining the needs of the site and the client to develop the landscape management program. The management program should be clear and detailed. Customers should know exactly what they are buying. Indicate the tasks involved, their frequency, and the desired quality level. Never forgo details or what the customer may or may not assume.

Maintenance take offs. Landscape management contractors have adopted a *take off* form for listing items from maintenance specifications, schedules, or programs. Take off forms make sure that nothing is omitted. Table 4.2 is a simple example of a take off form. Construct the form to include space for frequency, areas, type and amounts of material and equipment necessary, and other pertinent information.

Seasonal frequency. The maintenance program, the client's quality expectations and budget, the maintenance level of the site, and the region of the country, determine the frequency of each task.

Determining the area

The size of beds, lawns, and parking areas, and the exact number of trees and shrubs may be easily obtained from an as-built landscape plan from the client or designer. Specific areas can be measured by hand or with the aid of a planimeter. A *planimeter* is an instrument used to measure the area of regular or irregular segments. *As built* plans, unfortunately, are not always available.

Aerial photographs, in scales as large as 1 inch = 50 feet, are available from some county appraisers or other local government offices. Again, unit areas can be determined with the aid of a planimeter or geometry. Several contractors have mentioned the value of aerial photographs when bidding mowing, snow removal, and turfgrass care for apartments, commercial sites, or other large properties.

Check or determine the scale of aerial photography by physically measuring a building or other visible landmark. Compare the physical measurement to the photo scale.

Global Positioning Satellite (GPS) Technology makes it possible to develop accurate maps and determine areas. Accuracy of equipment allowed for consumer/commercial use has increased dramatically and the price has dropped markedly.

Table 4.1.

Estimating worksheet

This example worksheet illustrates the information necessary for developing an estimate, bid, or budget.

1	2	3	4	5	6	7	8	9
Maintenance activity or task	Frequency	Area or unit	Production rate	Production hours	Labor rate ($ /hr)	Material	Equipment rate	Equipment costs
Tasks from take off, specifications, or maintenance program	*(times per year)*	*(sq ft or unit)*	*(time per unit)*	*(2x 3 x 4)*	*($/hr)*	*(material cost x frequency)*	*(cost per hr or unit)*	*(2 x 3 x 8)*

Totals (sums of columns)

Table 4.2.
Maintenance take off

Job Title	
Location	
Specification or Bid	
Dates in Effect	
From:	
To:	

	Frequency						
Maintenance Activity	**Daily**	**Weekly**	**Monthly**	**Yearly**	**As Required**	**Unit or area**	**Material Needed**
Lawn Areas							
Irrigation							
Mowing							
Edging							
Weed control							
Pest control							
Fertilization							
Trash/debris removal							
Raking							
Aerating							
Other							
Planted Groundcover Areas							
Irrigation							
Edging/trimming							
Weed control							
Pest control							
Fertilization							
Trash/debris removal							
Other							
Shrubs							
Irrigation							
Pruning							
Weed control							
Pest control							
Fertilization							
Trash/debris removal							
Mulch/re-mulch							
Trees							
Irrigation							
Pruning							
Weed control							
Pest control							
Fertilization							
Other							
Public or Patio Area							
Trash/debris removal							
Sweeping							
Washing							
Snow Removal/deicing							
Other							
Parking Areas and Drives							
Trash/debris removal							
Sweeping							
Washing							
Snow Removal/deicing							
Re-stripe and mark							
Surface seal							

Table 4.2 (continued)

Snow Removal/deicing						
Re-stripe and mark						
Surface seal						
Other						
Walks						
Trash/debris removal						
Sweeping						
Washing						
Snow Removal/deicing						
Weeding cracks						
Other						
Walls and Fences						
And so on for the services offered						

Landscape managers and golf course superintendents are finding new ways to adapt the technology to their work.

The last and most common method is *physically measuring* the turf, paving, beds, and other areas with a measuring wheel or tape, and counting the trees and shrubs. Even if an as-built plan or aerial photo exists, a site visit is critical to determine topography and anything else that impedes management operations.

The degree to which the individual components of the site are broken down for bidding depends on the size and complexity of the job, the competitiveness of the marketplace, and the contractor's personal preference and methodology. At the very minimum, the square feet of turf, seasonal color beds, and shrub beds, and the number of trees must be cataloged. Measure parking areas and walks if snow removal or cleaning is included in the bid. Do not rely on windshield surveys or comparing a new property with an existing contract for size and complexity. This may result in a surprise.

Estimating Time. The *time* required for various jobs in landscape management is, literally, the $64,000 question. Labor is typically the largest part of direct costs for maintenance operations, sometimes up to 90 percent. Labor is also the most difficult part of landscape management pricing to accurately estimate.

Ask any contractor what it costs to mow a given area and answers range from, "I wish I knew," or "Probably more than I think," to pretty exact figures. Every contractor seeks a better handle on his/her costs, estimates, and profits.

Computers make keeping records, determining area, and unit costs much easier and time estimates more accurate. The majority of landscape contractors and site managers now use computer-based bidding and budgeting. Customize computer programs/spread sheets to reflect your price, labor, equipment, and other databases.

Estimating production time is a dilemma for every new contractor since new firms do not have historical records or experience to rely upon. They may also have a mixture of equipment, varying in serviceability and size.

Production rates. Numerous management firms use *production rates* or standards for estimating purposes. Production rates are the time required to mow, prune, spray, or perform other specific work on an individual or unit basis (per square foot, 1,000 square feet, acre, linear foot, or mile).

Figures for average production rates for landscape management tasks can be found in publications from Associated Landscape Contractors of America (ALCA), Professional Grounds Management Society (PGMS), and in several texts. Table 4.3 lists "typical" production numbers for various landscape maintenance functions gathered from various sources. Such figures are average estimates for average employees using average equipment on an average site. They serve only as guides, but at least provide a starting place for the young contractor. Some contractors have told me they would fire their employees if they could not produce more than that indicated in these publications. Others would love to replace their entire work force with these average workers.

Table 4.3.
Maintenance task production rates

Area and Operation	Average frequency per year	Average minutes per 1,000 Sq Ft
Turf Management		
Mowing		
21" self-propelled	30	6
36" self-propelled	30	4
48" rider	30	45 min/acre
72" rider	30	36 min/acre
Fertilization		
broadcast (PTO powered)	2	.25
36" drop spreader	2	4
Preemergent herbicide application	1	15
Postemergent herbicide application back-pack sprayer	2	15
15" boom, power	2	4
30" boom, power	2	8
Raking		
hand	1	60
power	1	10
Vacuum - 30" machine	3	10
Overseeding (machine)	1	30
Aeration (core aerator)	1	30
Edging	**Linear feet**	**Min./ 1,000 linear feet**
shrub bed - hand	10	60
power - walks	30	5
power - shrub beds	10	10
Trimming around objects		
string trimmer	25	10
chemical	2	10
Shrub Beds		**Min./1,000 sq ft**
Weeding		
hand	15	60
postemergent spot spray	3	15
Preemergent herbicide application	2	5
Policing-debris removal hand	30	15
vacuum	30	7
Pruning	2	60
Fertilization (broadcast)	2	5
Mulch	1	30
Pest control - spray	2	
Trees		**Min./small tree**
Pruning	2	20
Fertilization		
broadcast	2	5
deep root feed	1	30
Pest control - spray	3	15
Injection	1	10
Seasonal Color Beds		**Min./1000 sq ft**
Bed preparation	1	200
Weeding (no mulch)	15	60
Cultivation (no mulch)	15	30

Table 4.3 (continued)

Mulch	1	30
Weeding (in mulch)	7	20
Pest control (spray)	3	10
Preemergent herbicide (broadcast)	1	5
Fertilization (broadcast)	2	5
Policing-debris removal - hand	25	15
vacuum	5	10
Plant removal and clean-up	1	400
Paved Areas		**Min/1000 sq ft**
Walks		
sweeping - hand	15	25
vacuum	15	4
blower	25	2
Snow removal		
hand	?	60
power	?	12
Drives and Parking		
cleaning-vacuum	10	3
snow removal	?	10

Developing Production Rates. Production rates for each job and company depend on the equipment used, the skill and enthusiasm of the worker, and the condition and terrain of the area. The influence of size and speed on mowing is found in Table 4.4. Managers try to develop generalized figures that work in most situations. There are no average workers, as there are no average jobs. Adjustments to production figures will be discussed later.

Production rates can be developed from records of actual time-on-the-job from past contracts. Production figures can be developed by measuring the work by employees with different equipment with a stopwatch over a known area. Fine-tune and check production rates by comparing estimated time with actual times for specific tasks over the firm's many contracts.

Landscape contractors break down production rates into *unit areas*, such as square feet of turfgrass, linear feet of edging, square feet of bed, and number of trees and shrubs. Distinguish between the various size machines, such as mowers; the production time for each differs significantly.

Production rates or factors will be needed for each operation routinely performed, as well as

Table 4.4.
Average square feet mowed per hour using mowers of various deck widths at three mowing speeds.

Mower size	Mower type	Overlap	Net Mowing Width	Average area mowed per hour (rounded to 100 sq. ft.) Average speed (mph)		
				1	3	5
21 inch	push	4 in.	17 in.	7,600	22,700	38,000
36 inch	walk-behind	4 in.	32 in.	14,400	43,200	72,000
50 inch	walk-behind	4 in.	46 in.	20,500	61,500	102,500
60 inch	rider	6 in.	54 in.	23,800	71,400	119,000
72 inch	rider	6 in.	66 in.	28,500	85, 500	142,500
96 inch	rider	12 in.	84 in.	38,000	114,000	190,000
10 foot	rider	12 in.	9 ft.	47,500	142,500	237,500
12 foot	rider	12 in.	11 ft.	57,000	171,000	285,120
15 foot	rider	12 in.	14 ft.	71,300	213,900	356,500

those that are undertaken occasionally. Table 4.5 is a compilation of production rates from several contractors.

Adjustments to production rates. Production and efficiency vary with site. Adjustments to production rates reflect differences in conditions, difficulty, and other parameters. Adjustments to mowing production rates include increases for: collecting clippings; corner lots; hills and berms; cut-up areas (sidewalks and scattered ornamentals); jobs specifying end-of-the week mowing; and more frequent edging and trimming. Pruning time depends upon plant size and the degree of neglect. Weeding times depend on the present and past herbicide programs.

Adjustments to production rates are applied by adding a *percentage* to the final total of estimated hours or prices or by multiplying production rates or time estimates by an efficiency factor or *burden*. These adjustments vary with project and site difficulty and are determined by the estimator or manager.

Travel time. The time required for travel, unloading, and loading the equipment must be accounted for as part of the final price. Some contractors increase estimated hours by a standard percentage to account for these non-productive functions. Others calculate and list travel as a trip charge or "mobilization" charge. At least one company has a "debris removal" charge for each crew trip to the property that serves as the travel charge. How travel and other adjustments are handled will depend on the client, local market characteristics, and company philosophy.

On-site Staffing. Many firms staff regular personnel and equipment on site for some properties. Employees report directly to the site rather than the normal staging area. These customers may have special needs, require a vast amount of service, or have large properties requiring regular maintenance. Such clients include large condominium or apartment properties, college or business campuses, malls, military bases, resorts, and other commercial sites.

Typical candidates for on-site staging require regular and frequent detailed work. It may well be less expensive for the client to have an on-site contractor rather than in-house maintenance. On-site employees become familiar with the site and

---

Table 4.5.
Some of the many landscape operations for which a firm may want to develop production rates. Determining the time or *rate* required to perform the various tasks allows more rapid and accurate estimating. Develop production rates for each machine used and adjust the rate to reflect site and weather variations.

A. Turfgrass
1. Mowing
   a. For each size machine
   b. With/without collecting clippings
2. Edging and trimming
   a. Line trimmers
   b. Edgers
3. Fertilization/Pesticide
   a. Granules
   b. Liquid materials
4. Leaf removal
   a. Open areas with machines
   b. Small areas by hand

B. Shrubs and Groundcovers
1. Pruning
   a. By hand/Shearing
2. Fertilization/Pest control
3. Herbicide application
4. Hand weeding
5. Leaf removal and cleanup
6. Mulching

C. Trees and Large Evergreens
1. Pruning
2. Large
3. Small
4. Fertilization
5. Pest control

D. Seasonal Color
1. Bed preparation
2. Planting
3. Fertilization
4. Hand watering
5. Pest control
6. Pinching/dead heading
7. Removal/bed cleanup

E. Miscellaneous
1. Irrigation checks and adjustments
2. Travel
3. Loading
4. Unloading
5. Clean-up

users. Additional labor can be shifted to the site on days when mowing and other intensive regular events are required. Specialized labor, such as chemical application and arborist work can be scheduled as required without the need of having such expertise on site all the time.

On-site maintenance requires some special considerations. A cellular phone for the lead person and a fax machine are needed for communication. There should be on-site secure storage for equipment and material. Safe pesticide and chemical storage are necessary. Regular communication with the client is essential to make sure things run smoothly. Longer-term contracts are desirable in order that the extra equipment purchased or leased for the site does not go to waste.

Managing Service Routes. After the contracts are sold, developing efficient routes to service the clients is a key to success, satisfaction, and profit. How many sites can a route crew handle per day? Per week? How large should the crew be? Is special equipment or work required? How far apart are the sites? What is the potential for gaining new work to support a light route? What happens when the weather or breakdown delay work?

Experience, record keeping, and trial and error are the best teachers for developing and staffing routes. There is no magic or universal formula. Establish benchmarks, based on past and anticipated production, for routes and crew performance. Tested production records let the crew, manager, and scheduler know the time required to complete various maintenance tasks. Travel time, as well as unloading, loading, and cleanup must be estimated.

Plan new and evaluate old routes at the beginning of each season. Obtain input from full-time crews, supervisors and sales representatives to create a master plan. Check with key clients to determine if changes in a proposed schedule will meet their needs. It is better to ask than to risk cancellation over a schedule that could easily be changed.

Consider the effect of new and larger equipment and new or special techniques required. New employees will be less productive than seasoned veterans will.

Monitor every site, crew performance, and efficiency throughout the year. Clients will likely let you know if they are not satisfied, but not always. Change crew size and composition to maximize efficiency and quality.

Production Budgets. Time or *production budgets* for maintenance of a site can be developed from production rates. Production budgets supply crew supervisors and scheduling personnel with a planning tool. Production can be estimated so that workloads and routes can be planned accordingly. Production estimates provide field personnel with figures for exactly what is expected and how long each function should take. Budgeting also provides an efficient and accurate method to track actual versus estimated time by task. The contractor will know where problems lie, not simply that they exist.

Putting Estimates Together. *Bid summaries* bring labor, supplies, equipment and other costs for the maintenance program together. Each company develops estimate sheets to meet their needs. In every case, however, accuracy is everything. Compare the proposed services to the specifications - they must match.

Computer programs are available to take in job requirements, area measurements, production rates, and other information, and produce direct costs or estimates.

Determining Cost Estimates. Numerous costs must be determined and estimated to produce a bid or budget. Table 4.6 shows how these components blend to develop the final price or budget. Each segment of the process must be carefully derived and considered or the final product will be in error. No estimating system is perfect. Hopefully, the intrinsic errors inherent in every estimating process will be minor making the result acceptable to the client and to the estimator.

Project Costs. *Project* or *variable* costs include material, labor, equipment, subcontracting, and other expenses incurred by the firm that are directly attributed to the fulfillment of the contract or management of a site. The magnitude of individual costs will vary with each property, and can be directly correlated with the amount of work required, and quality expectations for the site.

Table 4.6.
Summary of inputs for an accurate estimate, bid, or budget

The final bid, estimate, or budget accounts for the **project costs** (labor, materials, and equipment and subcontracting expenses), a part of the total **overhead** of the firm, a **profit** for entrepreneurial companies, and possibly a **contingency** factor. If the project requires bonding, then the cost of the **bond** may be: 1) calculated as a *ratio* of the total price, if the cost of the bond is calculated as a percent of the total price; or 2) added into the final price if the cost of the bond is a flat fee.

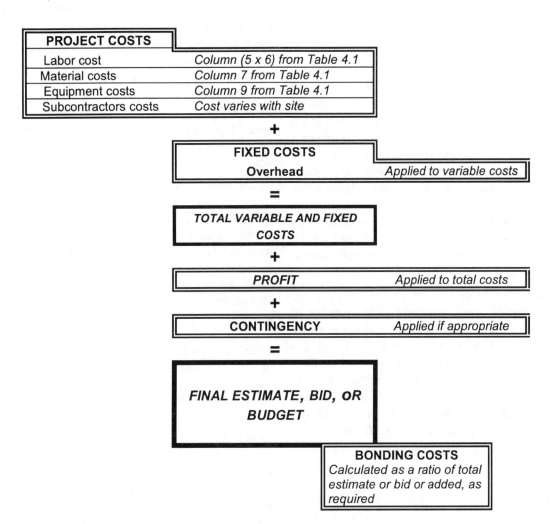

Materials

Material costs are probably the easiest expenses to calculate. The manager or estimator has a known area of turfgrass, landscape beds, and seasonal color for any property and a known amount of fertilizer, herbicide, insecticides, mulch, flowers, and other expendable materials that are applied or planted per unit area.

Each firm determines its philosophy as to whether materials will be estimated in *whole* or *partial units*. For instance, if a property requires 92 pounds of fertilizer for the turf, and fertilizer is purchased in 50-pound bags, is the material priced at 92 pounds or at two bags? This is an insignificant question when dealing with low cost items such as fertilizer or mulch; rounding to whole units will probably not make any difference in obtaining a competitive contract. Pricing per whole unit may increase material cost estimates dramatically with more expensive chemicals, such as pesticides. One should price these based on the amount actually used; partial containers will undoubtedly be used on subsequent jobs.

Material costs include more than simply the invoice price of materials divided by number of bags or pounds. Include freight and sales/excise tax. Apply a handling and storage cost to all materials, especially bulky items requiring handling time, or those requiring covered, secure, or special storage. Do not forget to add a factor for broken, damaged, and lost material. Also, add any interest incurred on the purchase from either a supplier or lending institution.

Labor costs

An *employee* costs the firm considerably more than his/her hourly wage. The actual cost to the company includes the base pay rate plus all mandatory and voluntary employer contributions to the employee. Legislated employer contributions, often referred to as *labor burden,* include: employer's share of FICA (Social Security); federal and state unemployment insurance; workers' compensation; and other statutory contributions. *Fringe benefits* or perks vary with company, but include: insurance benefits; retirement plans; paid holidays, vacations, and sick leave; uniform allowance; educational, license and meeting expenses; memberships; profit sharing or bonuses; and many others.

Some firms do not calculate employer-furnished insurance or pension plans as part of direct hourly labor rates. Since these costs are fixed on a monthly or annual basis, these employers prefer to establish them as part of overhead.

Several employers also incorporate a factor for unproductive time, such as rain days and breaks, when determining labor rates. Table 4.7 is useful in determining and understanding the total cost per hour of an employee.

Many managers also incorporate probable overtime in calculation of *effective* hourly rates. Contractors in some regions can schedule a uniform work program without overtime. In most areas, however, seasonal peaks, weather, and other happenstance must be addressed through overtime.

Midwest seasons run approximately 30 weeks from mid-April to mid-November. Some contractors plan for 11 weeks at six days per week and 19 weeks at five days per week. A labor budget may call for 11 weeks of 51 hours-per-week and 19 weeks of 42 hours. The increased wages for overtime can, therefore, be factored over a year and estimated as part of the hourly labor rates.

Equipment costs

Equipment costs are a significant expenditure of any management firm. Equipment expenses can be considered direct project costs or as part of overhead. There is no correct answer.

Developing equipment expenses as a project or variable cost allows realistic recognition of the cost of equipment on a per-job basis. This aids the manager in evaluating and differentiating between equipment- and labor-intensive procedures and makes his/her pricing of each more realistic and competitive. Hourly equipment and labor costs allow the manager to make efficient and economic decisions on equipment purchases, efficiency, and how changes in equipment will affect productivity, costs, and the bottom line.

Assigning equipment cost as part of overhead, however, is simpler. It is also more appropriate to assign costs of relatively inexpensive, long-lived, or seldom used machinery as overhead.

When determining the cost per hour or unit area (1,000 square feet, acre, or mile) of ownership and operation, manufacturer and suppliers' claims must be considered with a grain of salt, or

Table 4.7.
Labor cost estimating worksheet

COST ITEM	Employer Cost	Employee Income
Direct Wage Costs		
1. Total regular wages	$	$
2. Overtime wages		
3. Cash bonuses		
A. Total Wages (1+2+3)	$	$
Mandatory Wage Costs		
4. Employer's share FICA	$	$
5. Federal unemployment insurance		
6. State unemployment insurance		
7. Workers' compensation insurance		
8. Other		
B. Total Mandatory Wage Costs (4+5+6+7+8)	$	$
Fringe Benefits		
9. Insurance	$	$
Life		
Health		
Dental		
Other		
10. Retirement (employer's contribution)		
11. Uniforms		
12. Training/education		
13. Transportation allowance		
14. Other		
C. Total Fringe Benefits (9+10+11+12+13+14)	$	$
Other Benefits		
15. Holiday pay	$	$
16. Paid vacation leave		
17. Paid sick leave		
D. Total Other Benefits (15+16+17)	$	$
E. Total Employee Costs/Income (A + B + C + D)	$	$
F. Productive Hours Worked per Year[1]		
G. Average Cost Per Hour E divided by F		

[1]Productive hours do not include breaks, weather related down time, training, or any other non-productive time.

two. Evaluate and develop the hourly costs of ownership on realistic estimated annual hours of use and the useful life span of the machine. For instance, a mower used 30 weeks per year, five days per week, and six hours per day is operated for 900 hours per year. A machine kept for 5 seasons would be operated for 4,500 hours.

Table 4.8 is a worksheet that will be useful for determining the individual expenses that comprise the cost of operating landscape maintenance equipment.

Ownership costs. The *cost to purchase* a machine is the actual price plus finance charges. Some managers prefer to calculate actual cost for hourly computations based on the cost to replace the machine (*replacement cost*), rather than the original purchase price. Either calculation should deduct a realistic scrap or trade-in value (often around 10 percent) from the overall machine cost. Calculating equipment cost on replacement rather than purchase price may be more prudent during inflationary periods or for longer-lived machines.

The *cost of the money* used to purchase this equipment must also be included. If a contractor finances $4,000 of the cost of a $7,000 machine, then the interest paid can easily be seen and understood as part of the overall ownership expense.

Is there a cost for the $3,000 cash portion of the price? What if the owner paid for the entire purchase in cash? Business advisors urge judicious managers to consider a cost on the cash portions of down payment or purchase price. This return on cash, or *opportunity cost*, is the gain that can be realized if the cash portion of the purchase was invested in a safe income source, such as a certificate of deposit, money market certificate, or within the owner's own business. The opportunity cost is determined for the duration of the investment, just as finance charges. Opportunity costs should be considered for cash portions of equipment purchases, in addition to any finance costs.

Equipment operating costs. Include fuel and oil in *hourly operating costs.* Determine fuel consumption per hour under normal use. What will happen to fuel prices next year or even next month is a guess. Increases in fuel price affect the cost of operation, but the overall impact is actually quite small. The oil changes and other routine service are estimated based on records, experience, or manufacturer's recommendations.

Repairs and maintenance are estimated by including the cost of expected overhauls or major repairs, periodic tune-ups, and replaceable items (belts and blades) in the total operating expenses. Experience with similar machines, manufacturers and suppliers, and mechanics can provide information on repair costs.

Include the cost of insurance for a true cost of equipment operation. Some firms prefer to consider insurance as overhead since it is an annual fee. Most policies do not itemize charges for specific pieces of equipment, except for large equipment such as trucks.

Hourly costs for equipment can be carried to the extreme. The majority of contractors using the hourly charges develop costs for major equipment (vehicles, tractors, mowers). Some will compute the time cost for smaller equipment, such as blowers, edgers, and line trimmers. Other managers consider small machine costs as part of their overhead. Hourly figures are sometimes used to account for rakes, hoes, and other small tools. Basic small tool inventories, however, are best considered overhead. The estimator will go crazy trying to anticipate every minute a broom or pruner is used.

Subcontractors' costs

Subcontracting is a necessary and profitable part of landscape management. Subcontractors fill the gaps in services (Table 4.9). Trying to be an expert in too many business sectors compromises quality, increases costs, and wastes time. Only very large, diverse companies have all of the equipment and expertise to perform every required management task. Select subcontractors carefully; they represent your firm. Always request and check job references before hiring a subcontractor. Be sure the subcontractor carries proper insurance and licensing to protect the hiring firm and the client.

Subcontractors' costs are relatively easy to apply as direct costs. An estimate or bid from a subcontractor for their services is received. Many firms markup or add a percentage to the subcontractor's bid. The markup compensates for the hiring firm's time and expenses for monitoring the work. There is no accepted formula for

Table 4.8.
Worksheet for calculating equipment operation costs

The cost per hour for any machine or vehicle can be determined by adding its fixed and variable costs and dividing by the estimated use over its life. Estimated cost of repairs, operation, and life can be obtained from past records or manufacturer's literature.

Fixed or Ownership Costs

1. Purchase price	$
2. Salvage (10%) or trade-in	- $
3. Non recoverable price (1 minus 2)	= $
4. Finance or opportunity cost	- $
5. Insurance/taxes/licenses	- $

A. *Total Fixed Costs* (3+4+5)	= $

6. Fuel	+ $
7. Oil/lubricants/antifreeze	+ $
8. Estimated repairs	+ $
9. Tires	+ $

B. *Total Variable Costs (6+7+8+9)*	= $

Use

11. Estimated use per year (area, hours or miles)	
12. Estimated life (years)	

C. *Total Use (hour or area) of machine (11 x 12)*	=

Cost per Hour or Unit of Use

Fixed plus variable costs divided by total use (A+B ÷ C)	= $

Table 4.9.

Subcontracting:

- Allows the firm to offer the client complete management service.
- Extends the scope of work the firm is able to accomplish or participate.
- Provides additional personnel, specialized equipment, and expertise without extending the firm's resources.
- Can provide special licensing or knowledge of regulations.

Table 4.10.

Criteria for selecting subcontractors
- Performance quality
- Volume of work needed
- Financial backing
- Reliability
- Professionalism
- Risk

markups. Markups range from 10 to 50 percent of the subcontractor's price, depending on the complexity of the job, the budget, and the market. Ten percent is a common figure. The larger the job, however, the smaller the markup typically added.

Working as a subcontractor. Prompt payment and extended liability are the primary issues to consider when working as a subcontractor. General contractors may delay payment to the subcontractors until the job is finished and accepted. A subcontractor must be held responsible for his/her actions on site. However, make sure that the subcontracting firm will not share in liability for actions with which they were not concerned. Some general contractors like to spread the potential liability and "blame" among all of the participating subcontractors. Read the contract very carefully.

Overhead

Overhead is the cost of doing business. Overhead expenses cannot be directly attributed to any single job. Overhead expenses are incurred whether the company has work or not, and do not rise or fall based on what is charged for a job. Overhead includes salaries and benefits for administrative, management, secretarial, and accounting staff, payments or rent for land and buildings, and utilities (Table 4.11).

The salaries or wages of "non-working" supervisors or managers who coordinate a number of people or crews can be included as management overhead. Some contractors, however, consider these people as direct costs to the sites their crews are responsible for and apply their salary as an hourly expense. It is more efficient and reasonable to consider such employees as management overhead.

Applying overhead. There are as many ways to apply or factor overhead into a bid or estimate, as there are companies. Some companies simply determine labor and material costs and multiply by a magic number to cover overhead and profit. The numbers two and three seem to be the most common. This may be acceptable to some, as long as they are in the black at the end of the year. Successful business owners and managers feel that they must know and be able to control costs, especially in a competitive market.

Each property or contract must pay its share of the overhead costs. An accountant, business manager, or a consultant can assist in developing specific overhead figures and application formulae. The accounting is not difficult and annual expenditures by category must be determined for tax purposes anyway. Most overhead recovery systems develop a relationship (or ratio) between overhead and direct costs. Some overhead recovery systems are based upon a relationship or ratio between indirect costs and labor, since labor is the greatest direct cost.

Controlling overhead. Overhead for landscape management firms varies widely, from as much as 50 percent or more of sales, to as low as 14 percent. A 2001 ALCA survey of 106 landscape firms indicated that higher-profit firms, when compared to lower-profit firms:

- sometimes had a greater ratio of installation to maintenance revenue;

- had only a slight advantage over lower-profit firms in managing direct costs or project;

- had no cost advantage in managing indirect costs (wages; payroll taxes; shop, parts and repair expenses; and equipment depreciation); but,

Table 4.11.

Overhead categories reflect business expenses incurred whether or not the firm receives any work or income. Overhead is comprised of many, sometimes forgotten, but very important costs. The following illustrates some typical overhead expenses associated with landscape management.

Costs for Facilities
- Land - Payment or Rental
- Structure - Improvement and Upkeep
- Furniture and Furnishings
- Utilities
- Taxes and Fees
- Insurance
- Janitorial Service
- Grounds Care by Employees
- Security

Office Expenses
- Postage
- Office Equipment and Supplies
- Computers and Digitizers
- Telephone
- Radio and Communications Equipment

Contracted Services
- Labor and Materials Acquired by Contract
- Legal Fees, Audits
- Consultants
- Waste Disposal

Administrative/Management Expenses
- Administrative Wages and Benefits
- Management Wages and Benefits
- Support Wages and Benefits
- Secretarial and Accounting
- Finance Costs
- Advertising and Marketing
- Entertainment and Sales Costs
- Licenses/Fees/Permits
- Interest and Bank Charges
- Publications and Memberships
- Insurance
- Donations
- Travel/Meetings/Training
- Account Collections
- Bad Debts

Tools, Equipment and Vehicle Costs
- Purchase, Lease and Rental
- Service and Repair
- Replacement/Depreciation
- Fuel, and Fluids, and Parts
- Vehicle Insurance/Taxes/Licenses
- Storage
- Small Tool Inventory
- Mechanics Wages and Benefits

- were much more efficient in managing company overhead.

Look closely at the firm's overhead expenses and how they can be managed without affecting quality, production, or sales.

Other Costs. Supplements to total job costs may be added to the bid in some cases. For a new company, a new or difficult landscape, or unusual contract, a *contingency* factor is sometimes added. A contingency is an amount or percentage added to the calculated costs to protect from omission, gross error, or site factors that were unnoticed or unable to be factored into the bid. Contingencies are sometimes referred to as a fudge factor. They will serve as insurance if something was omitted or miscalculated, or a substantial boost in profits if everything was calculated correctly. Adding substantial contingencies, however, may result in losing the contract in competitive situations, since they will boost the bid.

The cost of *bid bonds* or *performance bonds*, if required, must be added after the entire bid, including profit, is calculated. The price for the bond, a guarantee of a surety, may be charged as a percentage of the total contract price, or as a flat fee. If the bonding fee is a percentage of the entire contract, include the fee in the final price using a ratio equation. Flat fee bond charges can be added to the total costs, plus profit, to determine the final price.

Some states require sales or excise taxes for materials and/or labor used in landscape maintenance. These should be added to the customer's price since they will have to be paid by the contractor.

Profit

Profit is not the only reason people go into business. It is, however, the principal inducement for remaining in business. As someone once said, "Work without profit is called exercise." The amount of profit, or return on investment, desired or required, must be determined by the firm's owners.

How much profit is enough? How much is too little? The profit margin of a firm is usually a variable floating around an ideal. Profit depends on several facets and is ultimately determined by how accurately costs were estimated. Hopefully, either the estimates will be reasonably accurate, or the shortfalls will be balanced by the windfalls to equal an acceptable overall rate of return. One benchmark for lowest level is current rate of returns on safe investments, such as certificates of deposit (CD). How much could the owner make if he/she sold everything today and invested in a 10-year CD? Why would the manager be willing to accept a lesser return with all of the work and headaches that go into operating a business?

The profit applied to individual properties is a figure within range influenced by need, size, risk, and the marketplace. What is the lowest and highest (without feeling guilty) profit acceptable on a job? If the firm needs the job to fill its schedule or a route, as an advertising point, to simply keep afloat, or as a point of honor, then it should be more willing to do it for a lower profit margin. The greater the need, the lower the profit the owner is willing to consider.

With risk comes an increased expectation of profit. If the job is risky from any of a number of views (labor, difficulty, or age of the landscape), then seek a greater profit. If the job is one that everyone can do, then be assured that everyone will bid on it. Larger jobs are sometimes bid at lower profits than are smaller properties. The lower profit rate is compensated for by increased volume and efficiency. Smaller jobs often have increased costs due to their scale and higher profit margins are applied.

The number of competitors in the marketplace causes a landscape management company to adjust its profit to become more competitive on specific jobs. Good work at a reasonable, or at least acceptable price, is always more honorable than a reputation as a low bidder at any price. Survey the competition to see if the firm is in line.

Profit is applied to the final price of any job according to the business statement and requirements of the owner. If *profit* is a *percentage of total costs or investment*, then the total cost of a job (direct + indirect) is multiplied by this figure. If the *profit* is a *percent of the final price, billing, or volume*, then it must be calculated by using a ratio equation. Again, seek the assistance of an accountant or a business consultant in setting up the firm's books and goals.

Pricing Strategies and Methods

A large number of companies have developed pricing systems in which direct costs, overhead, and profit are applied directly to hourly production rates. Total direct hours for labor during the past fiscal year are divided into the total income for the year. This yields a bid price per man-hour that includes direct, indirect, and profit. The hourly rate is adjusted to reflect the desired profit level. This pricing method depends on last year's business figures, so changes in costs, wages and inflation must be anticipated.

Companies using this system develop different hourly labor rates to reflect the amount or expense of equipment and materials involved. For instance, mowing is more expensive than general labor. Spraying and irrigation repair are more expensive than mowing.

One company used the following labor rates:

- $27.00 per hour for mowing, edging, trimming, and general labor;

- $80.00 per hour for herbicide application to shrub beds;

- $85.00 per hour for herbicide application to turf;

- $90.00 per hour for seasonal insect applications; and

- $60.00 per hour for irrigation checks, adjustment, or repair.

Hourly price differences reflect the equipment, material, and increased salary for technical and professional personnel for the individual operations.

Table 4.12.
Bid Comparison Form Example

Comparing actual versus estimated costs improves estimating accuracy and identifies true costs. The following simple example could be used to compare estimated or bid figures with actual costs or times. Actual costs are derived from job and time sheets.

Activity	Estimated Cost	Actual Cost	Difference	Reason
Material				
Pesticide				
Fertilizer				
Labor				
Mowing				
Tree care				
Shrub care				
Continued detailed listing of other operations				
Gross				

Other companies have extrapolated the income per man-hour to develop charges per unit area (1,000 square feet or acre) for mowing or chemical applications. Pruning is sometimes calculated on a per-plant basis, linear feet of hedge, or bed area. Seasonal color is frequently estimated on a per-flat, per-plant, per-bulb, or bed area charge.

Per-hour or per-unit estimating systems provide simple and rapid methods of determining charges. Per-hour charges are based on company history. Good managers monitor interim financial statements and cumulative costs for individual jobs. New companies adopting this practice tend to use per hour figures pulled from the air, usually very close to, but slightly below the larger firms in the area. The result is a large profit per hour during the first few seasons; however, total profit and profit-per-hour decline as overhead increases.

Some companies still just guess.

Budgeting for In-House Landscape Management

Budgeting landscape or turfgrass management for golf courses or other facilities where the work is done in house follows the same basic concepts as described for landscape management contractors. Costs depend on the type of facility, the quality of the infrastructure (equipment and maintenance, labor, availability of subcontractors,

etc.), the quality of the landscape design and installation, and the desires of the owner.

The manager develops a plan for routine management for the site for the entire year. The plan is the road map. Consider seasonal changes and pressures, and allow for contingencies.

Develop and keep good records. These serve to calculate production rates and as a basis for scheduling and decision-making. Software available from specialty vendors and printed forms can help tremendously.

Compare last year's budget to that of the current operating year. Was it adequate? Payroll is often 60 to 80 percent of the operating budget for in-house landscape management. What will be the effect of changes in salaries, wages, and payroll expenses? Experienced people will require higher pay to keep them. Was enough overtime paid to current employees to justify an additional employee?

Keep records of quantities and prices for materials used on site. Talk to vendors to determine expected price changes. Are there new herbicides, fungicides, insecticides, or fertilizers that will provide superior performance, eliminate applications, or reduce (or increase) costs? Check inventories to determine what is already on hand.

Evaluate equipment needs and condition. Are maintenance and repair costs in line? Develop a replacement plan for existing equipment based

87

on life expectancies and depreciation. When does it make sense to replace a machine rather than continue to repair it? Would replacing smaller equipment with larger models be cost effective?

When meeting with the budget approving authority, have data to backup and justify requests.

Do not overwhelm management with too much information. Provide written copies of the proposed budget well in advance of the budget meeting so it can be digested. At the budget meeting with decision makers, make sure your appearance is neat and demeanor professional.

Bibliography

1. Anonymous. 1985. Estimating techniques that will make you successful. *Landscape Contractor* 26(12):10.

2. Anonymous. 1987. Costing mowing jobs. *American Lawn Applicator* 9(3):44.

3. Anonymous. 1990. Equipment operating cost survey. *Pro* 2(7):30.

4. Anonymous. 1990. *Grounds Maintenance Estimating Guidelines.* 6th ed. Professional Grounds Management Society, Cockeysville, MD.

5. Anonymous. 1992. Calculating mowing costs. *Landscape Management* 31(1):22.

6. Anonymous. 1992. Subcontracting for pleasure and profit. *Landscape Contractor* 33(5):26.

7. Anonymous. 1993. Computing mower costs. *Lawn & Landscape Maintenance* 14(4):49.

8. Anonymous. 1996. Successful business owners do their math. *Lawn &Landscape* 17(12):56.

9. Anonymous. 1997. Details, details. *Lawn & Landscape* 18(2):56.

10. Buck, S. 1996. The labor cost prophecy. *Lawn & Landscape* 17(5):94.

11. Canute, T. 1999. Budgeting for golf course management. *Hawaii Landscape* 3(4):10.

12. Christian, P., III. 1990. When the rubber meets the road. *Grounds Maintenance* 29(6):36.

13. Church, B. 2001. Safe subcontracting. *Turf* Feb:24.

14. Copley, K. 1983. How to estimate the job. *Grounds Maintenance* 18(1):10.

15. Copley, K. and D. Lofgren. 1983. Estimating. *Grounds Maintenance* 18(2):18.

16. Dunham, G. 1999. Include subcontractors in your strategy. *Pro* 12(1):10.

17. Dunham, G. 1999. Subcontractors are no substitute for planning. *Pro* 12(1):6.

18. Farrington, B. 2001. A wage & hour law primer. *Tree Care Industry* 12(4):34.

19. Garber, T. 1990. Accurate estimating, pricing stems from a solid budget. *Lawn & Landscape Maintenance* 11(11):26.

20. Garber, T. 1990. Competition increases need for insightful bidding. *Lawn & Landscape Maintenance* 11(12):102.

21. Greenleaf, C. 2000. The business of bidding. *Lawn & Landscape* 21(4):92.

22. Greenleaf, C. 2001. Pricing sense. *Lawn & Landscape* 22(3):90.

23. Hampshire, K. 2001. Pricing for profit. *Lawn & Landscape* 22(1):83.

24. Hampshire, K. 2001. Commercial break. *Lawn & Landscape* 22(10):58.

25. Hampshire, K. 2001. Fill the gaps. *Lawn & Landscape* 22(7):96.

26. Haupt, S. 1993. What does $10 cost? *Tree Care Industry* 4(9):22.

27. Hearty, C. 2000. Subcontracting: More service can mean more sales. *Grounds Maintenance* 35(9):6.

28. Hoehn, C. 1994. Setting the right prices for contracted services. *Lawn & Landscape Maintenance* 15(1):52.

29. Howell, B. 1996. Look before you leap. *Lawn & Landscape* 17(1):60.

30. Huston, J. 1997. Pricing maintenance packages. *Landscape & Irrigation* 21(1):28.

31. Huston, J. 1998. Profitable pricing. *Landscape & Irrigation* 19(5):69

32. Huston, J. 1998. Pricing the job. *Lawn & Landscape* 19(54):115.

33. Huston, J. 2000. Sharpening your mental pencil. *American Nurseryman* 192(1):68.

34. Huston, J. 2000. Price for profit. *Turf* Oct:16.

35. Kendrick, J. 2000. Low-ballers and the lawn care food chain. *Turf* June:16.

36. Kehoe, K. 2001. How higher-profit companies do it. *ALCA advantage* Spring:28.

37. King, J. 1987. Three ILCA members help take the mystery out of estimating. *Landscape Contractor* 28(11):14.

38. Landis, D. 1989. Landscape bidding and job costing - a CPA's perspective. *Landscape Contractor* 30(5):10.

39. Legg, D. 1990. The cost of mowing. *Grounds Maintenance* 25(3):110.

40. Lofgren, D. 1978. Budgeting, estimating and management. In: *Manual of Site Management*. Environmental Design Press, Reston, VA

41. Lofgren, D. 1991. Projecting labor costs. *Grounds Maintenance* 26(11):38.

42. Martin, S. 1991. Multi-year contracts. *Grounds Maintenance* 26(10):16.

43. Marx, W. 1991. Job costing. *PRO* 3(5)5.

44. McVicker, M. 2001. Profits and profitability. *Tree Care Industry* 12(3):18.

45. Minor, D. 2000. In minor's league. *Lawn &Landscape* 21(9):20.

47. Moore, M. 1985. Bidding, installation and maintenance - how we do it. *Foliage News* 10(5):1.

47. Nilsson, P. 2003. Cutting yourself short? *Grounds Maintenance* 38(11):13.

48. Phillips, T. 1991. Pricing for profit: an introduction. *Landscape Management* 30(2):32.

49. Phillips, T. 1991. Pricing for profit II. *Landscape Management* 30(3):56.

50. Post, C. 1981. How to bid for profit. *American Nurseryman* 153(9):80.

51. Ross, F. 1998. Controlling overhead. *Lawn &Landscape* 19(8):51.

52. Tanzillo, K. 1995. Smart job-cost estimates build profits. *Lawn & Landscape Maintenance* 16(4):89.

53. Trusty, M. and S. Trusty. 1992. Making a profit at mowing. *Lawn & Landscape Maintenance* 13(12):27.

54. Tucker, D. 2000. Time is money. *Lawn & Landscape* 21(1):56.

55. Tucker, D. 2001. Accurate job costing. *Grounds Maintenance* 36(7):c1.

56. Vander Kooi, C. 1985. *Estimating and Management Principles for Landscape Contracting*. C. Vander Kooi, Littleton, CO.

57. Vander Kooi, C. 1989. Developing a bidding strategy. *Pro* 1(6):5.

58. Vander Kooi, C. 1998. The cost of labor. *Lawn &Landscape* 19(2):99.

59. Vander Kooi, C. 1998. Handling overhead. *Lawn &Landscape* 19(1):87.

60. Vander Kooi, C. 1999. Including a 'ding dong factor' in bids. *Pro* 12(1):16.

61. Ward, M. 1991. Pondering mowing costs. *Lawn & Landscape Maintenance* 12(2):3.

62. Wilbraham, S. 1989. How to bid large properties. *Pro* 1(6):4.

63. Wisniewski, N. 2000. Working with subs. *Lawn & Landscape* 21(1):94.

64. Wisniewski, N. 2001. Pricing pointers. *Lawn & Landscape* 22(3):112.

65.. Wisniewski, N. 2001. The game of bidding. *Lawn & Landscape* 22(7):86.

Chapter 5
Personnel Management [1]

Landscape management is a labor-intensive service industry. The largest single budget item for any landscape management project is labor. The greatest challenge to graduating students and new managers is not problem diagnosis or product knowledge, it is the lack of experience in supervising people. The quality of the workforce determines the success or failure of the company. Most of the problems discussed among landscape managers concern finding and keeping qualified labor. This will continue to be a dilemma in the future.

Interviewing and Hiring

There is more to hiring field employees and supervisors than running an ad and selecting the best person for the job. Managers and potential managers must be cognizant of employee's rights. Employee rights are at the forefront of changes encountered in the green industry. Wrongful discharge is one of the most rapidly expanding areas in the legal landscape. Anyone who applies for a position within a company deserves consideration and has certain rights guaranteed by law.

Hiring requires several critical steps to find the right person for a position. The manager must know what he/she wants in an employee before beginning the search process. To do this, write a *job description*. A job description lists the responsibilities and duties attached to the position. Obtain input from several appropriate people in

Photo 5.1/Photo 5.2. People are the strength, reputation, and future of every landscape management company. Photograph by James Robbins, University of Arkansas and Mr. Mark Yahn, Ground Control™ Landscaping and Maintenance, Orlando, FL.

[1]Special thanks to the late Glenda Hensley for assisting with this chapter. Her personnel experience and training as Administrative Assistant to the Dean of the College of Veterinary Medicine, Kansas State University and Contract Administrator with the Joint Institute of Marine and Atmospheric Research, University of Hawaii, were invaluable.

Table 5.1.

Job description

The following is a sample of a job description for a supervisor, or crew leader of an institutional or public landscape.

I. *Scope of Work:*

All exterior grounds, walks, roadways and facilities.

II. *General duties and responsibilities:*

1. Assign all tasks and jobs to landscape management employees on a timely basis.
2. Fill out time reports daily.
3. Plan and organize all work including scheduling and follow-up inspections on a routine basis.
4. Assist supervisors in the budgeting process, data collection, report preparation, and designing and analyzing training.
5. Cooperate with other departmental personnel in completing assigned tasks, either as a leader or as a member of a team.
6. Make routine purchases of material, services, rentals, repairs, and equipment as required and authorized.
7. Cooperate with other personnel and supervisors.
8. Fill-in, as needed, for grounds department personnel when others are absent or unavailable.
9. Participate in fire and disaster programs as directed.

III. *Qualifications:*

1. Good health with adequate physical strength and endurance to perform the work described.
2. Knowledge of how to work effectively and safely.
3. Willingness to be trained in any categories of grounds or personnel management that may be needed.
4. Knowledge of the safe use of hand and power equipment involved with grounds management.
5. Five (5) or more years working directly in horticulture, gardening, and/or landscaping.
6. Two (2) or more years supervisory experience of two more employees.
7. A valid drivers license.

IV. *Education:*

High school degree or equivalent. Some post-secondary horticultural courses are desirable.

Adapted from Professional Grounds Management Society. 1989. *Grounds Management Forms and Job Descriptions Guide. 3rd ed.,* Cockeysville, MD.

the company. If the position is supervisory, exclude input from the departing employee. The employee may exaggerate the complexity of the job or make invalid suggestions.

Realize that an opening provides the opportunity to restructure. Is a new employee needed or can the responsibilities be divided among existing staff? Should someone presently within the company be promoted to fill the vacancy?

Determine the skill level and experience required to handle the job effectively. What was it about the previous employee that made him/her effective in the position? What skills would have made them more effective? Criteria often considered include: education; experience; appearance;

and personality. Avoid the temptation of setting the qualifications too high. Are you willing or able to offer a pay and benefits package that a super star candidate will require?

Job Applications

Construct *application forms* so that they do not violate state or federal antidiscrimination laws. Many companies use commercially prepared forms specifically designed to avoid discrimination. Some application forms, however, have shortcomings.

Many historical questions on application forms have been ruled inappropriate and expose the firm to potential litigation. A company or manager can transgress by asking applicants, on application forms, or during an interview: their age; dates of public school attendance; birthplace; religion; citizenship; race; height and weight; color of hair, eyes or skin; marital or family status; non job-related handicaps; whether the applicant owns or rents a home; transportation arrangement for getting to work; type of military discharge; or the name or address of any relative. Employers may not inquire about an arrest record (you can ask about convictions in some states, but not all), whether the applicant has been sued, refused a surety bond or government security; hobbies, activities or memberships not related to job qualifications; or past workers' compensation claims.

Employers cannot ask questions that permit them to deduce an applicant's age, sex, or minority status. Requesting information on the applicant's height and weight, for example, might suggest that the applicant is a woman or a member of a certain racial or national group. These questions cannot be asked even if the information will become readily apparent during an interview. Photographs may not be requested as part of the application.

Where to Look

Field positions can be filled by advertising in the Help Wanted section of one or more local newspapers. Public employment assistance offices and programs can also provide applicants. Lawn and landscape companies face competition from the construction industry, factories, and other service industries such as fast food, retail, and delivery industries. Trade publications can provide a source of more experienced and supervisory candidates. Technical schools have names of qualified applicants for positions requiring specific training and/or advanced education.

Consider non-traditional employees, such as older people. Typically, entry-level workers are in their early 20's. Many firms successfully recruit employees in their 30's and 40's. They find that although these workers may require a higher wage, they provide additional skills, experience, and reduced turnover. The green industry is still dominated by men, but employers should recruit and consider the entire labor market: women; minorities; immigrants; and displaced workers.

Establish contacts with local and regional two- and four-year colleges. Build rapport with the various departments by meeting instructors, offering to present guest lectures to classes and student clubs, and field trips. Do not restrict the search for key or supervisory employees to horticulture, landscape architecture, and allied departments. Companies recruiting at universities seek people from agricultural economics, business, crop protection, agronomy, and a host of other departments.

Internships are mutually beneficial opportunities for students and management. Employers have a chance to assess prospective employees and the opportunity allows students to gain valuable experience and training. The internship should not necessarily be looked upon as a profitable position. Ideally, the student will gain experience in all phases of the company. An intern should be more than a summer employee. Managers should explain the how's and why's, as well as the what's. A surprising number of students who have completed good internships return to that company for their first full-time job.

Seasonal employees are an important resource during busy periods. Landscape management work is seasonal and the average landscape firm hires one to 10 seasonal workers annually. A lot of work must be done in a short time. Begin hiring seasonal employees early in the year; do not wait until the day before they are needed. Be aggressive – you are competing with retailers, food service, and other service industries. Hold mass

---

Table 5. 2.

Where to advertise for part-time or seasonal employees
- Daily/weekly newspapers
- School bulletin boards
- Word of mouth
- State employment agencies

hiring seminars at local schools. Retirees often make dependable seasonal employees.

Stress the importance of the part-time people to supervisors and existing crews. Ask for their tolerance and help in training the part-timer. Offer good part-time or seasonal employees as much work as possible throughout the year to keep them interested in the company.

As the company grows, consider appointing or hiring a personnel officer. This person can keep applicant files, learn and understand the necessary paperwork, maintain personnel records, and make the manager's life easier.

The general operation and management of the company play an important part in hiring, as well as employee retention. Develop programs that adequately train and reward employees. Create an environment that encourages people to seek career opportunities with the company.

Promotion From Within

A prime place to seek supervisory or management candidates is within the company. You are dealing with a known entity and do not have to research their background. The current employee is familiar with the organization, its goals, the management, equipment, and employees.

When comparing internal and external candidates, do not confuse credentials with accomplishments. Not every manager or supervisor need have a college degree. Possession of a degree does not assure expertise or ability to supervise people. Experience, motivation, and enthusiasm go a long way.

Promotion from within creates higher morale. The opportunity for upward movement shows employees that the company believes in their accomplishments, and abilities. Promotion also indicates to the employee that he/she has a career, rather than just a job.

There are also negative aspects of promoting from within. The applicant pool is limited. None of the employees may be suitable for the available position. A current employee that is interviewed but then not promoted may become disgruntled and a liability. The manager must assure the employee of his/her value to the organization or risk losing the disappointed person. Promotion from within still leaves a vacancy that must be filled. Other employees sometimes resent a former co-worker becoming their boss. Additionally, new talent or expertise has not been added to the company.

One difficult task for some firms is to expand the number of field crews for increased workloads. Good crew supervisors are difficult to find on short notice. One company anticipates crew expansion with a position of assistant crew supervisor on every field crew. The assistant supervisor has the opportunity to work directly under a supervisor and has leadership responsibilities in his/her absence. The assistant is paid slightly more than other field employees on the crew. The assistant

---

Table 5.3.

Qualities of a supervisor

Supervisors must be able to work with people. Evaluate people for supervisory or leadership roles in relation to the following:
- Does the person have adequate supervisory ability?
- How does the person work with others?
- Can the person communicate readily and clearly with employees, other supervisors, customers, and management?
- Can the prospect make decisions?
- How successfully can the individual delegate responsibility or assignments?
- Will the person overreact to the promotion or new authority?
- How will the person accept advice or criticisms from superiors?
- What is the emotional stability of the individual?
- Can the applicant assume the added responsibility?
- Does the prospect have sufficient stamina?

is familiar with the work routine and can assume a supervisor's position with minimal preparation when required.

Recruiters

Several employment firms have emerged to serve the green industry in recent years. Recruiters or "head hunters" aid managers in filling certain positions. Recruiters can sometimes find more candidates that are qualified in a shorter time. They can perform initial screening and provide potential people who meet pre-established qualifications.

Evaluating Résumés

The quality of the résumé and that of the candidate are not necessarily related. Many applicants seek the assistance of a professional résumé service. Hopefully, all of the information is true and accurate. When reading résumés, look for specific accomplishments such as sales increases, measurable productivity improvements, and examples of leadership.

Grades are not the most important indicator of knowledge or success. Grades, however, do indicate something about self-discipline, goal orientation, and intelligence.

Take note of noticeable gaps in work chronology. Do not eliminate a candidate for having had several jobs, but do inquire about it during the interview.

The résumé can indicate how hard the candidate will work. Look for instances where the person went beyond the call of duty. This may be evidenced by volunteer work and college club activities, especially committee chair and officer positions. Extra-curricular activities indicate high energy levels, a willingness to take responsibility, and ambition.

Seriously question résumés that: over-emphasize education or training; have distinct gaps in their background; contain trivia; those that sound egotistical or bitter; and those that appear too slick or too cute.

Read the cover letters carefully. In a cover letter, expect to learn what makes this applicant or student different from any of the others. The letter should be well written, grammatically correct, and typed without error. Again, there is plenty of assistance available in writing cover letters.

Interviewing

The interview is the period when the employer and employee meet and evaluate each other. Conduct the interview in as relaxed a setting as possible. Allow adequate time to answer the applicant's questions as well as have yours answered.

Plan the interview. Prepare by reading the credentials provided. Review the applicant's background and application with him/her to see if the information is correct and if there are any pertinent additions.

Check references. Over the years, I have assisted students in finding jobs throughout the green industry, and I have been appalled by how few employers bother to check references. Many feel that a person would not be listed as a reference unless he/she had positive comments about the applicant. In general, this is probably true. On the other hand, technical school and college instructors or advisors will likely provide an honest opinion of the person. They fully realize the student's limitations and are concerned about the success of the employer/employee relationship from both sides. Most instructors will not recommend students for positions they will not be able to handle.

Ask the right questions. When interviewing an applicant for any position, know what information is sought. Begin with small talk to become acquainted and make everyone comfortable. Have some planned questions. Know what points on the résumé or application require discussion. Assume a conversational tone rather than a direct question format. Encourage the candidate to do most of the talking and be a good listener using silence, nodding, and eye contact. Ask open-ended questions rather than those that can be answered yes or no.

Know what questions are appropriate and what behavior may be interpreted as discrimination. Ask only job-related questions using a reasonably structured format that uses the same set of basic questions for each candidate. Ask women the same questions asked of men. If physical standards are set, i.e., height, weight, or strength,

Table 5.4.

Twenty frequently asked interview questions

When interviewing applicants, know what information is sought. Encourage the applicant to do most of the talking and be a good listener. Ask open-ended questions rather than those that can be answered yes or no.

1. Tell me about yourself; expand on your résumé.
2. Why are you applying for this position?
3. What are your long-term career goals?
4. Where do you want to be in five or ten years?
5. Why do you feel that you will be successful in this position?
6. What supervisory or leadership roles or experience have you had?
7. What have been your most satisfying and most disappointing school or work experiences?
8. What are your strongest (weakest) personal qualities?
9. Give me some examples that support your interest in this (industry, position, or firm).
10. Why did you decide to interview with us?
11. What courses in school did you like best? Least? Why?
12. What did you learn or gain from your part-time, summer job, or internship experiences?
13. Would you prefer on-the-job training or a formal program?
14. What can you do for us right now?
15. What can we do for you right now and in the future?
16. Why are your grades low?
17. Why did you choose your major?
18. How do you spend your spare time?
19. Tell me about your extracurricular activities and interests.
20. Why did you quit your previous jobs?

then be prepared to show how they relate to the position.

Do not force issues that the applicant clearly wishes to avoid. Ask about perceived strengths, weaknesses, and responsibilities of their current position. Questions about the applicant's current job, previous successes, disappointments and problem solving reveal more information than the application. How would he/she describe the management style of their current supervisor? *"If I were to speak with your supervisor, what would he/she tell me about your job performance?"* Ask what strengths the applicant perceives they possess to make them a success in this position. Avoid trap questions, *"Are you any good at firing people?"*

Look at the candidate's communication skills and for continuing improvement. Does the candidate exhibit decision-making and problem solving ability? What is the person's ability to give and take, work as part of a team, and their openness to change?

Look for dependability (*"What was the biggest mistake you made at your last place of employment and what you did about it?"*) Are they quality oriented? Will they work safely?

Give extra credit to applicants who have done their homework and know something about your company. Find out why they are interested in this position and willing to leave their current position. Inquire about the applicant's goals over the next two to five years. Can they grow within the company?

Do not oversell the position. Explain the negatives about the job. What may be a negative to one person may be a positive to another. The applicant should have a true picture of their responsibilities to make an informed decision and reduce turnover.

Explain briefly the opportunities the company offers including: salary range; merit raises; benefits, insurance; any and all leave provided; and the payroll schedule.

Close the interview by asking for further questions from the applicant. Let the applicant know what to expect next – another interview, a phone call, or a letter with your decision. Give a date to

Table 5.5.

Killer questions for interviews

Avoid risky questions when interviewing potential employees. Do not ask anything that would hint of age, ethnic, sex, or religious discrimination.
- What is your date of birth?
- How old are you?
- What is your ancestry or racial or ethnic background?
- Are you married?
- Are you divorced?
- Do you have children? If not, do you have plans for a family?
- Who takes care of your children while you are at work?
- What is your religion?
- What church or synagogue do you attend?
- How is your health? (An exception is if health or physical ability relates directly to performance of the job, such as a good back for fieldwork.)
- What do you think about working with _____ (any protected class or race)?

expect notification of selection for the position, if possible.

Write down your opinions immediately after concluding the interview. What did you like and not like? If several people were interviewed for a position, they will blur and blend after a while. Interview the entire applicant pool before extending an offer. If a person appears perfect for the job, he/she will still be perfect after talking to the remaining applicants.

Make the offer to the selected candidate as quickly as possible by phone and by mail. Do not include anything that indicates the duration of the job, such as referring to a secure position. Do not promise anything that cannot be delivered. This can lead to trouble if the person does not work out. Ask the candidate for acknowledgment of acceptance and indicate that you are looking forward to working with him/her. Also, have the courtesy to inform unsuccessful applicants.

Salary

Determine the salary for the position based upon responsibilities and expectations. Know the current market value of the position being offered. Do not automatically base the new employee's wages on those of the previous. Exiting employees may have been paid more or less than they or the position is worth.

Salaries vary with market area, the size of the applicant pool, company policy, and budget. As the market for employees becomes more competitive, salaries are forced to increase. Employers should not only consider the starting salary but also develop equitable pay increase practices. Fringe benefits are very important to an employee trying to raise a family.

Salaries in landscape management are more competitive than in most other segments of the green industry. There is also greater concern about fringe benefits. This is based loosely on fact

Table 5.6.

Avoid indications of permanent employment

Giving an indication of a perceived or real intent to employ during the interview, or to retain a person or post-hiring orientation can lead to problem. Avoid these traps:
- You can (could) look forward to a long career here.
- After your probationary period, you will become a permanent employee.
- Just do a good job and you will not have any problems with job security.
- No one ever gets fired unless there is a really good reason.
- The company provides full health and dental benefits. (These are subject to acceptance of the employee by the insurance carrier.)

and a great deal on observation of offers and success of past students in various areas of ornamental horticulture. I have heard fewer concerns from prospective employees about salary levels in the landscape management business than in the nursery and garden center industries.

Reserve salary discussions until a job offer is made. However, I do encourage students to come away from an interview with at least some idea of a salary range. Schedules for evaluations and raises are probably as important as initial salary. An employee may be more willing to accept a lower starting salary during an evaluation or training period if there is promise and hope for fair, periodic increases based on production and the health of the company.

Non-competitive contracts

Some companies require new employees to sign *non-competitive contracts*. In essence, non-competitive contracts state that an employee will not compete with the company after leaving for any reason. The contracts are meant to prevent employees from starting his/her own business using the expertise and client base gained from the employer.

Some contracts are reasonable in their language and intent, others are not. One former student was asked to sign a contract a few days *after* arriving on a new job. He had not been informed of this requirement before accepting the position and moving his family. The contract prevented him from starting or working for any firm providing any landscape commercial or retail product or service within a 60-mile radius for three years after leaving the company. He thought the contract was inordinate and refused to sign it. He was dismissed a few days after beginning employment. He now has a very competitive and profitable firm in the same town. The employer deprived himself of an excellent employee and undoubtedly exposed the company to a nasty and expensive lawsuit had the employee elected to pursue it. That employer, by the way, is now out of business.

Courts have upheld some non-competitive contracts that protect the firm's customer lists, client base, and trade secrets. More often, however, courts throughout the country have found non-competitive contracts an unreasonable restriction on the employee and free trade.

Complying with Immigration Laws when Hiring

Under Section 274A of the Immigration and Nationality Act, it is unlawful to employ aliens who do not have proper employment authorization. At the same time, Section 274B of the Act establishes employment discrimination on the basis of an individual's national origin or citizenship status as an unfair and illegal immigration-related employment practice. Employers must tread a narrow line to assure compliance with Sections 274A and with 274B. The Immigration and Naturalization Service (INS) can be very aggressive in its enforcement of these provisions. Fines levied against employers can be and have been substantial.

The following guidelines may help avoid problems complying with immigration laws when hiring field and supervisory employees:

1. Employers are required to have a Form I-9, "Employment Eligibility Verification" completed for each employee hired since November 6, 1986. Establish a standard procedure for completing, verifying, and re-verifying I-9s. By consistently following this standard procedure, the company may avoid the perception that its hiring decisions are based on improper factors such as appearance, accent, or name.

2. Employers are responsible for ensuring that I-9s have been completed fully and accurately. Completing the Form I-9 should be part of every employee's first-day routine. Carefully review the document by the third day of employment. Check to see that the employee's identification documents presented are on the I-9 List of Acceptable Documents.

3. Allow the employee to choose which documents to present. If the documents appear to be genuine and are on the List of Acceptable Documents, an employer should not ask for more. Asking for additional documents may expose an employer to charges of immigration-related discrimination.

4. An employer may ask an employment applicant if he/she is currently authorized to work in the United States, but should not request information about citizenship or national origin. A simple "Yes" or "No" answer is enough.

5. Set up a reminder system to reconfirm authorizations for any employees who have time limits on their work documentation. The INS considers failure to reconfirm an employee's eligibility to work to be the same as knowingly employing an ineligible person.

6. Conduct periodic in-house audits to confirm that the company has I-9s for all employees. The forms should be completed fully and accurately. If information is missing or there are errors, this should be promptly corrected.

7. If problems or concerns arise, consult a labor or immigration attorney.

New Employee Orientation

Make every new employee feel welcome. Introduce him/her to everyone appropriate within the firm. Make sure that the employee understands the benefits available and correctly fills out all paperwork. A volume of paperwork has become necessary to assure compliance with the changes in the Immigration Reform and Control Act and other governmental mandates. Explain company policies and organization clearly. Make each employee feel that he/she is part of the team and will make valuable contributions to the team effort.

Provide each employee with an employee handbook. An alternative to a handbook is a brief history of the company and the organizational format. Include a written welcome from the owner if he/she is not affiliated with the firm's daily operations.

Employee Handbook

In most organizations, *employee handbooks* are used to summarize the relationship between the employer and the employee. Handbooks describe the employer's philosophy and set the tone for employee relations. Handbooks present rules and policies, standard procedures, and expected standards of conduct. They also explain what the employer provides the employee: benefits; services; and so on. Handbooks present the information necessary to make employees feel good about the company, build loyalty, and promote teamwork.

Another function of an employee handbook is to show the value of the benefits. It may be the only place where all of the employee's benefits are listed. A handbook can be a good recruiter, motivator, and aid in employee retention. Few employees realize the true dollar value of their benefits.

A well-prepared handbook saves time by answering routine questions like, *"How soon can I take a vacation?"*

Some firms contract a consultant or attorney to produce their employee handbook; other owner/managers write their own. Handbooks can be produced quickly and inexpensively using any of a number of available self-help books or software. Modify sample wording in these guides to fit the company's specific needs. Consult an attorney on specific legal questions. It is a good idea to have the firm's attorney quickly review the handbook before distribution. The following are general areas found in employee handbooks.

- **Introduction**. The *Introduction* describes the company's history and business philosophy. Make the tone of the handbook friendly and welcoming. Point out that the handbook does cover every possible situation and employees should contact their supervisor or the appropriate personnel person if they have specific questions.

- **Hours**. State the normal working hours for all employees. Explain the rules for overtime, how it is authorized and by whom.

- **Attendance**. Stress the importance of good attendance and punctuality. Discuss the types of absences that are considered as excused (illness, death of a family member, jury duty, National Guard service, etc). Indicate who should be contacted, and when, prior to the absence. Explain if unexcused absences or tardiness can be the basis for disciplinary action or dismissal.

- **Pay and salaries**. Be clear as to how pay and salaries are set and raises determined.

In small businesses, this simply may be a statement that pay levels are established and adjusted by the company owner/manager taking into consideration past performance, responsibilities of the position, cost-of-living changes, and the ability of the business to raise wages.

- **Benefits**. Employee benefits vary with the company. Benefits may typically include paid vacations, health insurance, dental insurance, sick pay and extended leaves for illness, pregnancy or family matters. Paid sick days or vacation days are not mandated by law; the firm sets the terms under which such benefits are granted. Be clear on whether employees can carry unused sick or vacation days into the next year. Clarify what happens to such benefits if an employee quits or is terminated. Describe any 401(k) or retirement benefits the company offers. Indicate that current job benefits can be changed at the company's discretion.

- **Drug and alcohol abuse**. Every business prohibits the use of alcohol or illegal drugs in the workplace. Some firms offer help to employees who have a substance-abuse problem and offer to pay for professional counseling. If the company provides this kind of service, state the terms involved. Discuss who determines when an employee needs counseling, the extent and duration of the counseling, approval of the counselor, and what happens if the counseling does not help.

- **Sexual harassment**. Sexual harassment is illegal. Let employees and managers know that inappropriate sexual comments or conduct in the workplace will not be tolerated, and the ramifications should it occur. Clearly state what constitutes a violation of the sexual harassment policy and make sure it agrees with legal requirements. Ensure that every employee and manager know that the firm takes sexual harassment seriously.

- **Discipline**. The discipline section of every employee handbook is particularly sensitive. List the types of conduct that will get employees in trouble, such as theft and vio-

lence. Remind employees that this is not an all-inclusive list and that the firm reserves the right to terminate an employee at any time and for reason.

- **Employee safety**. Employee safety is the first concern for every landscape management firm. Safety is a two-way street. The employer will provide the safest work environment possible and employees are expected to heed posted and normal safety rules. Encourage employees to call any potentially dangerous conditions they encounter at the workplace or on a job site to their supervisor's attention.

- **Smoking**. Most landscape management firms need a written policy for on-the-job smoking. Many cities and some states prohibit or restrict workplace smoking. If you do allow smoking at your company, clearly delineate the areas where it is permitted. Smoking on the job site is another matter. Employees should never be allowed to smoke on the client's site as a matter of professionalism and common courtesy.

- **Grievances**. Employees must know the procedures for filing grievances about evaluations, disciplinary action, violations of work rules, or other matters. If the company is large enough, consider establishing a grievance committee consisting of employees and management who meet informally and make recommendations on employment issues.

- **Appearance**. If the company has a dress code or policies on personal grooming, the employee handbook is the place to describe them.

- **Workplace civility**. Explain that employees are expected to treat each other with respect. The success of the business ultimately depends on cooperation and teamwork.

Potential implications of employee handbooks. There are also some legal implications of employee handbooks to consider. In some instances, an employee handbook is viewed as part of an explicit contract between the employee and employer. Handbooks provide written proof that

Table 5.7.

An example of an employee handbook discipline section

Employee conduct that, in the opinion of XYZ Landscape Management Company, interferes with or adversely affects our business is sufficient grounds for disciplinary action. Disciplinary action can range from verbal warnings to immediate dismissal. Depending on the conduct, it is the firm's general policy to take disciplinary steps in the following order:

- *Verbal warnings.*
- *Written warnings.*
- *Suspension.*
- *Termination.*

The seriousness of your conduct, your employment record, your ability to correct the conduct, actions the company has taken for similar conduct by other employees, how your action affects customers, and any other circumstances that may be related or extenuating will be considered before determining appropriate disciplinary action.

The following are some examples of conduct that may result in immediate dismissal. Immediate dismissal for cause is not limited to these examples.

- *Theft of company property.*
- *Excessive tardiness or absenteeism.*
- *Arguing or fighting with customers or co-workers.*
- *Using or possessing alcohol or illegal drugs at work.*
- *Coming to work under the influence of alcohol or illegal drugs.*
- *Failing to carry out reasonable job assignments.*
- *Making false statements on a job application.*
- *Violating company rules and regulations.*
- *Unlawful discrimination or harassment.*

the employees have been told the rules and policies. Some employers require the employee to sign a card indicating that he/she has read and understood the rules and policies in the handbook. If this is done, then be sure that the handbook is written so that it is understandable, and that it is available in as many different languages as necessary. Also, make sure that it has actually been read.

Regardless, avoid dangerous phrases, such as *"you are now part of the company family,"* or *"you can expect to be employed as long as you do a good job."* Refer to *permanent* employment as *regular* employment. These statements can be construed as promise of long-term employment.

Other specific areas of concern within employee handbooks include: grounds for dismissal; performance reviews; pay raises; and probationary periods. State specific offenses that are grounds for dismissal or discipline, but do not limit the firm to only these specific actions.

Refer to the probationary period as an orientation or introductory period. It may be interpreted that an employee can only be dismissed for cause after the probation.

Establish performance review procedures and conduct them fairly. Referring to annual reviews or "annual" pay increases may be interpreted as a yearlong employment contract. Salaries and subsequent adjustments can be described in terms of actual pay periods, with reference to *annual* rates only as an example.

The advantages of an employee handbook certainly outweigh any problems associated with it. These shortcomings can be neutralized with careful writing. The handbook must be fair, consistent, and updated to remain current. As with any potential legal document, write it with an eye toward interpretation and have an attorney review it.

Developing an employee handbook. Most handbooks provide general information about the company, including a letter from the chief executive, a brief history of the company, an organizational chart, and a statement of the company philosophy. Other areas included are employer services, work and discipline rules, and pay issues.

Cover the topics that pertain to the majority of employees. Avoid items that differ among classes of employees. Discussing the benefits for top management creates ill will among the troops.

Keep the book positive. Do not dwell on discipline. One of the aims should be to boost employee morale.

Do not try to discuss complicated topics. Refer employees to a designated person within the company for questions on health insurance and complicated benefits. Do not try to reprint the entire insurance policy. The personnel officer can handle this.

Determine how often the information in the handbook will change. Every time specific salaries, vacation, sick or holiday leaves are mentioned, you risk revision of the figures. On the other hand, if the handbook does not deal with specifics, then how useful is it?

Employee Benefits

Employers are required by governmental mandate to provide some fringe benefits to employees. These include Social Security, workers' compensation, and unemployment insurance. Other benefits are provided by agreement between the employer and employee. These include pension, profit sharing, bonuses, continuing education assistance, notary public service, paid vacation, holidays, sick leave, health insurance, life insurance, and many others.

Fringe benefits are important in recruiting and retaining employees and enhance the employer-employee relationship. It is, therefore, important to make employees aware of what the company provides for benefits and their costs.

Benefits packages and profit sharing plans improve and become more widely available as labor markets tighten. Fringe benefits boost the employee's real income because they are tax exempt. Fringe benefits can be beneficial to the employer because they may cost less than the comparable salary increase necessary for the employee to provide the same service him/herself.

Consider several items when evaluating fringe benefits for employee packages. First, determine which benefits are most advantageous for the employees. Medical plans are usually the most often requested. A 1995 industry survey indicated that 78 percent of hourly and 88 percent of salaried landscape employees received heath insurance or shared its cost with employers. Thirty percent of hourly and 40 percent of salaried employees received some dental insurance coverage. Seventy percent of hourly and 89 percent of salaried employees received an average of six paid holidays and ten paid vacation days.

To ensure the maximum effectiveness at minimal after-tax cost, an employee benefit should meet two tests.

Table 5.8.
Employee benefits offered by small businesses

Benefit	Percent of establishments offering
Paid vacations	88
Paid holidays	82
Employer-offered health insurance	66
Life insurance program	61
Paid sick leave	50
Retirement/pension plans	42
Employer-provided sickness/accident insurance	26

Data from: *US Bureau of Labor Statistics Employee Benefits Survey.*

1) The cost of providing the benefits should be tax deductible. A small company cannot economically embark on a program that does not permit the expenditure to be deducted.

2) The cost of the fringes should be tax-free to the employee.

The Tax Reform Act of 1986 imposed strict guidelines governing non-discrimination of fringe benefits. Each benefit has a set of eligibility tests to ensure that the plan does not discriminate against lower-paid employees. Check with an accountant to make sure the benefits meet the mandated requirements.

Evaluating Employees

Evaluation of employees is one of the most challenging functions for a manager. In a 2001 industry survey, 42 percent of landscape contractors surveyed annually evaluated all employees. Twenty three percent of the contractors conducted formal performance reviews for year-round employees, four percent evaluated only key managers, and 31 percent conducted no annual reviews.

Good evaluations are a pleasure. However, no one enjoys telling someone that his/her work is not up to par. Not many people know how to receive criticism. Employee performance is usually tied to pay increases, advancement, and job retention.

Interestingly, a survey of human resource managers reported that 90 percent would like to overhaul or eliminate their performance appraisal procedures. Only five percent of employees wanted to continue using their firms' current system.

Evaluations are easier when joined to job or task descriptions, goals, and *performance standards*. Some firms have a set of performance standards or goals for each job that are agreed upon by the supervisor and employee at the beginning of the evaluation period. Define performance standards so that everyone understands. Standards must be realistic, specific, and comprehensive. Use these same standards at evaluation time. Standards make it easier for the manager to evaluate the worker and for the employee to understand the evaluation. Goals encourage superior performance and should be re-negotiated each evaluation period.

Make the evaluation as positive as possible. Collect information and ask the recipient to prepare for the appraisal. Emphasize positive, strong points and indicate areas where the employee could improve. One aim of the evaluation should be to help and to educate the person as to how he/she can improve their effectiveness and efficiency. Using evaluations as gripe sessions and to berate the employee is not effective management. Do not wait until annual evaluations to discuss areas where the employee is not performing as expected or doing an excellent job. Allow the employee to input his/her opinion of performance. Do not allow friendship to cloud your perception of the person.

Managing Employees

"Keeping their jobs is the only motivation my employees need," according to some managers. Motivation by punishment, fear, and intimidation is the least effective management style. Unfortunately, it is too frequently used. Many supervisors think little of dressing-down, suspending, or firing employees.

Punishment and fear may achieve short-term results, but not long-term encouragement or efficiency. Adults are not inclined to remain in a position where they are threatened or intimidated. Yelling and threats create animosity toward a superior and the company. Employees may respond with hostility and subversion. Equipment will break more often and employee attitudes toward the client will reflect the supervisor's attitude toward them.

People-oriented management. Successful management of employees, whether they are entry level or salaried, requires thought, skill, and practice. Employees accomplish the goals of the company, not the owner. People work better, faster, and longer when they are informed, involved, and empowered.

People-oriented management is based on:

- *Communication* – providing information, consultation, and feedback;

- *Building people* – recognizing, developing, and using all of the capabilities of all of the people in the company; and

- *Leadership* – developing the shared vision and concern for the firm, delegation of authority, and requiring accountability from employees.

The manager must realize and communicate to his/her supervisors that the employee is the backbone of the business, the foundation of his/her reputation, and future. What attitudes are the owner and supervisors broadcasting verbally and nonverbally to the employees? If the supervisor is interested in performance levels, job satisfaction, and internal motivation of the workers, effective and demanding managerial strategies must be used.

Total Quality Management. *Total Quality Management* (TQM) and employee empowerment are common buzzwords in management style. Empowering employees can increase productivity, morale, and customer satisfaction. Like all management systems, TQM can work, but does not fit every situation. Management must be willing to give up some of the decision-making. Employees must want responsibility and accountability and buy into the entire scheme.

There is no specific recipe for successful management; read, study, learn, and change as necessary.

Motivating Employees

Peer pressure can induce higher levels of quality and performance. Encourage teamwork. Individuals are more concerned with living up to the expectations of fellow employees than those of their bosses. There is evidence that employees are more motivated when they perform a variety of tasks, as part of a crew, rather than a single, repetitive function, such as mowing. On some crews,

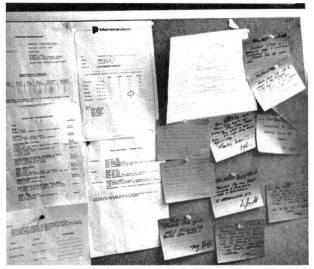

Photo 5.3. Pass compliments from clients to the crews. This company uses *gold cards* to show everyone in the shop compliments received for crews or individuals.

not all, it may be possible to rotate leadership, thereby building teamwork and experience.

Employees who are allowed to set their own performance levels will usually try to meet or exceed their own expectations. It is important to have the employee make a verbal commitment regarding written objectives. Individuals and groups are more likely to attain their goals when they make a public commitment to do so. They view verbal commitments with witnesses as promises and most people view themselves as the type who keeps their word.

Words of praise to an employee or crew that truly deserve it will lift their spirits. Master key phrases in the native language (and English) – *How are you today? Its time for a break. Lunch time! Good job! Thank you.* Improved self-image leads to an employee's greater interest in daily

---

Table 5.9.
Take the time to be a motivator

Motivated employees have a higher morale, work harder, and stay with the firm longer.
- Make sure employees understand how to properly complete the assigned job.
- Clearly indicate the expected results.
- Offer adequate and continuous support.
- Take steps to cultivate positive relationships.
- Be concerned for employees as individuals.
- Establish an appropriate recognition and reward system.
- Learn to communicate.
- Learn to communicate some encouraging phrases in the worker's native language.

work and a desire for improvement. Proper use of praise and rewards cannot be over-emphasized. Praise, after all, is free.

One company has a gold card system; any compliments to a crew or individual from clients are written up on a gold index card and posted on the bulletin board. This form of public recognition is well received. Even simple recognition such as an unannounced break augmented with cold drinks and snacks on especially hot days provides good return on investment.

Use of rewards is management based upon behavior modification. Recognition for praise from clients, greatest number of days without absence or a tardy, and performance beyond the call, are important. Workers will increase or repeat the desired work performance if they are given rewards or positive motivation. Poor performance is eliminated when the employee comprehends the relationship between commendable performance and rewards, at least in theory.

There are many bonus systems in the industry. Even small rewards, such as a free lunch, tickets to sporting events, or special jackets or clothing can be meaningful. Some employers provide additional time off in exchange for performance. Others tie bonuses to successful completion of classes, achieving certification, or licensing associated with the job. Some employers provide recognition dinners for employees and their families, and other inducements. Find out what would grab the attention of your employees. One or two employees may degrade these efforts. These are the type of people, however, that are not needed in the organization.

Rewards are successful motivators, but there can be complications. What may be an inducement to one individual is not to another. However, money talks! Bonuses funded from savings on contracts or performing under budget on a contract can be rewarded with a percentage of the windfall. Consider small bonus programs rather than salary increases. Salary increases are permanent.

Take care to develop a bonus program solidly based on performance. Make sure everyone understands the rules and that they are applied fairly. Also, remember the office staff when initiating any bonus program.

Some firms have developed a competition among crews and supervisors. The prizes may be cash, vacations, appliances, dinners, or plaques. The contest must be fair to all. If the same individual or group wins time after time, the motivation of the other workers declines.

Motivation is good management. Employees with a higher sense of worth are more valuable assets. Motivated employees save money, jobs go smoother, and equipment lasts longer. Employee turnover is also reduced and profits increase. Motivation requires planning and work on the part of the manager. After all, that is the manager's job: to manage and inspire.

Managing a Hispanic or Foreign-born Workforce

The expanding economy has put many employers into a difficult labor situation. Wages and benefits have increased to attract and retain employees and managers. The landscape service industry relies on a large amount of unskilled labor and turn over of field employees remains high. Labor for many jobs is difficult to find, regardless of the wages. Employers have increasingly relied on Hispanic and other foreign-born workers and increased mechanization to fill the void. Hispanic workers are now employed by a majority of landscape firms, making up about one-third of all industry employees. The South and West account for the heaviest concentrations.

The Hispanic workforce on the mainland and Filipino workforce in Hawaii and the Pacific Rim are diligent and intelligent employees with agricultural backgrounds and a solid work ethic. The service industry in the United States represents significant earning potential compared to their homeland.

Managing immigrant employees represents significant challenges for many landscape managers. The language barrier is the first and most obvious. Employers and lead people must maintain effective communication with the crew. The crew and lead people must be able to communicate effectively with customers and management. This can be a problem for some customers.

Identify and offer opportunities for regular crew employees to learn English; consider bonuses or pay increases as incentive for proficiency. Strongly encourage key employees in the organization to learn Spanish or the predominant language of the labor force. This will show employees the firm's commitment and long-term focus. Obtain or develop training resources in Spanish or other appropriate languages and take advantage of the increasing number of Spanish language training programs produced by many state and local associations for key employees.

Become aware of political and social situations that may cause friction. Just because the employee speaks Spanish, or English, does not mean that they all think and act alike. Each place or country of origin has particular customs and political considerations. Some groups do not want to work with other groups.

Open lines of communication are important. Employers must learn what employees need or expect from them, regardless of place of origin. Learn about cultural barriers, differences, and priorities. Employer-employee relationships are very important.

Some Hispanic and foreign-born workers are reluctant to pursue greater responsibility, even within the crew. In addition to the language challenge, there is the fear of the unknown in promotion. Raises are important incentives.

Retaining Employees

Attracting quality employees is only one management problem. Retaining employees, once the firm has invested time and money in their selection, training, and development, is another. Employees stay longer when they are happy, feel valued by the firm, and their career goals are being met.

Strategies for retaining employees are the same as those used to motivate workers:

- Maintain and review competitive compensation and benefits.

- Develop solid job descriptions – give employees a sense of purpose and some control.

- Develop an incentive program and reward outstanding performance.

- Provide verbal praise and reinforcement.

- Be consistent in review and reward.

- Pay attention to diversity issues.

- Make the effort to bridge cultural gaps and understand values.

- Offer opportunities for advancement and development in the company.

- Provide positive motivation.

Absenteeism

Absenteeism is an expensive problem in every industry. Besides illness, there are many reasons that employees do not come to work. Poor working conditions, boredom, uneven work distribution, undependable transportation, and substance abuse are but a few. An employee may also

---

Table 5.10.
What causes employee turnover?
Employee turnover is costly for any company. There are many reasons why employees move to different jobs. The following are some of the causes of turnover in the landscape industry in no particular order of importance.
- Money.
- Benefits.
- Hiring under- or over-qualified people.
- Feelings of isolation form the social groups at work.
- Employee is unable to adjust to the physical surroundings.
- Difficult or strenuous work.
- Poor supervision and management.
- Employer or supervisor attitude toward employees.
- Unclean or poor facilities.
- Little possibility of advancement - a dead end position.
- Stress or burnout.
- Personality problems with co-workers.

stay away because of work-related personality problems. Personality clashes between employees and jealousies are contributing factors. Minor conflicts among workers, if not settled by the supervisor, can develop into costly running feuds.

Poor relations with supervisors are a common problem. A surly and uncommunicative overseer can make for a miserable day. Lack of responsibility and recognition may also lead to job dissatisfaction and irregular attendance.

Solving absenteeism universally is impossible; however, improved management and motivation minimize the impact. Establish and adhere to a company policy on absenteeism. A continuing survey of the causes of absenteeism within each department can reveal chronic abusers and identify problems. Verbal recognition for a job well-done and other reward-related management, improve employees' esteem and attendance. Try to make the workplace a pleasant place. Keep lunchrooms and bathrooms clean. This reflects the employer's attitude toward the employees.

The manager should know his subordinates. Show interest, without prying, in their personal lives. Encourage employees to discuss problems as appropriate.

The manager should determine the needs and attitudes of the subordinates. Compare department and crew attendance between areas within the company. Absenteeism, like many employee problems, is a symptom, not a disease. A knowledgeable and progressive manager works with employees and supervisors to discover and rectify work-related causes.

Employee Theft

Many employees have dual standards. Those that would never think of taking a candy bar without paying for it may remove paper, pens, fertilizer, and chemicals from work, or make long-distance calls on the company phone without compunction. Casual theft and that is what it is, theft, costs employers billions of dollars annually. Time theft, workers leaving early, arriving late, or taking extra-long breaks, accounts for even more dollars lost to employers.

Make honesty a job standard. List theft and dishonesty as reasons for dismissal or disciplining employees. Let every employee know from the outset that honesty is expected.

A statement in the personnel handbook is not the only answer. The manager must lead by example; he/she cannot take home unauthorized supplies or leave early without recording the absence. This is part of management.

Employees that handle money can be bonded. This process is not excessively expensive and may be prudent if you are handling large amounts of cash. The bonding company (surety) can assist, usually with the police, in investigating loss and help compensate for theft. The surety attempts to recover stolen money from the employee. Bonding, however, is seldom done in the green industry.

When phone bills are inordinately high or a case of legal pads disappears, the manager should investigate. Ask employees what is going on. Many times this will end the problem. If the theft is serious, initiate an insurance or police investigation.

Adopt security measures, such as phone logs, or supply and equipment sign-outs. Many companies hold crews and employees personally responsible for the equipment they are issued. A few require employees to purchase their own small equipment (tools, pruners, shovels, etc.). Do not let anti-theft actions become a crusade. Such measures work best when instituted matter-of-factly and without personal or individual suspicion.

Terminating Employees

Dismissing employees should be the last resort. No one likes to be the bad guy and fire people. Dismissing incompetent, dishonest, or irreconcilable employees is sometimes the most expedient alternative. Termination should be carefully considered and done with caution. Dismissed employees have taken employers to court and won large settlements for wrongful dismissal. California seems to be the leader in this area.

When dismissing an employee, an employer should clearly state the reason for termination. In most instances, the manager must show that dismissal is the direct result of substandard performance, job-related negligence, or serious violation of policies. An example might be an employee who is a substance abuser. An alcoholic cannot and should not be dismissed because they have the disease. They may, however, be termi-

Table 5.11.

Common errors by employers when terminating an employee

Be aware of mistakes that can land the company in legal difficulties. Establish proper hiring and termination practices to reduce the possibility of litigation. Train supervisors to respect employee rights.

- Failure to put honest evaluations in writing.
- Failure to accumulate several written evaluations documenting inadequate performance before dismissal.
- Forcing an employee to resign by making working conditions intolerable.
- Including dangerous wording in employee handbooks.
- Company termination and grievance policy/procedures are vague and applied haphazardly.
- Making informal verbal contracts.
- Firing for bogus reasons.
- Terminating an employee for refusing a polygraph test without clear and sufficient justification.
- Terminating an employee for refusing to commit an unlawful act, violate public policy, or take other improper actions.

nated for negligence if he/she comes to work drunk or drinks on the job.

Discuss procedures for dismissal in the employee handbook. They must be adhered to. As a critical measure of protection, a manager must document substandard performance. Make sure solid documentation exists before initiating disciplinary action. In addition, document attempts to address and remedy the employee's problems. The importance of the proverbial paper trail cannot be overlooked.

Always conduct a pre-dismissal hearing before terminating anyone. Explain the reasons for dismissal and present the evidence resulting in the conclusion. Give the employee the opportunity to respond. Never dismiss an employee without a fair, thorough hearing. Again, document this. If a grievance procedure exists, then apprise the employee of his/her options.

Never use demeaning words or phrases when writing dismissal letters or during disciplinary conferences. Define *disloyalty* and *gross insubordination* if they are reasons for termination. Focus on the facts; absence of facts provides legal grounds for challenging the termination.

Employee dismissal is not punishment. Termination is the last resort after trying to rectify employee problems. Dismissal as a vendetta or punishment encourages mistakes, results in eventual problems, and is an abuse of power.

No one likes to fire people, however, it is part of the burden of management. Incidents of ter-

mination are reduced with careful hiring and orientation practices, regular review of policies and procedures, effective communication, and leadership.

Employee Education

Employee training and education are ongoing processes that improve attitudes and profits. Many companies spend significant time, money, and effort on employee training. However, this does not mean every training effort is effective or cost efficient. Poor training is costly. It contributes to employee turnover, customer callbacks, equipment abuse, violations, lost opportunities, and reduced profit.

Managers have greater opportunities for high quality employee training than at any other time in history. In the past, the owner or supervisors conducted employee training. Instructors from local colleges and universities, sales representatives and technicians, and consultants provided periodic programs and workshops. These opportunities still exist and are certainly viable.

Today there is a host of slide-tape programs, videotapes, CDs, computer programs, audiotapes, books and pamphlets, and other educational supplements available. These may be rented or purchased from local and regional professional associations, Extension services, colleges and universities, or other landscape management firms. Equipment manufacturers supply material on proper maintenance of their products. Some maintenance companies have produced very high-qual-

Table 5.12.

Who teaches training classes?

According to the Small Business Administration and US Census Bureau, colleges and universities are the most common source of employer-sponsored training. A large portion of this training for the landscape industry is through the Cooperative Extension Service. County Agents and State Specialists are resource people and provide training and programs for various aspects of agriculture, management, human resources, and sometimes business. To find out more, contact your Extension Service.

Source of training	Percentage
Colleges and universities	31
Professional trainers	16
Community colleges and technical schools	15
Professional, trade, and labor organizations	14
Vocational schools	7
Other school and community organizations	6
Government	6
Other	5

ity learning and training aids and videos internally. Topics range from safety, proper equipment use and care, pesticide safety and use, and horticultural techniques.

The number of voluntary and mandated certification programs is growing. When employees become certified, it increases their self-esteem and the firm's profitability. Support the employee's quest toward certification. Purchase the badges or caps recognizing certification by professional organizations for those who pass the examinations. Consider rewards for completing training or certification programs.

Employee training should not be relegated to rainy days or the dead of winter. It should be an on-going, organized process; repetition is a key to learning. Training should not be an event, viewed as punishment, or a chance to nap. Some companies have established training sessions during the orientation phase of an employee's tenure. Others continue with supervisor training and updates or whole-staff sessions on a regular basis.

Training must occur throughout the year, should involve many staff members, and should be frequently reviewed to attain maximum effectiveness. It has been suggested that 50 percent of the information gleaned during a training session is lost almost immediately. Approximately seventy percent of the new information is lost by the next day and seventy five percent is lost during the first

week. Eighty-five percent of the information is lost by the end of a month without review or reinforcement.

A review of the training after 24 hours increases information retention by 55 percent. Retention rates after one week and one month are

Photo 5.4. Employee safety is critical. Spraying pesticides without proper protection is dangerous to the applicator and bystanders. Photograph by James Robbins.

improved to 85 percent with periodic reinforcement or review.

Management should also reinforce training. Reinforcement may be simply showing some type of appreciation. Reinforcement and appreciation can be verbal or written. The company should adapt new techniques and practices learned.

Finally, make sure those that need and would benefit from the training, attend meetings and educational opportunities. Key employees without the benefit of college training should be given first priority. It seems that the company representative at most association meetings, field days, or educational meetings is the owner or manager. Would it not be more effective to send the people who are actually in the trenches?

Bibliography

1. Abrahamson, S. 1990. Retaining seasonal employees. *Grounds Maintenance* 28(8):93.

2. Anonymous. 1991. Uniforms. *Grounds Maintenance* 26(1):102.

3. Anonymous. 1991. The hiring game: who will succeed? *Lawn & Landscape Maintenance* 12(5)18.

4. Anonymous. 1995. Stop employee theft before it starts. *Lawn & Landscape* 16(11)130.

5. Anonymous. 1996. Labor survey: How do you compare? *Lawn & Landscape* 17(2):6.

6. Anonymous. 2001. Sting-free evaluations. *Lawn & Landscape* 22(12):13.

7. Arkin, J. 1990. Keeping your crew. *American Nurseryman* 172(7):51.

8. Arkin, J. 1997. Turnover and absenteeism. *Grounds Maintenance* 32(1):24.

9. Arkin Magazine Syndicate. 1989. Motivating your employees. *ALA/Maintenance* 10(1):66.

10. Baetz, R. 1989. Motivate your muscle. *American Nurseryman* 169(12):67.

11. Block, L. 1989. Mandated management. *American Nurseryman* 170(10):33.

12. Bruce, S. 1989. Employee handbooks. Timesaver and morale booster—or potential time bomb? *American Nurseryman* 170(10):24.

13. Carowitz, J. 1999. Recruiting and retaining a dependable work force. *Irrigation Business & Technology* 7(5):16.

14. Covington, S. 1989. Twelve questions to ask before selecting a supervisor. *Landscape Contractor* 30(9):40.

15. Curry-Swann, L. 1989. White-collar theft. *American Nurseryman* 170(10):123.

16. Davidson, J. 1992. Motivating entry-level employees. *Grounds Maintenance* 27(1)54.

17. Davis, S. 1978. Management by objectives in grounds management operation. In: *Manual of Site Management*. Environmental Design Press, Reston, VA.

18. Deyoung, J. 1989. People still call me "boy." *Pro* 1(2):14.

19. Dittmer, N. 1989. The cafeteria plan—an attractive employee benefit. *Landscape Contractor* 30(12):18.

20. Drexler, M. 1989. Maintenance professional on a proactive course to training. *ALA/Maintenance* 10(3):28-30.

21. Faizst, J. 1978. Labor relations and personnel management in site maintenance. In: *Manual of Site Management*. Environmental Design Press, Reston, VA.

22. Grahl, C. 1990. Bonuses, rewards popular in the race for employees. *Lawn & Landscape Maintenance* 11(10):40.

23. Gregg, R. 1989. Harassment. *American Nurseryman* 170(10):53.

24. Hensley, D. 1992. Off months are perfect times to replenish your workforce. *Nursery Manager* 8(1):73.

25. Hensley, D. 1992. Employee or independent contractor? *Hawaii Landscape Industry News* 6(5):16.

26. Hensley, D. 1992. Controlling workers' compensation costs. *Hawaii Landscape Industry News* 6(5):14.

27. Hensley, D. 1993. Ask the right questions when hiring. *Western Turf Manager* 4(1):24.

28. Hensley, D. 1997. Professionalism always victor over price-cutting. *Hawaii Landscape* 1(1):4.

29. Hensley, D. 1998. Disciplining landscape employees. *Hawaii Landscape* 2(2):10.

30. Howell, B. 1995. The challenge of empowering employees. *Lawn & Landscape Maintenance* 16(7):67.

31. Howell, B. 1995. Employee recognition goes a long way. *Lawn & Landscape Maintenance* 16(8): 76.

32. Human Resource Associates. 1990. Turnover: Your most expensive problem. *ALCA Personnel Notebook*, ALCA, Reston, VA.

33. Kujawa, R. 1998. Tapping in to seasonal workers. *Grounds Maintenance* 33(1):c12.

34. Jones, D. 1990. Designing programs to guide your firm's work force. *Lawn & Landscape Maintenance* 11(3):36.

35. Jones, D. 1990. An effective outline promotes favorable training. *Lawn & Landscape Maintenance* 11(4):40.

36. Jones, D. 1990. Follow up training increases task retention. *Lawn & Landscape Maintenance* 11(5):30.

37. King, J. 1987. Avoid hiring mistakes. *Landscape Contractor* 28(8):17.

38. Lehmann, D. and D. Hensley. 1991. Employee theft. An avoidable problem. *Northern Turf Manager* 2(8):37.

39. Mateffy, J. 1998. Choosing a great crew. *Landscape & Irrigation* 22(2):31.

40. Perry, P. 1993. Terminating Employees. *American Nurseryman* 177(2):85.

41. Perry, P. 1993. Let the employer beware. *American Nurseryman* 177(25):85.

42. Perry, P. 1998. Hold your fire. *American Nurseryman* 187(10):63.

43. Professional Grounds Management Society. 1989. *Grounds Management Forms and Job Descriptions Guide.* 3rd ed. Cockeysville, MD.

44. Ratcliff, C. 2003. Strength in diversity. *Grounds Maintenance* 38(11):20.

45. Roche, J. 1989. Whither comest the people? *Landscape Management* 28(10)20.

46. Roche, J. 1991. Employee education. *Landscape Management* 30(5):24.

47. Rosenberg, H. 1986. Learn how to use job descriptions. *American Nurseryman* 163(5):73.

48. Scholtz, C. and J. Arkin. 1989. Fringe benefits: finding the right mix for employer and employee. *Landscape Contractor* 30(11):18.

49. Shope, D. 1992. Focus on people. *Tree Care Industry* 3(3):18.

50. Smith, S. 1990. A top-notch performance evaluation. *American Nurseryman* 172(2):59.

51. Smith, S. 1990. Four steps to a happier staff. *American Nurseryman* 171(8):48.

52. Smucker, B. 1980. Fringe benefits—the hidden asset. *American Nurseryman* 151(8):102.

53. Snyder, E. 1993. A contract in disguise. *American Nurseryman* 178(7):73.

54. Steingold, F. 1990. The hazards of employers dealing with employees' rights. *Grounds Maintenance* 25(3):132.

55. Steingold, F. 1997. The how-to of employee handbooks. *American Nurseryman* 185(6):52.

56. Taylor, B. 1990. Finding the perfect employee. *Landscape Contractor* 31(3):34.

57. Toth, L. 1997. Retaining quality employees. *Irrigation Business and Technology.* 5(5):6.

58. Turner, T. 1990. The hire road to success. *American Nurseryman* 171(8):38.

59. Urbano, C. 1989. Labor. *American Nurseryman* 170(10):69.

60. Wandtke, E. 1990. Working overtime on morale. *Landscape Management* 29(6):52.

61. Wetzel, T. 1997. Thefts and accidents spoil productivity and profits. *Grounds Maintenance* 32(11):c10.

62. Wisniewski, N. 1999. On-site operations. *Lawn & Landscape* 20(9):53.

Chapter 6
Equipment Selection and Acquisition

Equipment is a major expenditure for every landscape management operation and one more challenge to the landscape manager. Equipment needs grow and change as a company increases its customer base and services. Equipment decisions must be carefully made before the manager commits precious capital.

Equipment Selection

The criteria for determining if a piece of equipment is needed or economical vary with each operation. The first question is whether or not the company needs, or can afford, the machine. If a piece of equipment can do the work more efficiently, inexpensively, or quickly than hand labor, the company can afford to operate it. Equipment is also important when it is necessary to do the work rapidly, such as plowing snow. Equipment that has a range of performance is easier to justify. Also consider how the equipment can grow into the company's future goals and plans. The bottom line is whether or not the equipment will make money for the company.

Know your needs. Maintenance contractors serving a variety of clients have the most difficult time making equipment decisions because the type of work they do constantly changes. Maintenance contractors and grounds managers for large facilities use their equipment in more predictable and well-defined ways.

Photo 6.1. Equipment, large and small, represents a major investment for in-house and contract landscape managers. Equipment selection requires knowledge and thought to maximize the return on the investment. Photograph courtesy of James Robbins.

Photo 6.2. Equipment that can be adapted for several uses is easier for the new or small firm to justify. Photograph courtesy of Hustler Turf Equipment, Hesston, KS.

113

Table 6.1.

Common equipment selection mistakes

In no particular order:
1. Not purchasing commercial-quality equipment.
2. Making the purchase decision on price alone.
3. Purchasing over- or under-powered machines.
4. Failing to consider service, the availability and cost of factory-authorized technicians, and parts.
5. Selecting machinery from too many different manufacturers. Parts are not interchangeable and the parts inventory becomes unmanageable and an economic burden.
6. Failing to obtain a pre-purchase demonstration on your site and with your personnel.
7. Not considering fuel source or 2- vs. 4-cycle, or gasoline vs. diesel engines, and purchasing the wrong one.
8. Failing to consider the machine's size and weight for maneuverability, transportability, and employee fatigue.
9. Not checking with other managers to confirm the sales pitch.
10. Relying solely upon brand name.

Landscape contractors starting out should select versatile equipment. Larger, established firms and in-house grounds managers may consider more specialized pieces of equipment.

Once the decision to buy a machine has been made, the manager's job has just begun. The manager must determine the brand, size, and capacity of the needed machine. The objective is to purchase the least costly piece of equipment that will do the job efficiently and correctly. Should the equipment be purchased, leased, or rented? Will the current employees be able to operate the machine safely, efficiently, and productively, or will operators have to be trained or hired? What problems can result from using the equipment?

New or used? The cost difference between new and used equipment is substantial. However, look at more than just price. Saving a few thousand dollars is not prudent if more money is spent keeping an older machine running. If the equipment must withstand rugged, stressful work, or is used frequently, then *new equipment* is a better buy. If the anticipated use will be light, undemanding work, then *used equipment* must be considered. Purchase infrequently used equipment as second-hand or plan to rent it.

Reconditioned equipment purchased from dealers often carries a short-term limited warranty. It is priced from 15 to 35 percent below the cost of new equipment. The selling dealer must usually service used equipment under warranty. Not all dealers are created equal.

Equipment acquired from individuals or purchased *as is* from dealers carries no warranty or guarantee. Such items are usually priced from 50 to 65 percent below the cost of a new machine. Check this equipment very carefully; what you see is what you get. List all items that require repair and add these estimated costs to the initial price for a true comparison with other used or new machines.

Photo 6.3. Specialized equipment, such as this Bedshaper® implement, is typically acquired as the management operation grows and matures. Photograph courtesy of Little Wonder Division of Schiller-Pfeiffer, Inc. Southampton, PA.

Table 6.2.
Buying used equipment

1. ***Compare.*** Do not buy the first unit evaluated. Compare models, brands, machine quality service, and warranty.
2. ***Try it.*** Ask the seller if you can operate the unit for a few days.
3. ***Look.*** Develop a checklist and inspect the general appearance, engine, oil, air cleaner, fuel tank, electrical system, drive system, gear box, safety equipment, and other crucial areas. Has the machine received proper care and service or is it dirty where it shouldn't be?
4. ***Ask.*** Obtain a complete service and repair record. If purchasing the unit from a dealer, obtain the name of the previous owner and contact him/her. If the dealer refuses to provide this information, keep looking.
5. ***Help.*** Have the machine inspected by a trustworthy mechanic if purchasing from an individual. Obtain a reasonable warranty or service agreement from a dealer.

Photo 6.4. Equipment must meet the needs of the site and operators. Larger equipment is generally more efficient and can pay for the price difference with increased production. Equipment must be versatile and appropriate for the type of sites most frequently encountered. Over-sized machines are liabilities if they cannot maneuver on the site or damage the property. Photo courtesy of Hustler Turf Equipment, Hesston, KS.

Photo 6.5. A new generation of equipment allowing access through smaller portals, such as this stand-up spreader-sprayer, has mechanized operations in areas previously requiring hand labor.

Table 6.3.
Selling used equipment

1. ***Determine the value.*** Consult the "blue" book and determine the local market for the unit.
2. ***Timing.*** Used equipment brings higher prices just before or during the normal season, especially if it is ready to go.
3. ***Quality.*** Make all necessary minor repairs, tighten loose bolts, and change fluids. Have the service history and records available. Spiff up the unit; some buyers associate cleanliness with quality. A coat of paint does hide a multitude of sins, but buyers are also well aware of this.

Table 6.4.
Top factors contributing to positive landscape manager-distributor relationships

	Percent survey respondents
Dependability	48
Price	23
Honesty	22
Understanding shared responsibility	13
Material and parts availability	13
After sale follow-up	8

Source of information: *Landscape Management*. 1998. 37(7).

Size. Purchase the largest piece of equipment that offers the most production using the least amount of labor available for the job. Labor is more costly than equipment over time. Within reason, larger equipment will do the task more rapidly and more efficiently and will offset price differences through labor savings.

Consider the maneuverability of the equipment in tight areas and the potential damage that an oversized unit could impose on the site or adjacent properties. A 48-inch walk-behind mower has a minimal effect on improving productivity if it must be taken through 28-inch gates.

Power Source. Many equipment manufacturers offer a choice of engines. Managers may choose between gasoline and diesel powered equipment, and sometimes between different power plant brands.

If you do not have experience with a particular engine or type, check references. Frequently, the engine manufacturer, not the equipment manufacturer, provides the warranty for the engine.

There have been many articles written on the advantages of one fuel type over another, and personal preference certainly plays a part. Diesel fuel offers advantages, but requires installation of an extra fuel reservoir. Fifty-five gallon drums are impractical because of the storage requirements and inconvenience. A mixed fleet using diesel and gasoline results in one fuel being used in a machine in which it should not. Count on it!

Many of the same comments can be made about two- and four-cycle engines. Select two-cycle engines with as near the same mixture as possible or select an oil-gas mixture that will operate efficiently in all. The mechanic, foreman, or someone with responsibility can mix an entire drum of fuel correctly from which everyone can fill their individual cans. Label two-cycle engines and fuel containers clearly.

Photo 6.6. / 6.7. Field days and trade shows are good places to see and try out equipment. Look at the options available and request a demonstration on your site.

Table 6.5.

Reducing accidents through training

Work related accidents are not a normal part of business. The primary causes of accidents in the landscape management industry are: *operator error*, usually linked with the extent and quality of training; and *equipment failure or defect*. Reducing or preventing accidents should be a primary goal of every employer. Here are some suggestions:

- Buy equipment from a reputable dealer.
- Dealers have a duty to warn the purchaser of any special operation or special hazards.
- Provide the operator's manual to employees and supervisors and make sure it is read.
- Take advantage of dealer safety programs.
- Train operators thoroughly and frequently.
- Inspect and maintain safety devices, including warning decals.
- Use equipment as it was designed and intended.
- Research the cause of accidents if they do occur.

Service. The availability of parts and qualified service from a local dealer is one of the most important aspects of equipment selection in the commercial arena. Service and dependability are as important as price in determining specific brands. Down time costs money. A piece of equipment is no good if it does not run or requires an inordinate amount of time for repair. Dealers commonly loan equipment if repairs cannot be completed within one or two days.

Warranties vary. Understand what is guaranteed, by whom, and for how long. Some equipment manufacturers purchase and modify engines, transmissions, and other major components. Determine who has responsibility for the warranty of these items.

Information. Before purchasing equipment, get as much information as possible. Be an informed consumer and plan. The worst time to buy a piece of equipment is when it is needed. Take advantage of off-season or trade show discounts that may be available.

Trade magazines and the manufacturer's literature and web sites provide specifications and operating information. Trade shows and equipment demonstrations allow the manager to see, stand behind, and compare different brands. Visit with other management companies that own the brand of machine being considered.

Do not be rushed into a decision by sales pressure. Go back to the office, lay out the facts and make an informed decision.

Whenever possible, arrange a demonstration of the equipment on the property where it will be used if purchased. Ideally, the person trying the equipment should be the operator who will use it.

Operators. Can current employees operate the machine profitably? Are qualified operators available? Allow the firm's most experienced people to break-in new equipment. If the sales representative provides an on-site preparation review or demonstration, include all crew members. The review should stress proper adjustment, maintenance checks, and safety.

Operators must have time to acclimate to the machine before their production rates reach an acceptable level. Some operators may decide the machine is no good before getting used to it. The manager must be patient, but persistent. Leaving new equipment in the garage wastes capital and time, while creating doubts about the manager's ability to make decisions.

Landscape equipment manufacturers have begun paying considerable attention to operator comfort and ergonomics. Equipment that reduces operator fatigue increases productivity and motivation.

Preparing Specifications

Public agencies live and die by specifications. The grounds manager must become familiar with the various brands of equipment available and take the time to list the capabilities, attachments, and other requirements for the planned purchase. He/she must also master the specification requirements imposed by the purchasing department for the agency or company.

Often the manager lists the brand and model requested, followed by the words *or equal*. This may be appropriate and save money if alternatives are acceptable. If several brands of equal equipment present bids, the lowest cost machine will be selected. Problems occur if the manager does not have a voice in determining what is equal and what is not. One way to increase the chance of obtaining the specific brand desired is to specify something unique for the desired brand or model that is not found on similar brands.

Replacing Existing Equipment

Replacing machinery produces serious questions that the manager must answer. Will the new equipment improve the profitability? Will new equipment cost less to own and operate? Will the new machine reduce direct labor costs or allow the crew to accomplish more with the same effort? Is the old machine obsolete? Will the new machine do a higher quality job?

Comparing costs. Determining true operation costs between old and new equipment requires careful analysis of ownership costs, interest, repairs, labor, and impact on cash flow. Nearly 85 percent of the cost of mowing is in labor, maintenance, downtime, and fuel. A machine that is paid for and fully depreciated for tax purposes can look a lot better when compared to the cash outlay for new equipment. The latest model brings with it the tax benefits of depreciation and interest, but also a drain of cash. These must be weighed against production costs, repairs, and downtime costs of keeping an old machine run-

Photo 6.8. Older equipment is often refurbished and saved for backups for front line machines. Backup pieces reduce down time and are critical if the firm relies on in-house service. Keep backup machines in good running order and ready to hit the road. Repairing a secondary machine before it can be used is frustrating and wastes time and money.

ning. Accurate records allow informed decisions.

Interest costs can be significant. Examine current and projected interest rates. Delay an equipment purchase or replacement if it will have a significant adverse impact on the company's cash position. When considering repair costs, a new machine should be relatively free of repairs during the first year. A comparison of buying new versus maintaining the old will generally lean in favor of the new purchase.

Productivity. New equipment should, by definition, improve productivity and justify itself on paper. Keep in mind that the advertised im-

---

Table 6.6.
Determine mower productivity

Productivity is a measure of the rate at which work can be performed. Mower manufacturers publish productivity information, in acres per hour, as part of product specifications. You can determine the area that a mower will cut in an hour by knowing the speed and mowing width.

$$\text{Acres/hour} = \frac{\text{Cutting width (in inches)} \times \text{speed (in mph)}}{100}$$

This figure is based on straight-ahead mowing, with no allowance for overlap, stops, turns, slopes, maneuvering, or obstacles.

Table 6.7.
Consumer concern for power equipment is real

- Excessive noise from landscape maintenance power equipment is a concern nationwide.
- California is the vanguard of the anti-blower movement.
- National, state, and local landscape groups and organizations have been and will be instrumental in keeping bans and restrictive ordinances to a minimum.
- Success of organizations comes from the membership; if you are not willing to join and help, do not complain.
- Quieter technology will be developed and may be a partial solution.
- Professional manners and common sense are part of the solution and are essential.

provements in production rates may never be achieved. Test the equipment on your sites with your operators. Manufacturer's claims assume the best of conditions and terrain. New or larger equipment can reduce costs and increase profitability by allowing a crew to do more work in a day. There is also a certain psychological impact with new equipment. Employees often feel that their work will be made easier or less physically demanding.

Obsolescence. Technological improvements evolve rapidly. A varied array of downsized equipment that can fit through a 36-inch gate is now available. Equipment becomes obsolete because of technology or because the manufacturer stops making it. Obsolescence alone is not a reason to purchase new equipment. The machine had distinct advantages and a positive effect on productivity when it was purchased. These reasons still hold true if ownership and repair costs have not escalated. If repairs become costly, parts become hard to find, or down time increases, newer equipment will be an economic alternative. There are situations, however, when older models of machines are superior to their new replacements. Don't let the *got to's* for a new, shiny machine obscure good judgment or the facts.

Noise and Air Pollution Issues

Power blowers were introduced in the early 1970s, replacing brooms, rakes, and hoses, and the labor to use them. Power blowers are used for a wide variety of tasks from cleanup of leaves and grass clippings, to cleaning streets, gutters, and even stadiums. They have become a mainstay for turf and landscape maintenance professionals. About 1.5 million power blowers are sold in the US each year; one-third of these are heavy-duty equipment for commercial users, and the remainder is aimed at the consumer market.

The City Council of Beverly Hills, California, responded to resident's complaints of dust and excessive noise by banning power blowers in 1976. This first ordinance restricting power blowers proved unenforceable. Complaints about the misuse of blowers and other power landscape equipment have increased, and many other communities have taken action.

Photo 6.9. Controversy over use of two-cycle power blowers and other landscape equipment has resulted in bans or restrictions in many communities. Use common sense and good manners when operating all power equipment in residential areas. Photograph courtesy of Mr. Mark Yahn, Ground Control™ Landscaping and Maintenance, Orlando, FL.

In 1997, an estimated 300 municipalities across the United States had imposed or were contemplating bans or restrictions on power blowers. Los Angeles banned use of power leaf blowers within the city limits as of January 1, 1998. It is interesting to note that Los Angeles required gardeners to use blowers, instead of water, to remove debris in the 1970s during one of the great California droughts.

In 2000, more than 450 communities in 20 states, Canada, and parts of Europe, had banned or restricted the use of power blowers by landscape professionals. Noise bans involving blowers and other landscape equipment also affect golf courses and municipal landscape management. Some ordinances have also included homeowners. Many of these ordinances, aimed primarily at power blowers, have restricted operational times, while others have established outright, very enforceable bans. Palo Alto, CA, requires landscapers to take a blower etiquette class, pass a written test, carry a license, and buy low-noise equipment.

Summonses have been issued, arrests have been made, and fines have been levied against landscape management firms. Some communities have expanded their legislation to regulate all lawn and garden equipment, not just leaf blowers.

The California Landscape Contractors Association (CLCA) estimates that it can take five times longer to clean the typical landscape site with a broom and rake than it would with a power blower. The CLCA estimates that the cost to the landscape firm will increase about 20 percent if they are required to perform the same functions without power blowers. The landscape firms estimate they can only pass on about one-third of their increased expenses to the consumer.

Reaction and efforts in some quarters of the landscape community have been reasonable and productive:

- Adoption of voluntary operation times for noisy power equipment.

- Initiation of educational programs by public and industry organizations to teach responsible equipment use.

- Trade-in programs from dealers and manufacturers to replace older, noisier equipment have been successful.

- Formation of coalitions of dealers, landscape professionals, and employees for education, training, and to work to overturn local bans through the legislative system.

  ○ Working for and promoting local initiatives to require public votes on local bans and restrictions on landscape equipment.

  ○ Lobbying for legislative initiatives in California to overturn local blower and landscape equipment bans through changes in state laws.

  ○ Promotion of state legislation establishing decibel limits of 65, which would supersede those local ordinances that were not established by referendum.

  ○ Establishing standards as a common ground for angry citizens, manufacturers, and users to begin constructive discussions.

Table 6.8.
Professional manners reduce noise complaints
- Operate blowers at lowest possible throttle setting.
- Use blowers or noisy equipment at reasonable hours.
- Avoid early morning and late evening, or other times when people may be disturbed.
- Keep 10 feet away from doors and windows when using blowers.
- Avoid open windows where dust and noise might be a nuisance.
- Use only one blower at a time on small residential sites.
- Use full blower extension to work close to the ground.
- Keep dust to a minimum.
- Use rakes and brooms where appropriate.

- Development of new technology to address noise issues.

Reaction by others in the landscape industry has been somewhat more militant.

- Deliberate disregard of ordinances and time restrictions.
- Belligerent public discussions with opponents.
- Court tests of equipment bans and legal questions of infringement of free trade.
- Civil disobedience, and even hunger strikes, by landscape employees in Los Angeles.

New technology has been and will continue to be developed to significantly reduce noise levels of blowers, line trimmers, and other landscape equipment. New blowers are at least 73 percent quieter than machines introduced in the early to mid-1990s, and up to 123 percent quieter than the late 1980s models.

In addition to the great noise debate, in 2000, the California Air Resource Board (CARB) initiated a multi-year stepwise reduction that will result in drastically stringent emission standards for small engines. Engines less than 65 cubic centimeters (cc) must reduce total emission of hydrocarbons and nitrogen oxides by 74 percent by 2010. Other small, non-road engine emission standards are also addressed in the legislation.

Manufacturers are working to meet the new stringent standards and some have threatened to pull out of the California market. However, since California is the 12th largest economy in the world, these are probably hollow threats.

The Environmental Protection Agency (EPA) has developed new, more rigorous non-road emis-

---

Table 6.9.

Noise by the numbers

The decibel (dB) is a unit used to measure the loudness of sound. Any sound above 85 dB can cause *hearing loss*, and the loss is related both to the power of the sound as well as the length of exposure. Eight hours of 90-dB sound can cause damage to some people's ears; exposure to 140-dB sound causes immediate damage (and actual pain). One in 10 Americans has some hearing loss affecting his/her ability to understand normal speech. Excessive noise exposure is the most common cause of hearing loss.

Approximate Decibel Level	Examples
0	The quietest sound you can hear.
20	Rustling leaves.
30	Whisper, quiet library.
40	Quiet home.
50	Quiet street.
60	Normal conversation, sewing machine, typewriter.
70	Inside an automobile.
80	Automobile (25 feet).
90	Lawnmower, shop tools, truck traffic, food blender (three feet). Eight hours per day is the maximum exposure protecting 90% of people.
100	Chainsaw, snowmobile, diesel truck (30 feet). Eight hours per day is the maximum exposure without ear protection.
115	Sandblasting, loud rock concert, auto horn. 15 minutes per day is the maximum exposure without protection.
120	Amplified Rock and Roll (six feet), gun muzzle blast, jet engine (100 feet), rock concert (good seats).
140	Noise causes pain and even brief exposure injures unprotected ears. Maximum allowed noise with hearing protector.

sion standards that will go into affect over an extended period. These emission standards will be similar to those in California, but the EPA standards will affect landscapers nationally.

Four-cycle engines will replace many 2-cycle engines on some landscape equipment to meet noise and emission standards. Survival of 2-cycle engines for professional and consumer landscape equipment is in doubt by many observers. These increased standards will undoubtedly raise the price of leaf blowers, line trimmers, and small mowers, most of which will likely be passed on to the consumer.

To Buy or Not to Buy

Once the type, capacity, and brand of equipment have been selected, the next dilemma facing the manager is whether to *buy* or *lease* the machine. Buying equipment, or *ownership*, has been the traditional means of acquiring control of machinery. In recent years, however, increasing numbers of firms have leased landscape management equipment. Manufacturers, distributors and dealers, financial institutions, and other opportunity-minded companies have entered the equipment leasing field.

Ownership, leasing, and other alternatives offer certain advantages for established or new companies. Investigate all options thoroughly, however, before committing capital. A lease or buy decision can be based on the estimated life of the equipment, the availability of cash flow, and advice from an accountant on tax ramifications.

Ownership

Purchasing the machine outright provides complete control. The owner makes all decisions. However, there are several potential disadvantages. Purchase requires a large capital commitment. The cost to the user is high if the machine is not used to capacity. There is also the risk of obsolescence. The owner also assumes all operation and maintenance responsibilities and costs.

The owner, however, has full freedom in using the machine. Depreciation and investment tax options belong to the owner. Some lending institutions and implement companies have creative financing available to match the cash flow of the maintenance industry.

There is also the intangible, pride of ownership factor. I have yet to visit a landscape management firm without eventually wandering to the shop to look at the equipment. Most managers take pride in discussing their purchases.

Leasing

A *lease* transfers control of equipment from the owner (lessor) to the user (lessee) for a specific period for an agreed price. Landscape equipment can be leased from three to five or more years. The lessee assumes ownership responsibilities, including taxes, insurance, maintenance, and repairs. A *full-service lease* provides all of these expenses as part of the lease agreement, but these are unusual in the landscape industry. The lessee may have the opportunity to purchase the equipment at the end of the lease. Terms and purchase agreements are often very favorable.

According to the American Association of Equipment Lessons, more than 80 percent of the nation's businesses acquire at least a portion of their equipment through leasing. This number is probably lower in the landscape management industry, but a large number of companies lease at least part of their field or office equipment.

Advantages. Leasing offers flexibility and some potential advantages. The popularity of leasing in landscape management is growing and new options continue to evolve to meet the green industry market.

Leasing does not require expansion of a company's credit line. Expensive credit can be used elsewhere in the company. Most leases require a modest down payment, allowing the manager to use his/her capital elsewhere. Leasing may be a viable option for a firm with considerable debt. Lease payments are fully deductible as a business operating expense. Leasing offers some before tax advantages in that the payments for a machine are usually lower. The long-term expenditure for equipment, however, is often greater over the period of the lease than if the item was purchased. A lease must recover the purchase price of the machine, interest, risk, overhead, and provide a profit for the lessor.

Equipment leasing results in higher annual operation cost than equipment ownership. This is due, in part to the seasonal nature of the landscape industry. However, the initial capital commitment is not as great. Manufacturers, dealers, and leasing firms offer varied payment schedules (to compensate for seasonality), low minimum leases, and alternatives for end-of-lease purchases.

Leasing may be especially attractive to the new operator. Most leasing companies are interested in selling and servicing new accounts. However, this does not mean that anyone can walk into a dealership and walk out with several thousand dollars in leased equipment by signing their name. Lessors require that potential lessees have a very good credit rating. Lessees must meet established requirements for net worth and collateral, and nearly all leasing companies require a credit analysis.

Disadvantages. There are disadvantages to leasing. Leases vary widely in their language, requirements, and eventual cost. Selection is limited to brands available from that particular dealer. There is still a risk of obsolescence before the end of the lease. The firm may be forced to operate an under-sized machine that would have been replaced as the operation grew.

The value of the equipment is lost at the end of the lease term, since the machinery is not owned. If a lease is canceled, even if the company goes belly-up, the firm may be required to pay a very large penalty or the entire amount owed.

Push a pencil before inking the line. All leases are not created equal; compare the actual costs of all acquisition options. Beware of hidden costs. Most leases have interest built in, some at very high rates. Others require one to three months payment up-front. Some leases require a processing fee. Leased equipment cannot be listed as an asset in financial statements.

Rentals. Equipment may be *rented* from dealers and rental companies by the hour, day, week, or longer. Infrequently used equipment can be rented as needed. Renting is also a source of short-term backup or extra machines.

Understand the rental contract before signing. In most instances, rental equipment is the renter's responsibility while in his/her possession. The renter is usually responsible for all maintenance and upkeep. It may be stipulated that the equipment be returned in the same condition as when rented, subject to ordinary wear and tear.

It is the intent that the property be returned undamaged.

The firm's insurance may or may not cover rented equipment. Check with the insurance carrier to determine if the company's policy covers rented items. Insurance is available from the rental company, but is always expensive. Rental insurance is not necessary if the equipment is protected by other policies.

Custom Hire. *Custom hire* is renting the *equipment and operator*. Custom hiring, or subcontracting, the work requiring specialized equipment or licensed and trained operators, such as heavy equipment or aerial trucks, may be the only viable option.

Shops and Service

Most management companies eventually initiate some sort of in-house equipment repair or service operation. In-house repair is more convenient and *may* cost less than outside repair. Some management consultants suggest that a firm should initiate in-house service by the time it reaches $1,000,000 in volume. There are many companies, however, that operate successful in-house service at far less than this benchmark. There is no magic number. The manager who

Photo 6.10. Custom hiring equipment requiring special operators saves time and dollars. Photo courtesy of Hustler Turf Equipment, Hesston, KS.

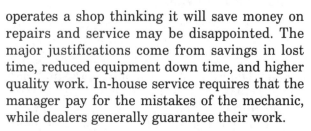

Photo 6.11. In-house serve shops can save time and money. In-house service is not always less expensive than dealer service, so carefully consider all of the costs. Establishing a shop brings its own management challenges.

Photo 6.12. Spare parts are essential to landscape operations of every size. Standardizing the brand of equipment simplifies parts stocking. Photograph courtesy of James Robbins.

operates a shop thinking it will save money on repairs and service may be disappointed. The major justifications come from savings in lost time, reduced equipment down time, and higher quality work. In-house service requires that the manager pay for the mistakes of the mechanic, while dealers generally guarantee their work.

Operate the in-house facility with profit in mind. Develop a system for allocating shop costs to equipment; usually a separate account is set up for the shop within the company's operating budget. Income (paper charges for parts and labor) and expenses (parts, labor, and overhead) can be recorded and analyzed. The charges for labor and parts should be competitive with those for local dealers for comparable service. If an in-house service operation costs more than a dealer, give careful thought to the necessity for the operation or find the reasons for the disparity.

A parts inventory and shop create their own challenges. The manager must deal with theft of parts and labor (mechanics working on their own vehicles or those of others during working hours).

Establishing a parts inventory. A parts inventory reduces equipment downtime and expenses. Having spare parts on-hand saves labor and capital. However, landscape management equipment is specialized. Finding parts, especially for older machines can be expensive and time consuming. It is impossible to stock quantities of every conceivable part for every possible machine.

Standardize equipment as much as possible. Regardless of the brand of the equipment, choose a favorite and make it the standard. At the least, keep the number of brands to a minimum within each machine category. New or smaller companies tend to have a mixture of brands, purchasing on price initiative and searching for the right brand. Larger and successful firms rely on one or a few major brands.

The mechanic will become more skilled by concentrating on and learning the peculiarities of fewer models. The parts inventory is simpler to determine. A single part will provide backup for several machines.

What parts and how many should be purchased and stocked? Parts are expensive. It will not take long to parlay the shop and parts inventory into a several thousand-dollar investment. Service records, experience of the manager and mechanic, the dealer, and the parts supplier will provide insight as to what and how many will be enough or too many.

Stock *common wear* items, those with predictably short lives, such as bearings, bushings, and seals. Purchase enough to take care of needs for a reasonable period. Take advantage of the quantity discounts. Landscape management firms, with or without a shop, stock routine and service items, such as oil, filters, belts, and blades.

Stock *routine breakage* items, such as hoses, starters, water pumps, and pulleys. The number on-hand depends on the likelihood of breakage. If the fleet loses one water pump every four months, then one in supply is adequate. Remember that service increases with the age of the equipment.

Plan for emergencies by stocking some *critical breakage* items. These items rarely break so parts departments seldom stock them. Infrequent breakage parts must be ordered from central supply, wherever that is. Having these on hand saves time and money by minimizing downtime, but requires capital commitment. Keeping critical parts on-hand is less critical if backup machines are available.

Spread the investment for a parts inventory over several years. Enlist the assistance of the company accountant to set up inventory procedures and cost recovery procedures for the parts inventory, as well as the shop in general.

***Records*.** Careful records promote good service, track costs, and assist in equipment purchase and replacement decisions. A *service chart* is a composite of the service schedule for a piece of equipment. Adjust service and oil changes to fit the operation. Keep the service chart for every machine listing date and type of service or repair where the operator, mechanic, or shop supervisor can easily consult it.

Adapt a simple, internal work order system for equipment repairs. *Work orders* should include a description of the problem, the repairs made, parts used and their cost, and the labor required.

Computerized maintenance management systems are available to keep records, schedule preventative maintenance, track maintenance history and organize maintenance departments. Large facilities have used such programs for years and several are available to help medium and small operators with equipment records and decisions.

***Service*.** Teach operators and crews to conduct *daily maintenance checks*. Equipment should be part of the company training and orientation program to instruct operators on how to check over, service, and operate their machines safely. A piece of equipment should never be started before the oil level is checked. This is *everyone's* responsibility.

Periodic or *seasonal service* and adjustments may be the responsibility of the crew or the mechanic. A shop can make a more thorough check and service of the machine. The crew or operator can use a backup while the mechanics give the front-line equipment the once over. Some companies have mechanics service equipment at night or during off days.

Equipment for the Crew

The tools and spare parts included with the crew depends on the equipment used, the skill of the operators or supervisor to diagnose and repair problems in the field, and the distance to the shop. Space is always at a premium, therefore, anything carried is considered valuable. At a minimum, pre-gapped spark plugs for each piece of field equipment and a spark plug wrench should be available. Also, include standard and Phillips screwdrivers, an adjustable wrench, pliers, and a reasonable selection of box and/or open-end wrenches. Metric wrenches are necessary to work on imported machines. Include a selection of bolts, nuts, washers, and cotter keys.

The inventory of equipment for maintenance trucks or teams varies widely between companies and even among crews within a company. Different firms provide different services and each team within a company may be faced with unique responsibilities according to the needs of each job site. Include pre-wound reels of line for line trimmers. Supply replacement nozzles, strainers and hose fittings to crews working with sprayers. Hardhats, safety glasses, gloves, and earplugs help prevent injury.

Keep the tools in a quality tool chest that can be secured to the truck. The toolbox should be able to be removed quickly when tools are needed

Photo 6.13. Organize equipment storage for efficiency and security. This firm paints the area for each crew a different color. Equipment can also be color coded. Part of each crew's daily responsibility must include cleaning and servicing equipment at the end of each shift. Photograph courtesy of James Robbins.

Table 6.10.
Employee safety is job number one for everyone

- Everyone using equipment should read and be familiar with the operator's manual.
- Handle fuel carefully and safely.
    - Use well-marked proper safety containers.
    - Make sure the right fuel is added to the tank.
- Be prepared for emergencies-a first aid kit in every vehicle is a must.
- Keep safety shields in place.
- Keep rollover protection in place.
- Make sure all safety devices are in place and working.
    - Never bypass the dead man switch.
- Never smoke while refueling or operating equipment.
- Never operate equipment when impaired by legal or illegal substances.
- Check the equipment every day before operating.
- Service tires safely, and maintain proper pressure.
- Check the area for debris before mowing or operating equipment.
- Wear protective clothing.
    - Loose fitting clothes, long slacks and closed–toe shoes with traction soles reduce injury.
    - Earplugs and earmuffs reduce uncomfortable noise and protect hearing.
- Never carry riders.
- Wear seat belts if furnished.
- Do not run engines indoors.
- Look before backing up.
- Lower all implements before storing a machine.
- Display a safety triangle or slow moving vehicle sign when operating equipment on or near roads.
- Avoid steep hillsides, ravines, and other risky areas where machines could slip or tip over.
- Be extra cautious when mowing or operating equipment near roadsides or in boulevard strips.
    - Discharge clippings away from traffic.
    - Be alert and cognizant of pedestrians, especially children attracted to the machines.

Photo 6.14. Open dove tail trailers are frequently used to transport equipment. The pickup provides quick access to tools and machines for the crew, but also for anyone else passing by.

on the work site or transferred between vehicles. Mark all tools and equipment or paint them a bright color. Establish responsibility for replacing tools that are stolen or abused.

Keep a first-aid kit with bandages, gauze pads, disinfectants, first-aid spray, pain relievers, and other simple first-aid appliances in each truck or toolbox. Replenish the first-aid kit frequently. Include a container of bottled water to flush skin, eyes, or clothing in case of an accidental chemical spill or exposure. Enclose phone numbers for a doctor, ambulance service, poison control center, and fire and police departments. Encase phone number and emergency instructions in plastic so they will remain readable. Instruct crew supervisors in simple first-aid and emergency procedures.

Photo 6.15. Enclosed vans, trucks, and trailers increase security for machines and other equipment. Photograph courtesy of James Robbins.

Bibliography

1. Anonymous. 1986. Rent, lease or buy? *Landscape Contractor* 27(9):9.

2. Anonymous. 1990. Maintenance checklist for commercial mower safety. *Lawn & Landscape Maintenance.* 11(6):48.

3. Anonymous. 1993. Computing mower costs. *Lawn & Landscape Maintenance* 14(4):49.

4. Anonymous. 1996. Equipment safety. *T&O Service Tech* 1(1):63.

5. Anonymous. 2004. Equip yourself. *American Nurseryman* 199(5):22.

6. Berkman, S. 1990. To buy of not to buy? *American Nurseryman* 172:(1):70.

7. Berens, S. 1998. Stock your maintenance truck, trailer efficiently. *Landscape & Irrigation* 22(3):8.

8. Berger, P. 1997. Computerized maintenance management systems. *Turf* (December):5.

9. Bradley, A., Jr. 1982. Lease or buy? *Landscape Contractor* 23(12):14.

10. Bridson, R. 2003. The wind, she blew. *Grounds Maintenance* 38(4):17.

11. Buckingham, F. 1986. Tools to send to the job site. *Grounds Maintenance* 21(3):40.

12. Buckingham, F. 1986. Should you rent, lease or buy equipment? *Grounds Maintenance* 21(7):60.

13. Buckingham, F. 1987. Buying and selling used equipment. *Grounds Maintenance* 22(7):12.

14. Clancy, D. 1999. What will be left? *Lawn & Landscape* 20(8):56.

15. Clark, B. 1989. Look before you lease. *Pro* 2(10):10.

16. Copley, K. 1986. Avoiding common equipment selection mistakes. *Grounds Maintenance* 21(2):58.

17. Dunlap, J. 1998. Small-engine emissions. *Grounds Maintenance* 33(2):12.

18. Fuller, J. 1990. Selecting a walk-behind. *Grounds Maintenance* 25(5):33.

19. Fultz, J. 1998. Power-tool engines made to limit noise and air pollution. *Landscape & Irrigation* 22(7):17.

20. Gilmore, D. 1998. Turf equipment: should you lease or finance? *California Fairways* 7(3):10.

21. Hammond, C. 1987. Save money and lives by using equipment properly. *American Nurseryman* 165(3):126.

22. Hayes, V. 1997. Is leasing equipment for you? *Arbor Age* 17(6):22.

23. Hensley, D. 1995. Mower safety. *Hawaii Landscape* 9(3):8.

24. Hollander, R. 2000. Multi-purpose equipment blooms. *Southwest Trees & Turf* 12(5):12.

25. Howard, H. 1989. Establishing a parts inventory. *Grounds Maintenance* 24(9):26.

26. Howard, H. 1990. Looking for Mr. good mechanic. *Grounds Maintenance* 25(1):74.

27. Liskey, J. 1998. Small-engine emissions. *Grounds Maintenance* 33(2):12.

28. Lillybeck, S. Make the most of rented equipment. *Landscape Management* 38(11):41.

29. Mohn, K. 2002. Service accessories. *Lawn & Landscape* 23(8):25.

30. Mollenkamp, B. 2003. Overblown? *Grounds Maintenance* 38(7):17.

31. Neal, C. and G. Howell. 1997. Knowing when to say when. *Lawn & Landscape* 18(10):32.

32. Pendergrast, R. 2003. The sound and the fury. *Golf Course Management* February:160.

33. Pinkus, R. 1985. Equipment costing systems. In: *A Guide to Developing a Landscape Maintenance Business*. Associated Landscape Contractors of America.

34. Skinner, D. 1988. Deciding to buy used equipment. *Grounds Maintenance* 23(11):32.

35. Ratcliff, 1999. Update on national emission bans. *Grounds Maintenance* 34(7):10.

36. Rodier, R. 1999. Choosing productive mowers. *Grounds Maintenance* 34(7):8.

37. Schrimpf, P. and B. West. 1997. Plugging Away. *Lawn & Landscape* 18(7):36.

38. Seaman, M. 1989. Love it? Lease it! *Pro* 1(10):11.

39. Siegfried, C., Jr. 1983. Why rent equipment? *Landscape Contractor* 24(9):12.

40. Smith, C. 1989. Alternatives to spending a fortune on your equipment. *ALA/Maintenance* 10(4):48.

41. Steele, B. 1990. Productivity is key to equipment purchasing decisions. *The Landscape Contractor* 31(11):12.

42. Steele, B. 1990. Rent, lease or buy: what's best for your business? *The Landscape Contractor* 31(11):14.

43. Sweitzer, S. 1995. The lowdown on leasing. *Landscape & Irrigation* 19(4):42.

44. Trusty, S. 1998. Equipment: lease or buy? *Landscape Management* 37(4):20.

45. Watson, J. and S. Williams. 1983. Before purchasing a new mower calculate the real cost. *Grounds Maintenance* 24(1):60.

46. West, B. 1998. The ultimate mowing machine. *Lawn & Landscape* 19(7):34.

47. Wilson, B. 2001. How to: buy a mower. *Grounds Maintenance* 36(5):30.

48. Wisniewski, N. 1999. A balancing act. *Lawn & Landscape* 20(7):22.

Chapter 7
Landscape Design and Grounds Management

Responsible design, as defined by one landscape architect, is sensitive to the environment, the client or user over an extended period of time, and to the requirements of maintenance personnel. A landscape that was truly designed to address and reduce maintenance will require minimal plant replacement, less-frequent hardscape repairs, and fewer time consuming horticultural tasks. The decisions by a landscape architect or designer have tremendous impact on site management for many years. Every landscape requires management; there are no maintenance-free designs.

Likewise, potential maintenance of the site affects the end product of the designer in infinite ways. A landscape is enhanced or destroyed by on-going management during its growth and maturation. Design has maintenance implications, and maintenance has design implications. With the designer's conception and the efforts of the landscape management personnel so intertwined, why is there so little communication between these two camps? They, after all, serve the aspirations of the same client.

Responsibilities of the Landscape Designer

It is the obligation and responsibility of the *landscape architect* or *designer* to produce a landscape proposal that is atheistically pleasing, that addresses the client's wishes, and that is atten-

tive to the site. He/she must also create a project capable of being efficiently maintained. Landscape architects and designers must have a strong knowledge of horticulture in order to use this information as a tool for design. The design intent must also be communicated in some way to the eventual site manager.

It is also the designer's obligation to develop the project within the management resources that will be available or budgeted in the future. These resources may be in terms of money or labor for the commercial client, or time and willingness for a homeowner. The designer must assess the owner's commitment to provide for long-term maintenance.

The designer can assist the owner in establishing yearly budgets. These budgets, however, must be realistic, not figures pulled from the air to sell the project. Unfortunately, many landscape architects today lack experience and knowledge about the maintenance field. When in doubt, the designer should seek the expertise of a management contractor or consultant to obtain a credible ball park figure for maintaining the property.

The designer may be called upon for a maintenance schedule or specifications as part of the contract documents. The designer, however, must first understand maintenance processes before he/she can suggest what the management requirements will be.

The Landscape Manager

The *site manager*, whether part of an internally budgeted or entrepreneurial organization, must maintain the landscape at the highest quality and efficiency feasible within budgetary constraints. The professional manager will not sacrifice quality for price. Landscape management contractors and managers must educate clients about what low or reduced maintenance design really means for their proprieties.

The site manager must be able to communicate management requirements, operations, and goals in a way that the owner and designer can realize and understand. Few site managers or contractors for established properties request or study the original plan to determine how the existing compares with the proposed. Communication is most effective if there is an arrangement for the designer to periodically evaluate the work as it grows and develops. Adjustments can be made. This may be somewhat idealistic, but it can be achieved. It will perhaps be easier in the public realm than in the private.

Landscape management is more than mowing the grass and pruning the shrubs. Management has developed into a highly specialized field involving administrative, scientific, economic, social, and political functions. Site managers must be competent stewards of time, machinery, and capital, and adopt technology as it becomes available. Quality training and supervision for maintenance personnel are essential. The gardener of old, who accomplished everything by hand, has been in large part replaced by specialists and technology.

The Landscape

A *landscape* is not analogous to a building. A building is at its optimum condition on opening day. A building requires continual maintenance to delay its deterioration and obsolescence. A landscape, however, requires many years of management to develop as the designer and client envisioned. The fertilizing, spraying, pruning, and turf management continue for as long as the landscape exists. Many European gardens have been continually maintained for hundreds of years, adhering to the original design tenets, but shaping the landscape to present a civility that would soon disappear without thoughtful care.

Relative Costs within the Landscape

Some authors estimate that maintenance may account for 75 percent of the total lifetime costs of any specific project. One Texas landscape contractor estimated the annual cost of the average maintenance project to be as much as 20 to 25 percent of the installation cost.

Trees, the most expensive part of a landscape installation, require the least maintenance.

Table 7.1.
Relative maintenance requirement of landscape plants

Highest

Lowest

Turf
Plants requiring special care,
   such as espalier and topiary
Annual and perennial flowers
Groundcovers
Deciduous and evergreen
   shrubs
Evergreen trees
Deciduous trees

Photo 7.1. Turf provides many desirable aspects to active and passive landscapes. Careful selection of turf reduces maintenance cost. Areas with regular or heavy traffic, such as this outdoor banquet area, require additional care to alleviate compaction and maintain a reasonable quality.

Shrubs and groundcovers require more management, but usually have a lower initial cost. All of these require much less management input than color beds and turf. With the stroke of a pen, a designer inserts the largest elements in typical management budgets. Differences in initial versus long-term maintenance costs must be brought to the owner's attention.

Budgets

Landscape work comes toward the end of construction when funds run short. There is the obvious tendency on the part of some owners to skimp, that is, to reduce the landscape construction budget. Everyone involved (especially the owner) must realize that while plants will grow and eventually achieve the desired results, a reduced installation budget forces significant change.

Groundcovers may be planted further apart and smaller trees and shrubs may be installed. Less expensive species can be substituted for those on the plant list. These actions increase maintenance costs, especially in the early years of the project. Skimping on quality installation results in potential dissatisfaction by the owner, designer, installer, and landscape management contractor. A thing of beauty has in actuality become a headache for everyone because of poor budgeting.

Landscape management budgets may be reduced because of economic or business forces. Redesigning and changing problem maintenance areas can reduce costs. Spending a little money now can produce long-term savings.

When changing or re-designing any landscape, maintenance should be a primary consideration. The designer can actively seek the input and expertise of those familiar with the site and its peculiarities.

Designing To Reduce Maintenance

Each landscape site, client, designer, and proposal is different. The design must be sensitive to the needs and requirements of the client, the site, aesthetics, and function. There are, however, common considerations, usually combinations of common sense and horticultural knowledge, which can and do affect site maintenance requirements. The following discussions may not have a place in every landscape. They are, however, concepts that the designer, the landscape management supervisor, and the owner may wish to consider.

Installation. Establish the *best possible soil conditions* before planting. A good root environment enhances plant growth and quality and reduces landscape maintenance. Particular attention should be paid to soil structure and porosity, since these cannot be changed once the landscape and lawn are installed. Improper grading, poor soil quality, failure to amend the soil, improper planting, and relying on magic will reveal themselves to the client and the site manager in time.

Photo 7.2. The quality of landscape installation affects long-term maintenance. The landscape maintenance contractor or supervisor must deal with the problems and complaints resulting from poor installation and poor quality nursery stock.

131

Photo 7.3. A very difficult area to mow. Consider alternatives to turf for steep areas. Photograph courtesy of James Robbins.

Photo 7.4. The same area replanted in a groundcover. Photograph courtesy of James Robbins.

Topography. Changing topography, the rise and fall of the land, results in more appealing designs, but also influences management expenditures. The optimum slope for a maintained landscape is around two percent; a slope of three to five percent is common around structures to assure dry foundations. Avoid flat sites (zero percent slope). Inadequate surface drainage and standing water increase disease, reduce oxygen within the root zone, and make mowing difficult in wet weather. Standing water also increases the likelihood of personal injury from slipping and falling.

Slopes of 15 to 20 percent are often pleasing aesthetically and within the range usually considered maintainable with standard equipment. Berms increase mowing time but are frequently justified from a design standpoint. Slopes over about 30 percent make mowing and other operations more dangerous and expensive. Steep slopes

Photo 7.5. Selection of walk and hardscape materials should reflect the intended function, anticipated level of use, and the environment.

can be planted in groundcover or terraced to avoid mowing.

Hardscape. Man-made landscape features (patios, decks, walks, walls, fences, benches, and light fixtures) must be maintained against normal wear, the elements, insects and decay, and plant invasion. When considering landscape and construction materials, compare the initial cost to long-term maintenance and durability. Using the highest quality, strongest, most durable material or equipment available saves money in the future.

Material selection should reflect the intended function or anticipated use. The type and frequency of maintenance to the surface varies with the material selected. A wooden deck or brick surface is expensive to maintain in a heavily used or trafficked area. Concrete may be less aesthetic, but it is a more maintenance-free choice.

Use decay resistant or preserved woods and avoid painting wood when possible. If the surface is painted, carefully consider the use of vines or other types of vegetation allowed to grow on the structure. Removing tangled vines or over grown vegetation for painting every few years is a major expense and problem.

Anticipate problems before they occur. A preventive maintenance program decreases maintenance time and expensive repairs.

Paved Surfaces. Apart from the intrinsic beauty of a lawn, its most notable characteristic is that of being a planted surface that can be walked and played upon. However, this generali-

132

Table 7.2.
Overall maintenance requirements for common landscape surfaces

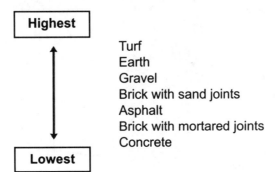

Highest	
↕	Turf
	Earth
	Gravel
	Brick with sand joints
	Asphalt
	Brick with mortared joints
Lowest	Concrete

zation has distinct limitations. Location and use must be considered. Paved surfaces cost less to maintain than turf in areas where significant or frequent traffic occurs.

Design walks to accommodate the anticipated amount of pedestrian traffic. The walk surface and texture should correspond to potential environmental conditions. Heavily textured walks make snow removal difficult. A major walk in commercial circumstances should be a minimum of six to eight feet wide; minor walks need to be four to five feet wide. Residential walks should allow two people to walk comfortably side-by-side.

Design walks to direct pedestrians to their destination in the straightest possible or reasonable manner, and to define entrances. People in a hurry tend to make their own path; the shortest distance between two points is a straight line. This can be witnessed on any college campus.

Avoid 90-degree angles with paved surfaces where possible. Rounded corners reduce stop and go mowing and deterioration of the turf or landscape by people cutting corners. When possible, walks, patios, and edging around beds should be low and flat, permitting a mower to ride up over the surface and reducing the need for hand odg ing.

Consider access of maintenance equipment throughout the landscape. Gates and entrances should be wide enough to anticipate maintenance

equipment. Large backyards should allow for entrance of more than a 20-inch mower.

In the Snow Belt, design walks to accommodate and facilitate snow removal. Clearing steps and stairs requires hand shoveling and sweeping. Gentle slopes provide better access to physically challenged patrons and can be cleared with equipment. Plan for areas for dumping and storing snow on site. Natural snow fences can be created by proper placement of plants and raised plant-

Photo 7.6. Poorly designed parking divider. The planting bed is too narrow; the trees will be wounded by automobiles.

133

ers. Poor plant placement, however, accumulates snow on walks and drives.

Parking. Design *adequate parking* space to avoid parking on grassed areas. Place a gravel or bark mulch strip along the edge areas where cars nose in to park. The mulched strip prevents cars from hanging out over the mowing area. Mowing and trimming time is decreased. Damage to the grass from engine heat and leaking fluids is eliminated. Potential scratching of the cars is reduced.

Water Features. *Water features* are notorious for requiring inordinate care and upkeep. Avoid water features in reduced maintenance landscapes. Locate any water feature where it can easily be serviced.

Locate swimming pools away from deciduous trees to reduce leaf removal. Direct water overflow from pools and fountains away from plantings and building entrances.

Gutters and down spouts reduce excessive water run-off, erosion, and washing of mulch. Where gutters are impractical or displeasing, consider installing a modified French drain or gravel strips beneath the drip line to carry away water and reduce splashing.

Plant Selection. Select only *culturally adapted, pest-free plants* that stay within the size limits afforded by the area or design criteria. Plants requiring different degrees of sun, shade, or irrigation will not grow well together.

Some projects contain inexpensive, fast growing shrubs, such as honeysuckle. These plants grow quickly in the nursery and in the landscape, but they are the most expensive and least efficient to maintain.

Designers, nurserymen, and clients tend to push the hardiness zones of plants, regardless of the region. People in central Texas try to grow plants that prefer southern Texas. People in Missouri like to try plants that prefer central Texas or Tennessee. Every few years, however, Mother Nature sets everything back to normal with an exceptional winter. The cycle then begins again.

There are many newer cultivars of common and favorite plants that are less susceptible to age-old maladies. Crabapples serve as good examples. Some cultivars are resistant to apple scab, rust, and fireblight (and fruitless to boot). Other crabapples are susceptible to all three diseases

Photo 7.7. Maintenance around this pond is reduced by use of a stone edge or *coping*. The edge eliminates trimming along the water's edge and provides footing for mowers.

Photo 7.8. Select plants that stay within the space allotted or the design criteria.

Photo 7.9. Common lilac is prone to powdery mildew in many areas. Excessive shade and moisture aggravate the situation. Consider more easily maintainable plants in troublesome areas and avoid problem plants all together.

134

with fruit the size of 'Jonathon' apples. Which requires less maintenance? Why the nursery industry still plants and sells crabapple cultivars that are defoliated by June is a mystery.

Some plants are notorious for their susceptibility to chronic problems. Some are too successful and become overgrown or invasive pests. Avoiding these is a professional responsibility to the client and management of the site. Although plant problems vary with location, the following are a few that require constant attention:

- Norway maple (*Acer platanoides*) is unable to withstand urban, heat, and drought stresses leading to sunscald and decline. In areas where Norway maple grows well, it has become a serious invasive pest.

- Silver maple (*Acer saccharinum*) hosts numerous diseases and insects problems. Its limbs are brittle and prone to breaking under wind, snow, or ice load.

- Ixora (*Ixora* spp.) have serious problems with alkaline pH.

- Japanese Euonymus (*Euonymus japonica*) is widely over planted and highly susceptible to aphids, crown gall, powdery mildew, and most seriously, scale insects. If you must, plant some of the less susceptible species and cultivars. .

- Non-resistant crabapples (*Malus* spp. and cultivars) are susceptible to fireblight, cedar-apple rust, and/or apple scab. Suscep-

tible cultivars such as 'Dorthia,' Henry F. Dupont' 'Hopa,' Van Eseltine,' and many others should be avoided in favor of selections resistant to all three major diseases.

- Fraser photinia (*Photinia x fraseri*) is widely over planted in the South and prone to several pests, including a defoliating leaf spot. It may also require significant pruning to maintain a desired size if used in the wrong place.

- American sycamore (*Platanus occidentalis*) is tolerant of poor soils and environmental stress, but it is highly susceptible to anthracnose. Leaves and fruit are nuisances.

- Colorado spruce (*Picea pungens*) is beautiful in the West and cooler, dry northern Midwest, but short lived and susceptible to Cytospora canker, spruce gall adelgid, and spruce budworm in warmer, higher rainfall areas.

Photo 7.11. Leaf cleanup for some trees is no problem, as with this thornless honey locust. If leaf removal will be a major undertaking, carefully consider tree species for the site, locate trees near roadways or other access points, keep trees away from water features and pools, and invest in adequate power leaf removal equipment. Photograph courtesy of James Robbins.

Photo 7.10. Avoid trees with messy fruit around walks, roadways, or where people gather. Photograph courtesy of James Robbins.

Table 7.3.

Good plants gone bad

Innocently introduced as ornamental plants, the following, and many more species and cultivars have escaped and pose serious ecological threats to native environments. This is by no means an inclusive list and the number of escapees continues to grow every year. Information adapted from: Plant Conservation Alliance, Bureau of Land Management, Washington, DC 20240

Common name	Botanical name	Notes
Trees		
Norway maple	*Acer platanoides*	Serious invasive pest in woodlands in East.
Tree-of -Heaven	*Ailanthus altissima*	Widely distributed, occurring in 42 states: Maine to FL and west to CA.
Silk tree	*Albizia julibrissin*	Introduced in 1745. Naturalized from NJ to LA and in CA.
Carrotwood	*Cupaniopsis anacardioides*	Popular ornamental in FL, occurs in natural areas in 14 counties. Used ornamentally in CA, but no reports of naturalized populations, perhaps due to drier climate.
Russian olive	*Elaeagnus angustifolia*	Introduced in late 1800s; recommended by US Soil Conservation Service for wildlife plantings and windbreaks until recently. Found in central, western US, and in East (VA to PA).
Melaleuca (paperbark)	*Melaleuca quinquenervia*	Occupies several million acres within the FL Everglades.
Princess tree	*Paulownia tomentosa*	Introduced as a landscape tree around 1840. Found in 25 states, from ME to TX.
White popular	*Populus alba*	Introduced in 1748, now found in 43 states throughout US.
Black locust	*Robinia pseudoacacia*	Naturalized throughout US, within and outside of its historical range. Cultivars may also pose a threat.
Salt cedar	*Tamarix* spp.	Introduced as an ornamental in early 1800s, now occurs in the intermountain region western US, the Great Basin, CA, and TX.
Shrubs		
Bush honeysuckles: Fragrant, Amur, Morrow's, Tartarian, Standish's, European fly, and hybrid pretty honeysuckle	*Lonicera fragrantissima, L. maackii, L. Morrowii, L. standishii, L. tatarica, L. xylosteum, L. x bella and cultivars*	Amur, Tartarian, Morrow's, and pretty honeysuckle range from the central Great Plains to southern New England, and south to TN and NC. The remaining species are sporadically distributed.
Common buckthorn	*Rhamnus cathartica*	Common buckthorn naturalized from Nova Scotia to Saskatchewan, south to MO, and east to New England.
Multiflora rose	*Rosa multiflora*	Introduced to East in 1866 as rootstock. US Soil Conservation Service promoted it in 1930s for erosion control and as living fences. Occurs throughout US, except Rocky Mountains, southeastern Coastal Plain, and deserts of CA and NV.
Japanese spiraea	*Spiraea japonica*	Introduced in 1870, now naturalized throughout much of the Northeast, Southeast, and Midwest.

Vines

Fiveleaf akebia	*Akebia quinata*	Introduced in 1845 and has since naturalized in 16 states in eastern US, from MI to CT, south to GA.
Procelainberry	*Ampelopsis brevipedunculata*	Species and cultivars still sold as an ornamental; naturalized from New England to NC and west to MI.
Oriental bittersweet	*Celastrus orbiculatus*	Introduced in 1860s, occurs from NY to NC, and westward to IL.
Climbing euonymus	*Euonymus fortunei*	Introduced in 1907 as ornamental ground cover, currently scattered throughout the eastern US in populated areas.
English ivy	*Hedera helix*	Widely sold as an ornamental. Occurs in 26 states and District of Columbia. One of the most abundant and widespread invasives.
Japanese honeysuckle	*Lonicera japonica*	Introduced in the early 1800's, occurs across the southern US, CA to New England, and in Great Lakes region.
Kudzu	*Pueraria montana var. lobata*	Introduced at the 1876 Philadelphia Centennial Exposition, promoted as forage and an ornamental. Common throughout most of the southeastern US and found as far north as PA.
Wisterias, exotic	*Wisteria floribunda* and *sinensis*	Chinese wisteria introduced in 1816 and Japanese wisteria introduced around 1830, both found now extensively throughout the eastern states.

Herbaceous plants

Giant reed	*Arundo donax*	Introduced in Los Angeles in the early 1800's. Now distributed from AR and TX to CA and in the east, from VA to KY, and MO southward.
Cogon grass	*Imperata cylindrica*	Sold as an ornamental grass, distributed throughout the south and southeastern US as far west as TX
Purple loosestrife	*Lythrum salicaria)*	Introduced in the 1800s as an ornamental; still widely sold, except in MN, WI, and IL. Now occurs in every state except FL.
Burma reed	*Neyraudia reynaudiana*	Introduced 1916 by USDA as potential ornamental, escaped and now widespread in southern FL.
Fountain grass	*Pennisetum setaceum*	First collected in HI in 1914, introduced as an ornamental to many parts of the world. Found in AZ, CA, CO, HI, FL, LA, and TN.
Japanese knotweed (aka Mexican bamboo, Japanese fleece flower, or Reynoutria)	*Polygonum cuspidatum*	Introduced in late 1800s as an ornamental, now found in 36 states, ME to WI south to LA, and scattered Midwest and West, and in AK.
Lesser celandine	*Ranunculus ficaria*	Still commercially available in US, currently found in 20 NE states and OR and WA.

- Pin Oak (*Quercus palustris*) succumbs to iron chlorosis if soil pH is greater than 6.5. The cure, is not plant them.

- Azaleas, rhododendrons (*Rhododendron* spp.), and other ericaceous plants will fail in soil with a pH above 6.5, in heavy soils, and in poorly drained situations.

- Roses (*Rosa* spp. and cultivars) are noted for blackspot, mildew, winter injury and an enormous amount of labor.

Select *compact cultivars*, rather that fighting to make a 12-foot tall plant stay beneath a four-foot window. Plants that overgrow the allotted space require continual pruning. Place and space plants so that they will have room to mature without being crowded. Plants with invasive root systems cause trouble with other plantings, pavement, curbs, walks, and underground utilities.

Select trees that are strong-wooded. Avoid species that surface root or sucker badly. Avoid trees with fruit or pods or excessive leaf drop that litter walks or lawns. If messy trees are used, keep them away from walks, patios, areas that require extra cleanup, or where pedestrians might slip and fall.

Some landscape managers feel that trees with small leaves require less maintenance than those with large foliage. Small leaves do not distract from the landscape as much as large leaves that have fallen. There is some merit to the fact that raking and removal of small leaves requires less effort than large leaves. Contrast the effort required for thornless honeylocust (*Gleditsia tricanthos* var. *inermis*) and sycamore (*Platanus occidentalis*). Honeylocust foliage is simply macerated and spread by mowing; no raking is usually involved. Sycamore leaves, however, hit the ground with a resounding thud and apparently multiply once they have fallen.

Turfgrass

The *type of grass* selected for lawn areas seriously affects maintenance. Select species on the basis of use and traffic, the level of management available, and those adapted to the region. Trying to grow cool- or warm-season grasses out of their element results in added management and replacement costs. The turf management chapter of this text provides detailed information on efficient maintenance of turfgrass.

Great differences between species and cultivars in water and fertilization requirements, as well as disease, insect, and stress susceptibility are documented. For instance, management requirements for tall fescue in much of the transition zone is much less exacting than bluegrass to maintain acceptable quality. Many new, improved selections of bluegrasses and fescues require higher levels of water and nitrogen than the common species.

Some turfgrass species are more invasive of planted landscape beds. Bunch-type grasses require less frequent edging to keep them out of plant beds than do bermudagrass, bluegrass, or

Photo 7.12. Eliminate needless turf areas that require labor to maintain and serve little or no purpose.

Photo 7.13. Groundcovers can reduce landscape management. The groundcover in the parking island is less maintenance intensive than turf and produces a quality appearance. Additionally, people are less apt to walk across a groundcover planting than turf, reducing compaction.

Photo 7.14. Concentrate color beds in critical areas. Photograph courtesy of James Robbins.

Photo 7.15. Wildflower mixes are popular for low maintenance or stressful sites. Native forbs and grasses are better able to tolerate local conditions with less input than turf and some exotic species. Native plants add local flavor and character to the landscape.

other creeping species. Finally, since grass requires large amounts of maintenance input, eliminating turf in small areas by using groundcovers or mulched beds significantly affects long-term budgets.

Groundcovers

Groundcovers are some of the most useful plants in landscape design. In addition to providing a finished look, groundcovers suppress weed development in landscape beds. Groundcovers substitute for turfgrasses in heavy shade, and areas too wet or dry to support a quality lawn. Plant slopes too steep to mow safely or efficiently to a groundcover. Groundcover small, odd-shaped landscape areas where maintenance with power tools would be unreasonable. Beds of groundcovers at the base of fences or other structures will help eliminate trimming. Since some groundcovers have lower water use requirements than turf, they can be utilized in water conservation or xeriscape landscapes.

Groundcovers are expensive to install and require vigilance in watering, fertilization, and weed control during establishment. The long-term inputs required to grow many groundcovers, however, are significantly less than that of lawn grasses, especially in less than favorable turf environments.

Some groundcovers grow rampantly and require frequent trimming to keep them in bounds, are prone to insect and diseases, or have other problems. Select groundcovers carefully. Do not trade one maintenance problem for another.

Seasonal Color

Seasonal color beds of annuals and perennials require large inputs of resources and labor to maintain quality. Some landscape managers indicate that weekly care of color beds may be more time-consuming than mowing. In low maintenance situations, color beds should be concentrated in key, high impact areas and kept to a minimum. Keeping the color beds together, rather than scattered throughout the landscape, reduces maintenance time. Select durable species and cultivars adapted to the particular environment in which they will be used, i.e., sun, shade, moist, or dry.

Table 7.4.
Uses for groundcovers
- *Slopes* where turf is difficult or dangerous to maintain.
- *In combination with pavers and paths* to soften these elements.
- *Narrow strips* between streets and walks or others too narrow for shrubs or turf.
- *Shady areas* where maintaining turf is difficult or impossible.

In addition to environmental tolerances, select annuals for herbicide tolerance. There have been dramatic strides in labeling of weed control products for use in annual and perennial flowers. However, there remain differences in tolerance among cultivars and species to pre- and post-emergent herbicides. Limit selection to those that can withstand herbicides and hand weeding may be essentially eliminated.

Native Species

Native plants may require less attention than some exotic species. These plants are successful in their native range because they can withstand the rigors of the environment and pest pressures. Large sections of the Kansas City International Airport, Kansas City, MO have been re-established to native prairie species. These native grasses and forbs require significantly less frequent mowing than the turf-type grasses initially planted. They receive little fertilization or no irrigation.

Native plants are not a panacea, however. The compacted, urbanized, drastically disturbed landscape site the native plant is exposed to is far different from the pristine environment in which it developed. Just because a plant is native to a region does not necessarily mean that it is more drought tolerant or appropriate for the site than exotic species. A native plant placed in an unfriendly foreign environment will fail.

Mulches

Mulches have become a standard design and management element for landscape plantings. Mulch is any material that is used to cover the soil for beneficial purposes. Using mulch in planting beds maximizes watering efficiency, minimizes watering, weed competition, and soil compaction and moderate temperature extremes. Mulches help keep plants healthy, beautify and unify landscape plantings and are a key to reducing landscape maintenance. Organic mulches improve the soil.

Mulches can assist landscape maintenance by providing a safety zone that protects planting beds, shrubs, and trees from lawnmower and line trimmer damage. Trees have extensive root systems and it is not often practical to mulch the entire root zone of a mature tree. However, applying a three to four foot circle of mulch surrounding a tree is easy to maintain and can be a pleasing addition to the landscape.

Landscape mulches may be inorganic or organic. *Inorganic mulches* do not decompose but do require occasional raking and refreshing. Inorganic mulches are useful for areas such as paths and passageways, and they have a place in certain types of display gardens. Common inorganic mulch materials are stones, gravel, marble, lava rock, and shredded recycled rubber tires.

Photo 7.16. A mowing problem that could be solved easily and inexpensively by mulching.

Photo 7.17. Inorganic mulches do not decompose; they do require occasional raking and refreshing.

Table 7.5.

A comparison of longevity, availability and relative cost for several mulches in a Midwest market. Costs are relative and vary with market, supply, and transportation costs.

	Replacement (in years)	Availability - (Manhattan, KS)	Relative cost (per yd³)	Texture
Organic Mulches:				
Straw	Less than 1	High	Low	oarse
Leaves	Less than 1	High	Low	Coarse
Leaf mold	Less than 1	High	High	Medium
Pine needles	1	Medium	Medium	Fine
Peat moss	1	High	High	Medium
Cocoa-bean hulls	1 – 2	Low	Medium	Medium
Shredded bark	2 – 3	High	Medium	Medium
Wood chips	1 – 2	High	Low	Coarse
Sawdust	1 – 2	Medium	Low	Fine
Compost	1	High	Medium	Medium
Pecan hulls	1 – 2	Low	High	Medium
Inorganic Mulches:				
Marble chips	-	Medium	Very high	Varies
Limestone	-	High	High	Varies
Granite chips	-	Low	Very high	Varies
Volcanic rock	-	Medium	High	Varies
River gravel	-	Medium	Medium	Varies
Crushed brick	-	Low	High	Varies

Inorganic materials are not necessarily recommended for mulching trees and landscape beds. Mowers, landscape equipment, or vandals can throw stones and gravel. Some inorganic materials affect plant growth and vigor. Marble and crushed coral, for example, are calcium carbonate (lime), which makes soil pH more alkaline, resulting in nutrient deficiencies and yellowing of pH-sensitive plants such as azalea, rhodendrons, gardenia, and ixora.

Do not use impermeable bed coverings, such as black plastic, beneath mulch. Impermeable coverings reduce soil gas exchange and water infiltration. Open weave mulch liners allow normal water and air movement into the soil. Mulch blankets, however, do not guarantee a weed-free landscape. They will not control some ambitious perennial weeds, weeds germinating from wind blown seeds landing on the mulch, or weeds growing through openings made to plant the ornamentals.

Organic mulches are materials derived from living sources. Organic mulches improve the soil

Photo 7.18. Mulching gives a finished look to the landscape, modifies the environment, and reduces maintenance. Organic mulch must be replaced periodically.

over time as they decompose, and must be replaced periodically. Desirable organic mulches are woody, fibrous materials that will degrade slowly and are in large enough pieces to allow for good air circulation. Mulches are usually graded by size: fine, medium, or coarse. Medium and coarse grades of organic mulch are preferred for use around plants. Fine textured materials have a lot of surface area for their volume, causing them to break down rapidly requiring frequent replacement. Fine textured mulches can also pack and form a barrier to air and water entering the root zone. Smaller particles are more prone to blow or float away easily. Common organic materials vary with region and include: shredded bark; shredded coconut husks; pine straw, pine, fir and redwood bark; wood chips; aged wood bark; and other local materials.

For many years, well-aged bark was the standard mulch used in landscapes. It contained little wood and was so thoroughly decomposed that few of the fungi living in it produced fruiting bodies. The demand for organic landscape mulches has increased to a point that wood with some bark residue is collected from a wide variety of sources and processed into mulch. These new sources include waste from lumber and paper mills, ground or shredded materials from arboricultural and land-clearing operations (green waste or landscape debris), and material from wooden pallet disposal facilities. Many of these products are rarely composted and may not even be aged before use. One segment of the industry is devoted to coloring fresh wood chips prior to use as mulch.

The increase in wood content in landscape mulch, as well as the decrease in the length of time mulches are composted or aged, raises several concerns among residential and commercial clients that landscape professionals must regularly address.

- Will insects harmful to the building or landscape, or disease-causing organisms be brought to the site with the mulch?

- Will unsightly things or something that could cause damage to the structure, site residents or users, grow in the mulch?

Termites are the primary insect of concern to clients. Termites do not live or breed in mulch piles or in the thin layer of mulch on landscape beds. Termites are opportunistic foragers and may feed on uncomposted or raw wood in mulch if they encounter it. Duryea (1999) showed that subterranean would use commercially available shredded cypress, shredded eucalyptus, pine bark, pine straw mulches, or uncomposted green waste (con-

Photo 7.19. Dog vomit fungus is one of many organisms that decompose wood and bark mulch. Dog vomit fungus is actually a slime mold. It poses no threat to plants, animals, or children, but might be distracting at a Garden tour or barbecue.

taining primarily oak), but not melaleuca mulch, as a food source in laboratory studies.

Carpenter ants live and nest in exposed wood, but not breed mulch or compost piles or in mulch applied to landscape beds. Bark beetles, wood borers, and pine wood nematodes may survive for a short time in fresh wood ships. Composting or aging the wood for four weeks or more eliminates this problem.

There is a small chance that certain vascular diseases, such as verticillium and oak wilt, could survive in fresh wood chips derived from infected trees. Disease causing organisms will not survive composting or aging for four or more weeks in piles at least eight feet high.

Wood, and other organic materials, decomposes over time primarily from the action of a variety of bacteria and fungi. These organisms use the wood and bark as a carbon source and are harmless to plants and animals, with the exception of some mushrooms and toadstools. Mushrooms and toadstools are fungal fruiting bodies, and some are poisonous, especially to small children, if eaten. Mushrooms should be removed if they occur.

Artillery fungus (*Sphaerobolus* spp.) is a wood decomposing fungi that has caused problems in the Northeast and along the East Coast in recent years. The fruiting body of the artillery fungus orients itself toward bright surfaces such as light-colored buildings or parked vehicles. The artillery fungus shoots its sticky black spore mass up to six feet high. The spore masses can reach the sec-

Photo 7.20. Too mulch of a good thing. Applying mulch deeper than three or so inches can damage plants. Anaerobic respiration can occur, producing plant damaging byproducts. Excessive or volcano mulching around trees is also unsightly. Photograph courtesy of James Robbins.

ond story of a building with the aid of the wind. The spore mass, resembling a small speck of tar, may stick to the sides of buildings, vehicles, lawn furniture or the underside of leaves of plants growing in mulched beds.

Once in place, the spore mass is very difficult to remove without damaging the surface to which it is attached. When removed, a stain remains that is also very difficult to remove. A few fungal spore masses are barely noticeable, but they accumulate and can become unsightly on buildings or vehicles. Landscapers have been required to remove or replace infected mulch and pay for removal of the spots or repainting the vehicle or building.

There is no control for artillery fungus at this time, but research is underway. Preliminary findings indicate that artillery fungus may not grow well on wood or bark derived from decay resis-

tant tree species (cedar, cypress, or redwood). Pure pine bark mulch does not appear to support growth of artillery fungus. Wood, green waste, or bark mulches composted with sewage sludge also do not appear to support the fungus.

The chances for importing insect or disease problems into the site through mulch application are very small. The few problems that could occur are avoided by only using composted or well-aged material.

How much mulch is needed? A mulch layer three to four inches deep is recommended for most situations. One cubic yard of mulch covers 105 square feet when applied three inches deep, and 80 square feet when applied four inches deep. To determine how much mulch is needed for a specific area, measure the area to be covered and use the formula in Figure 7.1.

If purchasing mulch in two-cubic foot bags, multiply the number of cubic yards by 13.5 (27 sq ft = 1 cu yd) to find the number of bags needed.

Mowing Strips and Edging

Mowing strips and edging along planting beds assist in keeping grass from encroaching into planted areas. Edging should be used around all beds to reduce trimming and prevent mulch from moving on to turf areas.

Use steel or hard edgings instead of plastic. Plastic edging sticks up higher than steel exposing it to damage from mowers and maintenance activities. Steel and hard edgings are much more durable.

Bed Design

Mowing is more difficult when plants are scattered in open lawn areas. Keep plants in beds and the landscape area as free of scattered ornamen-

Figure 7.1

Specific area to cover (in square feet) x depth of mulch desired (in inches) x 0.0032 = approximate cubic yards of mulch required

For example: to cover an area of 100 square feet with 3 inches of mulch:

100 sq ft x 3 in. deep x 0.0032 = 0.96 cu yd of mulch

Photo 7.22. Mowing barrier for trees in turf made from ground and colored recycled tires. Photograph by James Robbins.

Photo 7.23. Edging slows spread of grass into planting beds, speeds mowing, and gives a clean edge. Many suitable materials are available. Photograph courtesy of James Robbins.

Photo 7.24. The concrete edging in this photo provides an effective edge, but is too expensive for most landscapes.

Photo 7.25. When possible, include landscape trees in planting beds.

tals as possible. Scattered beds are more costly to maintain.

Design planting beds with a continuous sweep and straight lines for easier mowing. Gentle curves are more pleasing aesthetically than complicated curves and shapes. Avoid sharp corners or narrow strips that mowers cannot reach.

In northern climates, keep snow removal and deicing salts in mind when selecting and placing plants and choosing paved surfaces. Select salt plants for use near entrances and walkways.

Massing Plants

In commercial landscape designs, designers tend to use fewer plant varieties, partially due to maintenance concerns. Designers find that simple arrangements and statements or broad masses require less diverse and exacting maintenance and read atheistically much quicker by people using and viewing the site. Massing produces a cleaner design and increased impact.

Plants in mass require less pruning, weed control, and general care than individuals. Placing several species in compositions or groupings reduces maintenance only if they have similar cultural requirements. Plants should have similar requirements for water, light, soil pH, and fertilization.

Meadows. Large expanses of turf can be converted to interesting *meadows* reducing irrigation, mowing, and chemical inputs once established. Some periodic care is required to control vigorous or invasive weeds, trees, or shrubs. Meadows also reinforce naturalistic and sustainable landscape themes.

144

Photo 7.26. Massing plants reduces maintenance and is an effective design tool.

Photo 7.27. A wetland landscape provides interest and may solve a drainage problem.

Irrigation

A *well-designed, automated irrigation system* is one of the most important and cost effective methods of establishing a manageable, superior landscape in most regions of the country. A poorly designed or installed irrigation system, however, results in increased maintenance costs and innumerable woes. Make sure the designer and installer know their business.

Separate the control zones for woody beds from the turfgrass irrigation zones. The water requirements for the two are vastly different. Make sure the system can be winterized and there is room for expansion as it becomes necessary.

Mission Impossible Areas

There are places in some landscapes where it is simply impossible to grow plants. These may be small or narrow areas between buildings and walks, narrow non-irrigated spots on the south side of a wall or structure, or portions of a bed beneath an extended overhang.

Regardless of planning, there may be spots where the microclimate makes plant growth unachievable or incredibly expensive. Use permanent mulch for impracticable areas. Do not sacrifice plantings that are doomed to failure.

Understand the Client

Understanding the landscape requirements, desires, capabilities, as well as the daily operation of the client's business, produces a more maintainable landscape. For instance, simply installing trash receptacles where necessary enhances the appearance and reduces maintenance costs dramatically.

The designer must understand and plan for the maintenance capabilities and interest of the client. If he/she is only willing or capable of mowing grass, then nothing more than open lawn should be included in the final design. Do not impose a high-dollar landscape when only a shoestring maintenance budget will be provided. Everyone comes out the loser in the end.

Starting Over

Excellent landscape management practices and dedication of the site manager and crew cannot overcome disasters created by poor design or atrocious installation practices. Sometimes it is just time to punt. It is often more cost effective to start over with a new plan, the right plants, and correct installation, than to try to make a silk purse from a sow's ear. Work with the client to do it right the second time.

Photo 7.28. An impossible area to grow plants because of vehicles blocking access, engine heat and fluids, confined space, and lack of irrigation. Stone or mulch is the best choice for this and many areas where plants would become living sacrifices.

Photo 7.29. Learning the operation and needs of the client and site users saves landscape maintenance dollars. Items as simple as strategically placed waste receptacles reduce unsightly trash, debris removal, mowing time, and produce a higher-quality landscape.

Table 7.6
Guidelines for designing a landscape for reduced maintenance

- Avoid plants that require regular pruning or that overgrow the intended space.
- Choose plants tolerant to the environmental and site conditions.
- Choose pest resistant plants.
- Avoid plants with leaves, fruits, or seed pods that become excessive litter.
- Mulch all beds and use a durable edging.
- Use turfgrass where appropriate, but provide alternative surfaces for traffic where necessary.
- Lay out planting beds for efficient equipment operation.
- Keep plants in beds; avoid scattered landscape elements.
- Understand the client's needs and maintenance abilities.

Bibliography

1. Anonymous. 1992. *Low maintenance landscaping.* Kansas State Univ. Coop. Ext. Serv. Pub. MF-1046.

2. Appleton, B. and J. Derr. 1990. Growth and root penetration by large crabgrass and bermudagrass through mulch and fabric barriers. *Journal of Arboriculture* 8(4):197.

3. Balge, R. 2003. Mulch: the great mediator. *American Nurseryman* 198(6):18.

4. Billeaud, L. and J. Zajicek. 1989. Mulching for weed control. *Grounds Maintenance* 24(2):16.

5. Carlson, C. 2001. Too mulch of a good thing can be bad. *Arborist News* 10(6):35.

6. Clarke, A. 1979. Designing for low maintenance. *Proceedings of the Second Annual Ornamentals Short Course.* Hawaii Institute of Tropical Agriculture and Human Research, Univ. of Hawaii at Manoa, HI.

7. Chung, R. 2001. Simplified landscape design adds elegance. *Hawaii Landscape* 5(2):3.

8. Church, B. Cutting time. *Grounds Maintenance* 26(2):100.

9. DeTurk, P. 1995. Design focus: Design for easy maintenance. *Indiana Nurseryman.* (8):20.

10. Durand, L. 1987. How to design landscapes for maintenance economy. *American Nurseryman* 165(4):51.

11. Duryea, M. *et al.* 1999. Will subterranean termites consume landscape mulches? *Journal of Arboriculture* 25(3):143.

12. Fech, J. 2000. Sustainable landscape design. *Lawn & Landscape.* 21(1):44.

13. Fech, J. 2002. Ground covers in the landscape. *Turf* May:A6.

14. Fink, M. and D. Hensley. 1992. Let Mother Nature help with landscape design. *Nursery Manager* 8(5):54.

15. Gogue, G. 1978. The correlation between landscape design and maintenance considerations. In: *Manual of Site Management.* Environmental Design Press, Reston, VA.

16. Hamilton, D. and R. Plack. 1998. *Low maintenance landscapes.* Univ. of Florida Coop. Ext. Serv. Fact Sheet ENH-24.

17. Harper, J. 2000. The pleasures of a no-lawn landscape. *Fine Gardening.* 70(1):28.

18. Hensley, D. 1990. Designers should plan with maintenance in mind. *Nursery Manager* 6(5):70.

19. Hensley, D. 1990. Designing to reduce costs of maintenance. *Nursery Manager* 6(7):95.

20. Hensley, D. 1991. Low-maintenance trees. *Grounds Maintenance* 26(2):36.

21. Hensley, D. 1993. Irrigating to conserve water. *Hawaii Landscape* 7(3):14.

22. Hensley, D., C. Murdoch and J. Tavares. 1993. Lazy man's (person's) grass. *Hawaii Landscape* 7(4):14.

23. Hensley, D. 1994. Maintaining landscapes in-house doesn't always save money. *Hawaii Landscape* 8(2):8.

24. Hensley, D. 1994. Mulches. *Hawaii Landscape* 8(2):12.

25. Hensley, D., C. Murdoch, and J. Tavares. 1994. *Centipedegrass.* HITAHR Instant Information Sheet No. 16.

26. Hensley, D. 1995. Big plants-little places. *T&O Service Tech* 1(1):53.

27. Hensley, D. 1996. Low maintenance roadblocks. *Lawn & Landscape* 17(2):48.

28. Hensley, D. 1996. Maintenance efficiency results from design evaluation. *Hawaii Landscape* 10(4):4.

29. Hensley, D. 1996. Money-saving tips for new and existing landscapes. *Building Management Hawaii.* 13(7):26.

30. Hensley, D. 1997. Drip irrigation saves water, money and plants. *Building Management Hawaii.* 14(1):19.

31. Hensley, D. 1997. Design to reduce maintenance. *Landscape and Irrigation.* 21(3)36.

32. Inouye, L. 2000. Landscaping takes lifestyles into consideration. *Hawaii Landscape* 14(1):3.

33. Koch, J. 1990. Designing for snow removal. *Grounds Maintenance* 25(11):44.

34. Kuhns, L., D. Davis, and E. Brantley. 1997. *What is growing in my landscape mulch?* Pennsylvania State Univ. Coop. Ext. Bul. AGR97-27.

35. Kuhns, L., D. Davis, and E. Brantley. 2002. Mulch ado about nothing? *Grounds Maintenance* 37(3):26.

36. Meade, G. and D. Hensley. 1997. *Mulching for healthier landscape plants.* Univ. Hawaii Coop. Ext. Bul. L-3.

37. Morris, B. and D. Devitt. 2000. Mulching magic. *Southwest Trees & Turf.* 5(12):5.

38. Niedenthal, A. 1983. *Landscape design for minimum maintenance.* Purdue Univ. Coop. Ext. Serv. Bulletin HO-176.

39. Neary, B. 1998. Steer clear of troublesome plants. *Grounds Maintenance.* 33(2):66.

40. Roche, J. 1992. Mulch: Perfect for beauty in landscapes. *Landscape Management* 31(4):18.

41. Roche, J. 1998. From maintenance standpoint, environmental landscapes are well worth the extra effort. *Landscape Management* 37(11):8.

42. Rodie, S. and A. Streich. 2000. *Landscape sustainability.* Univ. of Nebraska Coop. Ext. Serv. Pub. GOO-1405-A.

43. Russ, K. and B. Polomski. 1999. *Low-maintenance landscape ideas.* Clemson Univ. Coop. Ext. Serv. Pub. HGIC 1703.

44. Shrock, D. 1998. *Low-maintenance Landscaping.* Univ. of Missouri Coop. Ext. Serv. Pub. G6902.

45. Squire, J. 1978. Initial design as a factor in ultimate site management. In: *Manual of Site Management.* Environmental Design Press, Reston, VA.

46. Svenson, S. and W. Witte. 1989. Mulch toxicity. *American Nurseryman* 169(2):45.

47. Wade, G. 1990. Low-maintenance landscaping. *Landscape Management* 29(10)48.

48. Walsh, M. 1999. Design with maintenance in mind. *Landscape and Irrigation.* 23(10):26.

49. West, B. 1996. Want more for less. *Lawn & Landscape.* 15 (2):46

50. Williams, E. 1978. How design should recognize and be influenced by maintenance at public scale today. In: *Manual of Site Management.* Environmental Design Press, Reston, VA.

51. Wisniewski, N. 1999. Hands off! *Lawn & Landscape.* 20(2):84

52. Wisniewski, N. 2001. Dodging design disasters. *Lawn & Landscape.* 22(11):60

53. Wolfe, J. III and J. Sajicek. 1998. Are ornamental grasses acceptable alternatives for low maintenance landscapes? *Journal Environmental Horticulture.* 16(1):8.

Chapter 8
Pruning

Pruning, the removal of plant parts to control size or improve form, is an annual maintenance event for most shrubs and many trees, especially in their early development. Some landscape plants require pruning several times every season. Pruning is the most frequently misunderstood, but critical function in directing the development of plants to fulfill the intent of the landscape designer. Proper pruning requires time and understanding of the plant's habit, biology, and function in the design.

Why Prune?

The primary reason for pruning is to *maintain the size and natural form* of landscape plants. Correct pruning and training extend the useful life of a plant in the landscape.

Pruning also *maintains the health* of landscape plants by removing dead, diseased, rubbing, or damaged branches.

Pruning is used to *train young trees* to their proper form for future development.

Removing spent flower heads or fruit *encourages development of flowers and fruits* next season, as with *Rhododendron* spp. Pruning also *encourages flowers* on plants which bloom on their current season's growth, such as *Buddleia* spp., *Hydrangea arborescens, Hydrangea paniculata, Lagerstroemia* spp., and many *Spiraea* spp. by providing additional leaf area, carbohydrates, and blooming sites.

Pruning is necessary to ensure *safety* in the landscape. Prune limbs rubbing against a structure or restricting vision from windows or traffic. Limbs interfering with power distribution lines must be removed to protect the physical safety of the client and others, as well as prevent interruption of service. Trees interfering with electrical distribution lines are the number one cause of power outages. Hazardous limbs must also be removed for safety of the client and passers-by and reduction of owner liability.

Pruning can maintain plants in *unnatural shapes* as with hedges and screens, formal gardens, and topiary shaping of plants.

Pruning is used to *renovate* old, overgrown plants and restore them to their proper landscape function and size.

Pruning trees can *reduce shade and wind resistance*. Turf, groundcovers, or shrubs can receive more light when live foliage of a tree is removed from the crowns of large overstory trees. The tree's resistance to wind can also be reduced with pruning.

Pruning can compensate for *root loss* at planting. Research, however, has indicated marked species differences. The benefit of pruning at planting for some species is questionable, but pruning has a positive response in survival and establishment of other landscape plants.

Developing and Scheduling a Pruning Program

It is the responsibility of the landscape manager to develop a *program* for the proper timing and pruning of trees and shrubs on each property maintained. A well-managed pruning program requires trained personnel, proper equipment, proper timing (scheduling), and efficient handling of brush.

Pruning is an annual maintenance event and even more frequent in some situations. Schedule pruning when it is needed and appropriate. Pruning is an intricate part of landscape management, not an interference with other duties. Problems occur when pruning is postponed until there is a slow-down in other work, or until the supervisor is looking for something to keep the crew busy. Allowing plants to grow out of bounds means that extensive cutting will be required later. Remedial pruning is more costly and disruptive to the landscape, and will probably not make the client happy.

Site Inventory. The quantity, type, age, general condition, and location of the plants are aspects used to develop and price a pruning program. Some firms classify plants in broad categories based on flowering habit and plant type (deciduous or evergreen, tree or shrub). An example of general categories might include:

A. *Deciduous shrubs*

1. Inconspicuous flowering (prune any time during the dormant season).

2. Early flowering (flowers borne on one-year-old wood—prune after flowering).

3. Late flowering (flowers borne on current season's wood—prune during dormant season).

4. Shrubs with prized fruit (prune lightly during the dormant season).

B. *Evergreen shrubs*

1. Needle-leaf evergreens (prune during the dormant season).

2. Broadleaf evergreens (prune based on flowering habit as with deciduous shrubs).

3. Pines (pinch new candles when new needles ½ normal size).

Photo 8.1. Pruning vines growing on large buildings requires specialized equipment. Schedule vine pruning based on flowering habit.

C. *Roses* (Require frequent dead-heading and pruning).

D. *Vines* (Pruning is based upon flowering habit; specialized equipment required for tall-growing vines).

E. *Flowering trees*

1. Early flowering (flowers borne on one-year-old wood—prune after flowering).

2. Late flowering (flowers borne on current season's wood—prune in dormant season).

3. Prized fruit (late flowering under shrubs—prune lightly during the dormant season).

F. *Large or shade trees*

1. Separate bleeders and non-bleeders.

G. *Pine or other large conifers.*

H. *Groundcovers* requiring mowing or pruning.

This is not the only way to schedule or categorize pruning. Groupings should reflect regional variations in species, timing, and crew organization. Select an inventory system complex enough to be worth the effort, yet simple enough to understand, explain, and use. Breaking down the plants on a property within pruning groups provides basic information for determining bids, budgeting personnel and equipment, and scheduling.

Personnel. Pruning is handled differently among professional operations. Some landscape managers use specialized crews to prune as necessary for all of their properties. Other landscape managers have one or more members of a general crew assigned to prune the sites for which they are responsible. With some companies, however, everyone prunes everything. Each method has advantages and disadvantages.

Regardless of the organization, the personnel or supervisor responsible for pruning should know the names and be able to identify the various plants on site. It is difficult to know when or how to prune if no one knows what is to be pruned.

Do not assign just anyone to prune or supervise a pruning crew. Select people with interest in, and respect for plants. Such employees respond to training and produce the desired results. Training specialized pruning crews or personnel in plant identification, prescribed pruning techniques, and operation of specialized equipment is beneficial and profitable. Specialized personnel can also prune more efficiently and profitably, and their work is easier to estimate.

It may be more efficient and cost effective for some in-house operations to contract an outside firm for pruning. Contract pruning eliminates the need to purchase infrequently used equipment and train current employees. A certified arborist with the proper training, experience, and equipment should handle high work in trees. Trying to do tree work beyond the firm's or employee's capabilities is a good way to get someone hurt, make the problem worse, and fall behind in other areas.

Scheduling. Scheduling on a calendar basis, using dates when pruning was done the previous year, is common, but not completely valid. Weather conditions modify blooming dates and growth flushes. However, recording the dates when pruning is accomplished each year serves as a basis or reminder in future seasons. Schedule specific dates for pruning according to the current year's growth pattern. If practical, schedule pruning to meet the needs of as many plants on the site as possible to minimize return trips and simplify clean up. Pruning to clear areas for painting, construction, or other emergency operations, such as storm clean up, are not part of the normal landscape management contracts. Price special jobs separately.

Avoid interfering with classes, meetings, or other activities on the site with noise from chainsaws, chippers, and power equipment. Avoiding scheduled events may require special arrangements or overtime work. Understanding the client will help to develop friendly and long-lasting relations.

Brush. Brush or debris disposal is the final aspect of a pruning program. Dealing with brush becomes even more important as the number of public landfills limiting or restricting dumping of organic material increases. Chipping reduces volume, permits recycling of the chips as mulch, avoids a tangled brush pile, and reduces landfill charges or storage space. Chippers are indispensable to large operations, but they are expensive and noisy. They can be rented or leased for the period of greatest use.

Standards. The International Society of Arboriculture (ISA) produced updated *Tree Pruning* Guidelines in 1995. The Guidelines can be used to explain tree pruning concepts to clients, and can be included in specifications. This document presents a concise description of the basic concepts of tree pruning and provides common language with which they can be discussed and specified.

The American National Standards Institute (ANSI), a private, non-profit organization, develops voluntary consensus standards for various industries. The latest tree pruning standards, (ANSI A300) was updated in 2001. These standards may be of assistance in preparing specifications for bids or contracts.

Timing

Proper timing for pruning is extremely important because it affects future flower development. Appropriate pruning time depends upon the plant species, its condition, and the desired results. Remove diseased, broken, or damaged branches anytime. If flowering is not important, then plants can be pruned anytime during the dormant season. To maximize blossoms, however, correct timing depends on the plant's flowering habit.

Prune plants that flower *early in the spring* from buds formed during the past season (one-year-old wood) at the end of their blooming period. Pruning during the dormant season before flowering removes flower buds. Early flowering species include forsythia (*Forsythia* spp.), quince (*Chaenomeles* spp.*)*, magnolias (*Magnolia* spp.), and the majority of other flowering deciduous landscape plants.

Trees and shrubs *flowering during the summer or fall* do so from buds formed during the *current season's growth*. These species include crape myrtle (*Lagerstroemia* spp.), buddleia (*Buddleia* spp.), clethra (*Clethra* spp.), rose-of-sharon (*Hibiscus syriacus*), pomegranate (*Punica granatum*), oleander (*Nerium* spp.), frangipani (*Plumeria* spp.), cassia (*Cassia* spp.), jacaranda (*Jacaranda* spp.), and others. Such species should be pruned during the dormant season, generally before growth begins.

Prune plants *prized for their fruit* display (*Malus* spp., *Ilex* spp., and others) lightly during the dormant season. This reduces next year's blossoms only slightly, yet allows the site manager to direct and control growth.

Needle-leaf evergreens can be pruned during the dormant season anytime the wood is not frozen. Pruning apparently has the least effect on growth if conducted just before spring growth begins. Juniper and other needle-leaf evergreens should be pruned lightly on an annual basis or somewhat heavier every other year.

Broadleaf evergreens prized for their flowers should be pruned after flowering. Prune other broadleaf evergreens where flowers are inconspicuous or not an issue during the dormant season just before spring growth begins.

Avoid pruning during *late summer* in areas where winter damage can be potentially significant. Pruning during late August or September may force new growth that cannot harden sufficiently before winter. This most commonly occurs during periods of significant fall rain or irrigation, coupled with high nitrogen fertilization and an early winter.

Delay pruning *plants routinely susceptible to winter damage* until growth begins in the spring. Waiting makes it easier to determine the extent of cold injury and the portions to be removed.

Closure of *pruning wounds on trees* will be somewhat more rapid if cuts are made shortly before or just after growth begins. Research has shown that pruning wounds to ash (*Fraxinus pennsylvanica*), honey locust (*Gleditsia tricanthos*), and pin oak (*Quercus palustris*) were slower to callus when made in the fall [*Journal of Arboriculture* 1979. 5:135]. Pruning during the dormant season also makes it easier to see the operation.

Some trees, known as *bleeders*, lose considerable amounts of sap if pruned in the early spring. This is not particularly harmful to the tree, but may be objectionable to the client. Species predisposed to bleeding include maple (*Acer* spp.), birch (*Betula* spp.), yellowwood (*Cladrastis kentukea)*, walnut (*Juglans* spp.), and elm (*Ulmus* spp.). Prune bleeders in summer, late fall, or early winter instead of late winter and early spring. Sap loss is also minimized if only small cuts are made.

Equipment

Proper tool selection and use minimize injury to the plant and the employee, and complete the task efficiently. There are many brands and types of pruning equipment available in the market place. As with most purchases, the buyer generally receives what he/she pays for. Durable, dependable, quality equipment is expensive. The professional, however, requires more durable equipment than do homeowners. Also, purchase extra blades, handles, and parts so repairs and replacements can be made quickly.

Hand pruners. The most frequently used pruning tool is the *hand pruner*. Hand pruners cut limbs or suckers up to one-half inch diameter; cutting larger material damages the shrub and the tool. Two types of hand pruners are available. *Draw-cut* or *scissors-action* hand pruners use a sharpened blade that cuts with a scissors action. *Anvil* or *snap-cut* types feature a sharpened blade that cuts against a broad, grooved head. The scissors-action pruners are preferred because they cut through the twig more easily without crushing tissue.

Photo 8.2. Hand pruners are the most common equipment used by landscape managers. Select professional quality equipment. *Draw-cut* pruners will provide a cleaner cut and are the choice of most professionals. Photograph courtesy of FELCO SA and Pygar Inc., Kirkland, WA

Photo 8.3. *Anvil* type hand pruners feature a sharpened blade that cuts against a broad, grooved head. Hand pruners are available with many different blade sizes and angle for specialized work and comfort. Photograph courtesy of FELCO SA and Pygar Inc., Kirkland, WA

Ratchet-action hand pruners increase leverage, thereby reducing the force needed to cut a given branch. Ratchet pruners are useful in cases of a weak grip, but they require more time per cut. They also are not durable enough for the professional. Regardless of type, use of a belt sheath will keep the pruners handy, reduce loss, and increase the life of one's bluejeans.

Another handy tool for pruning small branches is the *pruning knife*, with its heavy, hooked blade. Pruning knives require a fair degree of skill to use effectively and efficiently. In trained hands, a pruning knife is a versatile tool. In the hands of an amateur, however, the knife can be dangerous to the plant and the employee.

Loppers. *Lopping shears* or *loppers* prune limbs exceeding the capacity of hand pruners. Loppers are designed to remove limbs up to one inch or so in diameter. Loppers with larger cutting heads are available to handle larger limbs, up to 2 - 2½ inches. Again, hook and blade or scissors-action (parrot beak) heads are preferred to anvil types. The length of the handle determines the leverage and therefore, ease of the cut. Typi-

cally, handles range from 24 to 35 inches and are made of wood, steel, or fiberglass, with or without vinyl or rubber handgrips. Better quality units have replacement blades and parts available.

Gear-driven and ratchet loppers are available. These modifications increase the force and the size of limbs that can be cut effectively.

Pole Pruners. *Pole pruners* aid cutting limbs higher in the tree. The pole pruner consists of a pruning head mounted on a wood, metal, or fiberglass handle approximately six feet in length. Extension handles increase the working length of the unit. Although fiberglass is heaviest, it is the safest material for working near electrical wires. Models with telescoping poles are available and add versatility.

The pruning head of pole pruners consists of a heavier scissors-action blade, as found on loppers, operated by a rope. The size of the limb a pole pruner will effectively cut varies between one and 2½ inch, depending on the model, cutting head size, and quality. Curved pruning saws for removing larger limbs can be fitted to the pole. Pruning head-saw combinations are available. Cutting large limbs from below with a pole pruner is frustrating, time-consuming, and can be dangerous.

Power Pole Pruners. Power pole pruners are an all-in-one pruner-lopper-saw with a two-cycle gasoline engine at one end of a telescoping pole, and a 10-inch or 12-inch chainsaw at the other end. Several brands are available and power pole pruners are capable of cuts up to 20 feet off the ground. Despite the dangers associated with power tools, power pruners are still safer than using standard chainsaws, or for non-arborist trained employees climbing trees or ladders. Two-cycle power pole pruners cost $400 to $800.

Photo 8.4. Loppers cut limbs and branches too large for a hand pruner, up to one inch or so in diameter. Anvil and draw-cut blades are available. Select a lopper for durability and comfort. Rubber bumpers between the bases of the blades cushion the jar caused by closing the handles and increase worker safety and comfort. Photograph courtesy of FELCO SA and Pygar Inc., Kirkland, WA

Electric-powered pole pruners are available with a small electric chainsaw mounted at the business end. While less expensive then their two-cycle counterparts, electric-powered pole pruners are heavier and more difficult to balance, especially when extended. Electric-powered pole pruners must be used close to an electrical outlet or be coupled with a generator, which adds to the overall cost of the tool.

Pruning Saws. *Pruning saws* are essential for removing branches two inches or larger in diameter. Pruning saws are available with straight or curved blades of different lengths. Each distinct type and size has a particular use. Pruning saws differ from carpenter's saws in several respects: pruning saws usually have curved blades for working around limbs, and they cut on the draw or pull stroke. Pruning saws are coarse (five to six teeth per inch) for rapidly cutting though wet wood and the teeth are arranged in "V" alternately bent to either side when the saw is viewed down the length of the blade. Finer teeth (eight to 10 per inch) are useful in removing small branches.

A *bow saw* with a flat blade of 15 inches or larger is useful for open limbs, but it cannot be maneuvered among closely growing limbs or into dense shrubs. Bow saws cut with surprising ease and most have a replaceable blade. *Chainsaws* have similar limitations but are the most effective and efficient tool when removing large limbs or entire plants.

Another potentially useful tool is a *wire saw* or hand-powered chainsaw. A wire saw uses a short length of special saw chain attached between two lengths of rope or wire. A small weight is attached and the device thrown over the limb to be cut. The wire saw is designed to cut in both directions as it is pulled back and forth over the limb. Wire or rope saws are also useful in removing older stems from tangled shrubs.

Hedge Shears. *Hedge shears* are for pruning hedges, period. Never use shears to prune landscape shrubs. Unfortunately, they are the most common pruning tools used by some landscape managers and many homeowners. Hedge shears feature flat scissors, sometimes serrated, blades eight inches or more in length. For heavy use, hedge shears with neoprene, rubber, or spring shock absorbers between the handles are preferred.

Photo 8.5. *Pruning saws* are essential for working with trees and large shrubs. Pruning saws are available with straight or curved blades of different lengths. Each distinct type and size has a particular use. Photograph courtesy of FELCO SA and Pygar Inc., Kirkland, WA

Photo 8.6. Three types of pruning saws. The saw on the left is a *limb saw*. Limb saws are curved for better access to limbs and available in many different lengths, widths, and angles. The *bow saw* in the middle makes quick work of limbs but is difficult to maneuver in tight spaces. Several sizes are on the market. The *folding saw* on the right is handy for carrying in the truck, tool box, or work belt to remove the occasional limb.

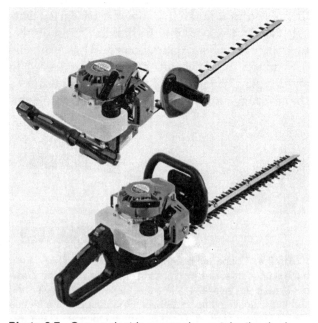

Photo 8.7. Gas or electric power shears take the drudgery out of large shearing jobs. Photograph courtesy of Little Wonder Division of Schiller-Pfeiffer, Inc., Southampton, PA.

Photo 8.8. Some brands of power shears offer extended reach and articulating cutting heads that can pivot and rotate 180 degrees. Photograph courtesy of Little Wonder Division of Schiller-Pfeiffer, Inc., Southampton, PA.

Electric or *gasoline powered hedge shears* have a moving blade resembling a sickle bar mower. Power units take much of the drudgery from pruning extensive or tall hedges. Some hedge shearing units can be adapted to chainsaws or commercial line trimmers. Some brands offer an extended and articulating cutting head that can pivot and rotate 180 degrees. The articulating feature keeps the tool comfortably balanced and makes it easier and more efficient to prune tops of taller hedges and even groundcovers.

Gasoline units avoid the need for a portable generator to power electric shears, extension cords, and the inevitable cut power cord. However, noise can be an issue with gas-powered shears. As more communities and states are beefing up their restrictions on noise pollution, major manufacturers are making strides to bring down the 2-cycle hedger's decibel levels. Pay attention to the decibel output of the power hedge shears when purchasing or replacing existing equipment, especially if your jobs are in upscale neighborhoods.

Pruning Technique – Shrubs

Shrubs, deciduous or evergreen, are most frequently pruned for size control. If keeping the plant in bounds requires frequent and extensive pruning, then it is the wrong plant for the particular use or location. Extremely large and fast growing plants are frequently found in home and commercial landscapes due to nursery marketing and production practices (such species can be produced rapidly and inexpensively).

Many landscape architects and designers have little understanding or knowledge of mature plant size, and desire a finished look as rapidly as possible. These are insufficient reasons to justify continued indiscriminate use of monster plants at the long-term expense of requisite, constant butchering, and aesthetics. There are landscape situations where use of large, rapid-growing plants is planned and desirable. The grounds manager, however, most frequently encounters them where smaller-growing or compact plants would better serve the purpose, the client, and the maintenance budget. Replacement with appropriate plant material is the most economical long-term maintenance decision.

Shearing. Too frequently, shrubs, regardless of habit or design intent, are headed back or pruned with hedge shears resulting in unnatural shapes. *Shearing* results in exceptional growth of branch side shoots, thickening of the interior of the plant to the point where there are no leaves, die back of the branches, and thinning of the base of the plant.

This type of pruning is sometimes requested by clients who require their plants to grow as cute

Photo 8.9. Shearing plants to unusual shapes, or *topiary,* has long been a part of landscape horticulture. Formal gardens of royalty in Europe and Asia often contained manicured topiary in the form of animals, geometric forms, and other symbols.

155

little balls or cubes. Sometimes, there is no accounting for taste.

Shrubs are sometimes sheared by untrained, unprofessional hacks. More often, however, the heading back or shearing is the result of the landscape manager or contractor trying to maintain fast growing plants in confined locations, while trying to be financially competitive. More than one landscape contractor has indicated that the client wants the work completed as quickly and cheaply as possible; many do not really care what the plants look like. Unfortunate, but it is too often true.

Indiscriminate shearing is faster and less expensive than pruning correctly. If a true pruning/thinning program is initiated from installation of the landscape, however, the time to properly prune each plant is not that much greater than shearing. In addition, shearing is not the only way to keep the plant below the windows. If costs and aesthetics are true concerns, removal and replacement of plants requiring frequent pruning is a realistic alternative.

Every landscape manager or contractor professes quality work to be their hallmark, rationale for the firm's pricing structure, and their most effective advertisement. Quality workmanship extends beyond a well-managed lawn to include proper pruning and care of shrubs and trees. Are you a professional grounds manager or a hack? It is the professional and ethical duty of the landscape designer to provide a maintainable landscape, the nursery and the installer to provide the best, even though possibly more costly plants, and that of the landscape manager to consider the design intent before unpacking the gas-powered shears. It is time for the green industry to educate clients about quality landscape design and to help them recover from the low bid mentality.

Compact species

Slow growing or compact species, especially broadleaf evergreens, produce most of their growth from terminal buds or buds near terminals. The result is a slowly expanding symmetrical shrub that develops a dense outer layer of foliage. Few leaves develop in the interior. Little pruning is required, except occasional removal of a branch that outgrows the general form. Light thinning can open up a compact shrub and stimulate interior foliage, if desired. Compact landscape plants should not be sheared.

Thinning technique

Most rapid growing shrubs, especially deciduous species, sprout vigorously from the base. Others develop a main framework from which most new shoots arise. Large-growing deciduous shrubs require regular, severe pruning to keep them attractive and reasonably contained.

Deciduous shrubs, except those described earlier as compact or slow growing, should be pruned with a *thinning technique*. Thinning preserves the natural shape, allows internal growth, and reduces shading and, therefore, leggy plants.

Photo 8.10. Shearing landscape shrubs is not pruning. Distinguish between the two operations when preparing specifications and maintenance programs for bid by contractors. Photograph by James Robbins.

Photo 8.11. Slow-growing or compact shrubs seldom need pruning or shaping.

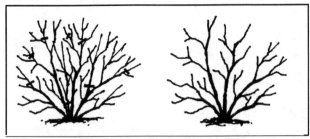

Illustration 8.1. The thinning technique for pruning shrubs retains the natural form and opens the inside of the plant to light. Make pruning cuts to an out-facing bud or lateral branch. Reduce the length of branches or canes at various heights throughout the plant. See Table 8.1 for a more detailed pruning sequence. Illustration by Cameron Rees.

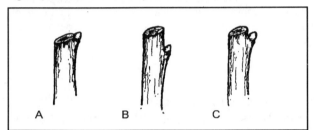

Illustration 8.2. *Cut A* is too close; the bud may die, resulting in several lower buds breaking and subsequent twiggy growth. *Cut B* is too high above the target bud; several lower buds may also break. *Cut C* is one-fourth inch above the new terminal bud. It will become the leader on the branch and the natural form is retained. Illustration by Cameron Rees.

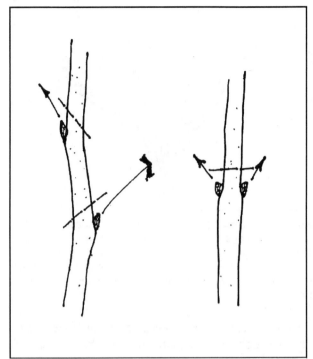

Illustration 8.3. The direction of new growth can be controlled when pruning by selecting the new *leader*. Cut to an out facing bud to direct the growth away from the center of the plant and to retain the natural shape. For plants with opposite buds, rub off or prune through the inside bud to avoid a fork. Illustration by Cameron Rees.

Table 8.1.
The thinning technique for shrubs ordinarily follows a sequence of pruning decisions and cuts

- Remove all diseased, broken, weak branches.
- Remove all crossing, rubbing branches, and those that lay on the ground.
- Remove some of the older, heavy interior growth (10-20 percent).
- Reduce length of other different branches at varying lengths.
- Remove some of the new or sucker growth, especially from extremely vigorous species and those tending to develop numerous suckers.
- Visualize what the plant will look like without the branch or cane before each cut.
- Prune with an eye to the overall health and vigor of the plant. Consider the plant's age and growing conditions, especially where weather conditions are extreme.
- Prune carefully, avoid injury to surrounding growth and leave clean cuts without torn edges.
- When pruning for disease control, disinfect the pruners after each cut.

This pruning technique, however, requires more time and training to accomplish correctly. It must be performed with hand pruners and each plant must be individually assessed and pruned.

Make pruning cuts about ¼-inch above an out-facing bud or lateral branch. Cutting too close to the remaining bud can damage it, while cutting too far away may allow additional buds to break.

Buds can be selected to direct future growth. When pruning plants with opposite buds, the interior bud should be rubbed off with the thumb or the cut angled to damage or remove it. This results in a single bud becoming the new terminal rather than two, and the subsequent fork.

Evergreen shrubs can also be pruned with a thinning technique similar to that described for

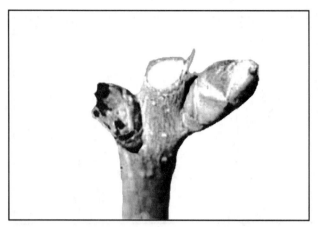

Photo 8.12. When pruning shrubs with opposite buds, remove or damage the interior bud by rubbing it off with the thumb or cutting at an angle so as to damage or remove it. This results in a single bud becoming the new terminals, rather than two, and the subsequent fork. Photograph by James Robbins.

Photo 8.13. Needle leaf evergreens can be pruned with a thinning technique to retain their natural shape and control size. Make cuts back to an out-facing lateral branch or bud.

deciduous shrubs. Make cuts to an outfacing lateral branch. Tips can be headed back later if thicker growth is desired. Non-green portions of arborvitae (*Thuja* spp.*)*, juniper (*Juniperous* spp.), and most other needle evergreens do not have active adventitious buds. Pruning evergreen shrubs severely into this brown, leafless area will not result in new growth. Yews (*Taxus* spp.) are an exception.

Shrubs with *colorful canes*, such as red- and yellowed-twigged shrub dogwoods (*Cornus* spp.), are best thinned annually after the shrub is three to five years old. Older twigs lose their brilliant coloration with age and renewal thinning maintains a supply of colorful, new canes.

Remedial Pruning

Many grounds managers and management firms inherit sites where their predecessors pruned the trees and shrubs improperly, or where the plants are terribly overgrown. Ideally, of course, plantings should be designed so that remedial pruning is minimal. If the ideal were commonplace, however, many people would be taller and have considerably more hair.

Some problems in a poorly maintained or overgrown planting can be solved with corrective pruning, while others cannot. With few exceptions, conifers will not sprout new growth from their trunks or older branches if they are severely pruned.

Conversely, most (but not all) broadleaf evergreen trees and shrubs will bud out and grow again from even quite old stems and branches. Deciduous plants regenerate most rapidly and will usually be presentable in the first season or two after severe pruning.

Overgrown privet (*Ligustrum* spp.), hydrangea (*Hydrangea* spp.), forsythia, and some spiraeas *(Spiraea* spp.), can be pruned to within four to six inches of the ground. A thick growth of new canes and sprouts will result. The new growth must be thinned severely and proper pruning established the following year. Unhealthy shrubs that are in poor vigor or that have been long ne-

Photo 8.14. Large, overgrown shrubs can be renovated and returned to a useful place in the landscape. The best solution, however, is to select plants that will not overgrow their space and to prune regularly. Photograph by James Robbins.

158

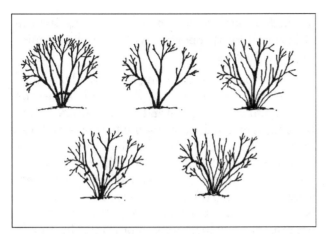

Illustration 8.4. *Renovation pruning* over several seasons can restore some over-grown shrubs. Remove one-third to one-half of the oldest canes or shoots in the first year. Thin the new growth and remove the next one-half to one-third of the oldest growth during the second season. During the third season, begin a normal thinning pruning program and remove the remaining one-third of the old growth, if the renovation is over three seasons. Illustration by Cameron Rees.

glected may not respond well to severe measures. These plants should be renovated over two or three years, as described below. Grafted lilac (*Syringa* spp.) or other species should not be cut to the ground. The grafted clone will be removed and replaced by shoots from the undesirable rootstock.

Selective thinning of tops to restore the natural appearance might be preferable to total rejuvenation of a shrub or group of shrubs. Renovation over two to three seasons is successful with lilac, honeysuckle (*Lonicera* spp.), and most deciduous shrubs. Remove one-third to one-half of the oldest growth during the winter of the first year. Prune out the remainder during the dormant season of the second, and possibly third year. The time required to renovate older shrubs depends on their size, age, vigor, and the budget. Growth during and after renovation will be vigorous, so diligent thinning and pruning to remove suckers and re-establish the form and density is absolute. Removal of some of the oldest canes will be required annually or the plant will soon be overgrown again.

Azaleas (*Rhododendron* spp.), camellias (*Camellia* spp.), hollies (*Ilex* spp.), junipers, yews, and other shrubs that have been globed can be restored by not hedging back the new growth. Reduce excessive height by shortening or removing several selected branches annually using a thin-

ning technique. Remove and thin a number of the oldest branches annually.

Overgrown rhododendrons (*Rhododendron* spp.) can be, but are not frequently, rejuvenated by cutting back to 12-inch stubs. A more reasonable approach would be to renovate rhododendrons and other broadleaf evergreens over two to three years by removing a portion of the oldest branches annually as described previously.

Hedges

Hedges serve various functional and aesthetic purposes in the landscape: visual and traffic barriers; backgrounds; separation of space; and creation of formal landscapes. Hedges may be successfully formed from almost any species. Many old and beautiful hedges from maple, hornbeam (*Carpinus* spp.), beech (*Fagus* spp.), and pine (*Pinus* spp.), species not usually thought of as hedge plants, are found in formal gardens throughout the world. Hedges are more commonly established from rapidly growing deciduous species such as privet, or slower growing evergreens such as yew or boxwood (*Buxus* spp.).

When establishing a hedge, no pruning except heading back the plants at planting is required the first year. This allows the plants to become well established. During the second year, cut (head) shoots of broadleaf plants to within four to six inches of their height at planting. Narrowleaf evergreens are tip pruned. Head back

Photo 8.15. A large beech hedge at the Royal Botanic Garden, Edinburgh, Scotland.

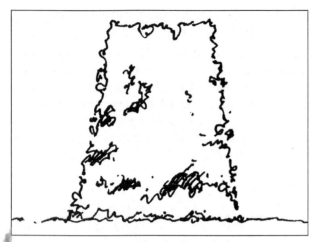

Illustration 8.5. A properly pruned hedge is always wider at the base than at the top. Illustration by Cameron Rees

new shoots one-half to two-thirds of their length each time they grow six to 12 inches, until they reach desired height. This technique develops a dense, low branching structure, and encourages the plants to spread. Hedges, regardless of species, should always be pruned so they are wider at the base than at the top.

After the hedge reaches the desired height, it is sheared. Base time of shearing on the amount and cycle of growth. Shearing effects last longer if performed as growth ceases for the season. Shear down to three new leaves and buds. This forms a dense outer cloak of foliage and reduces growth. Species that grow continuously or produce multiple flushes during the growing season will be pruned several times during the year.

Most broadleaf hedge plants, in contrast to conifers or narrowleaf evergreens, can be pruned back severely. If the hedge has outgrown its desired size or becomes unkempt and ragged, cut it back to one-half of the existing height and width. The desired height and form will redevelop after shearing a few times. Pruning this heavily is best accomplished just before growth begins so that the hedge is bare for the shortest period.

Pruning Techniques – Trees

Pruning at planting. There are several current opinions on *pruning at time of planting*. Traditional recommendations call for removal of one-fourth to one-third of the branches, and thus potential leaf area, of bareroot and balled and burlapped woody plants at planting. The theory or wisdom behind this advice is to bring the top of the plant into proportion with the roots remaining after harvest.

Bare rooting and balling remove a large portion of the functional root system, the larger the tree or shrub, the greater the percentage of active roots removed. Some estimates place root loss at 90 to 95 percent of the original mass. Reduction of potential leaf area would, therefore, reduce water loss via transpiration. Container-grown plants are seldom severely pruned, as there is no reduction of the root system. Post-transplant pruning of container-grown material is limited to cleaning up stray or broken branches.

Opponents of pruning at planting suggest there is no benefit and that pruning the top reduces photosynthetic capability. Some of the evidence put forth in support of not pruning is based on singular studies and somewhat shaky interpretation of the data.

More reliable work with Newport plum (*Prunus cerasifera* 'Newport') and Sargent crabapple (*Malus sargentii*) by Evans and Klett, Colorado State University, and others, indicated no significant differences in root production when leaf:new root ratios of variously top-pruned plants were compared to control trees. Pruning did not appear to improve first-year survival or overall growth of these easily established species. The investigators cautioned that their results should not be extrapolated for other woody species similarly pruned.

In other studies, moderate shoot pruning of Norway maple (*Acer platanoides*) at planting improved structure and did not harm the plants. Research with oaks, a significantly more difficult species to transplant, showed advantages in survival when plants were pruned at planting. Many reliable nurseries and plant experts still recommend top pruning of all new transplanted bare root liners.

A compromise with the existing data and opinions is probably in order. It is doubtful that moderate pruning at planting will benefit survival or growth of relatively easily established species on sites with adequate irrigation and post-plant management. On the other hand, moderate pruning will not harm, and will likely benefit, more difficult to establish species or those plants with little or no post-plant irrigation and maintenance.

Pruning at planting does not require the shortening of every branch by 25 to 33 percent. All landscape professionals agree that this damages the plant's form. Correct pruning of a transplanted tree is accomplished by removing the least needed branches or those that will interfere with the form or future development of the tree.

Any well-grown tree has several limbs that can be removed, either wholly or in part, without seriously affecting the plant's size or shape. Thin closely spaced limbs. Shorten or remove one of any two branches in a weak, V-shaped crotch.

Small trees usually have a number of small side shoots in lower regions of the trunk that will be free of branches in a few years. At least some of these side shoots should remain, but they can be shortened at time of transplanting. Research with pin oak indicated that the tree made greater total shoot growth in the first few seasons after transplanting if some of the side branches were not removed. Selective pruning will establish and likely improve the tree's future form.

Training. Trees should be trained and pruned routinely while they are young, during the first ten or so years after planting, to avoid severe pruning when they are older. Properly pruned younger trees will not likely need to be repruned for one to two years. Middle-aged trees can grow for longer periods without pruning.

Train the tree according to its natural form. Plants with *excurrent*, or central leader growth habit, pin and Shumard oak (*Quercus shumardii*), are trained differently than those with *decurrent*, or multiple leader growth habit (maple or ash).

A tree is a three dimensional object. Train limbs to develop in all directions (*radically*). Establish *alternate branching* early in the tree's career. Major scaffold branches should develop at least six to 12 inches apart to allow for future growth. Damaged, diseased, and broken branches must be removed. Branches that touch or rub against another will cause future problems and should be removed. Remove interior branches as these receive little light and will grow slowly, eventually dying. Prune away water sprouts and suckers.

Select the broadest-angled branches possible; branches that diverge from the main stem at less than a 40-degree angle should be removed. Wide crotch-angle branches have greater structural strength and resistance to wind, ice, and snow. Some species such as halesia (*Halesia* spp), yellowwood (*Cladstris kentuckea (lutea)*), and silver maple are prone to narrow or weak crotch angles. In these cases, prune to direct limbs so they grow more laterally, rather than upright.

The lowest branches will be removed over time, as the tree develops. Do not remove all branches that ultimately need to be taken out at one time. Trees limbed-up too soon develop weaker trunks. The crown height of the tree

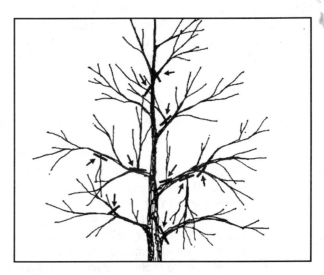

Illustration 8.6. Begin training a tree at planting. Remove unnecessary and injured branches. Illustration by Cameron Rees.

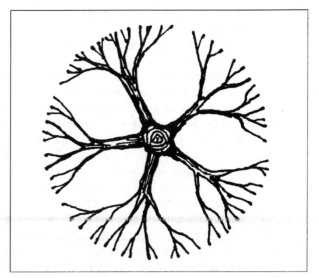

Illustration 8.7. Establish radial spacing of branches. A tree is a three-dimensional object. Illustration by Cameron Rees.

161

should be proportional to the trunk. A ratio of crown to clear trunk of 3:1 is sometimes used as a guide. Under city conditions, branches lower than seven to 10 feet should be eventually removed, particularly along major streets. It is not necessary to raise the height of the limbs all at once, however, shorten side limbs and remove over time. This height may be increased to 15 feet to provide truck body clearance.

Special consideration and training are required for 'Bradford' flowering pear (*Pyrus calleryana* 'Bradford'). This cultivar possesses many attributes that have resulted in its widespread use. It is one of the most popular flowering trees in the country. Branch arrangement and angle, however, are not two of its better characteristics. The plant develops four or more major scaffold branches at the same level on the trunk. The tragic result is loss of entire sections of the plant due to wind or snow after the plant is 10 to 15 years old. This can be corrected by proper training, but unfortunately training is not frequently accomplished during nursery production. As a result, many 'Bradford' flowering pears established in landscapes are too large to successfully remove some of the scaffolds and establish alternate branching.

The solution to the problem is to avoid 'Bradford' flowering pear and select other species of flowering trees or select flowering pear cultivars with superior branching habits. A number of such cultivars of Callery pear such as 'Aristocrat', 'Chanticleer', and 'Trinity', are available in the trade.

Table 8.2.
Objectives and criteria for pruning trees

- Allow all trees to grow to their natural form and size unless specifically exempted by design criteria. Prune to retain the natural growth habit of a tree by removing undesirable growth detracting from the normal shape of each species.
- Tree pruning should promote the tree's structural strength, accentuate its natural form and features, assure the safety of the landscape users, and enhance the health of the tree by removing dead, damaged, or diseased parts.
- Prune trees to protect persons and property around and under the tree from injury or damage.
- Prune trees to select and develop permanent scaffold branches that are smaller in diameter than the trunk or branch to which they are attached.
- Prune trees to improve the structure of the tree by establishing appropriate scaffolding, and removing crossing or crowded branches, shoots, or suckers that compete with the tree's leaders.
- Trees with multiple leaders or a branched main trunk system should be pruned to select and develop permanent scaffold branches that have vertical spacing from 18 to 24 inches. Where possible, eliminate V-shaped, narrow branch forks that lack strength. Space branches vertically and radially so as not to overlay one another.
- Dense crowns may be thinned to enhance the plant's natural wind resistance.
- Young, developing trees should not have the lower branches stripped (raised up). Lower limbs should be retained and tipped or pinched to retain as much foliage as possible to promote trunk growth and caliper. Lower branches should be removed only after the tree is able to stand erect without support.
- Remove all suckers (adventitious shoots), water sprouts, root suckers, and crisscrossing, dead, diseased or broken branches.
- Remove branches by pruning to, but not through, the branch collar. Do not leave stubs.
- Large limbs should be removed with a three-cut method. Smaller limbs removed with a saw should be undercut to reduce tears and bark rips.
- Prune trees according to the latest International Society of Arboriculture Pruning Guidelines.
- All debris should be removed from the site and disposed of properly.

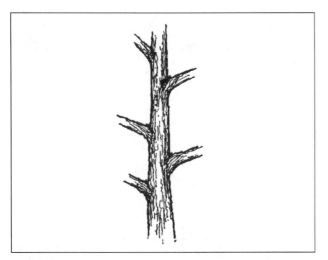

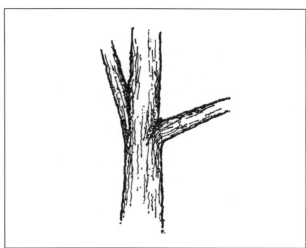

Illustration 8.8. Establish alternate branching. Branches should emerge throughout the radial plane of the tree and be spaced far enough apart so they will not cause problems as they increase in size. Illustration by Cameron Rees.

Illustration 8.9. Remove branches with narrow branch angles, if possible. Narrow branch angles are weaker and more likely to break under snow or ice loads, or during high winds. Illustration by Cameron Rees.

Photo 8.16. Prune trees to establish a crown to trunk ratio of 3:1. Photograph by James Robbins.

Photo 8.17. 'Bradford' callery pair forms all of the tree's major scaffolds at one level. In 10 to 15 years major portions of the tree will be lost to wind or snow load. Train the trees to alternate branching in the nursery or landscape while they are small or select cultivars with better branch architecture. Photograph by Robert McNiel.

Removing Limbs

Previous recommendations have been to remove tree branches as close as possible to the stem or lateral branch. This process is known as flush cutting. Research by Dr. Alex Shigo, US Forest Service, indicated that this practice delays closure of the pruning wounds.

Branch collars. At the point where a branch attaches to the stem or trunk of a tree, the branch and stem tissues remain separate, but are contiguous. The *branch collar* is a shoulder or buldge formed at the base of the branch by the annual production of overlapping layers of branch and stem tissues. Remove branches so that the branch collar is not injured. Cutting into the collar destroys natural defense mechanisms, creates a larger wound, and opens the tree to infection.

Some species have prominent and easily detectable branch collars, while others are not so easily discernible. Shigo developed guidelines to determine where a cut should be made. These *natural target pruning* (NTP) procedures are:

- Locate the ridge of bark formed above the branch at the union, or crotch, of the stem and branch.

- Locate the branch collar surrounding the branch, usually a slight swelling near the main stem or trunk.

- Remove the branch by cutting outside both the bark ridge and the branch collar.

- Where an obvious swelling or collar is not present, cut outside the branch bark ridge and at an angle opposite that formed by the ridge.

- Limbs over two inches in diameter or long, heavy branches should be removed by the three-step method described below.

Old stubs resulting from previous natural damage or poor pruning methods should be removed carefully. In many cases, callus tissue may have begun to form near the stub base. An enlarged area enclosing the lower portion or remainder of the stub can identify this callus region. Remove the stub just outside the swollen callus region. If an enlarged callus area is not visible or the stub is recent, remove it at the branch collar.

Three-step removal for large branches. Remove branches larger than two inches in diameter with a *three-step process* to avoid tearing the bark beneath the limb. The first cut is made on the underside of the branch one to two feet from the crotch. Cut the branch one-fourth to one-third of the way through or until the saw begins to bind. The sec-

Photo 8.18. Limbs are only truly joined to the stem on the underside of the branch. This photograph is courtesy of Lawrence Hensley and Ernest Hensley and their chainsaw and wood splitter.

Photo 8.19. Branch collars are prominent in some species, but difficult to discern in others. Photograph by James Robbins.

Photo sequence 8.20, 8.21, 8.22. When removing limbs from tree species without a distinct branch collar, cut outside the branch bark ridge and at an angle opposite that formed by the ridge. Photographs by James Robbins.

Illustration 8.10. Three-cut branch removal. Make the *first cut* one-third of the way through the branch from the underside. Make the *second cut* a few inches further out the branch from the top. The branch will break and drop at the first undercut. Remove the stub with the *third cut*. Support the stub to avoid tearing the bark. Illustration by Cameron Rees.

ond cut is made from the top of the limb and two or three inches further out on the limb than the first. Saw until the limb breaks off; the break will occur at the first, lower cut.

The third and final cut is made at the branch collar or crotch. Do not leave the stub, as it will be slow to callus or will decay. Scribing or breaking the bark on the lower side of the branch with

the saw before making the final cut through reduces the possibility of bark tearing should the limb slip. Large limb stubs should be removed with two cuts, the first from the bottom and the second from the top. A heavy stub can be supported with a rope sling to aid the cutting operation and prevent bark tears.

Shaping pruning cuts. Remove loose or torn bark at the point where it is attached to the limb or trunk. Some publications refer to shaping or paring the pruning wound with a sharp knife. *Paring* is cutting the thick bark around the pruning wound and rounding the edges of the cut to provide a smooth, even surface. Although the wound may appear neater, paring does not aid closure or callusing and requires additional effort. Rounding of the edge of a pruning wound may actually delay callus formation and wound closure.

Pruning Paint and Wound Dressings

The practice of painting or covering pruning cuts and tree wounds to protect against insects and diseases and to reduce decay has been recommended for centuries. Many sources persist in advising to cover any pruning cut larger than one-inch diameter with asphalt-based pruning paints or wound dressings. This counsel continues in spite of research dating back to 1934, repeated by numerous scientists since, showing conclusively that dressings do not reduce decay or speed closure, and are of no value in preventing insect or disease infestations. Some materials delay callus formation and growth. There should remain no controversy over this topic; the purpose of pruning paint is cosmetic rather than practical. Pruning paint and wound dressings should only be used at the insistence of the client or manager who clings to the old habits without regard to, or possibly knowledge of, published findings. If a dressing must be used for cosmetic purposes, then only a thin coating of a non-toxic material should be applied. Aerosol formulations are especially useful for a small, quick application.

Naphthaleneacetic acid (NAA) products can be applied to pruning cuts or in a pruning compound to reduce regrowth of tree sprouts following pruning. These materials are labeled for use on many species prone to suckering.

Interest in developing and testing new materials for wound treatment has waned, except in the area of tree fruit production, where tests of dressings to control wound pathogens has continued. Lac Balsam, an artificial resin emulsion used in Europe, has found some favor in this country. Binab, a commercial formulation of two species of *Trichoderma* fungi, applied alone or with Lac Balsam, purportedly has inhibitory action on an array of wood rotting fungi. Hudler and

Photo 8.23. Pruning paints are strictly cosmetic. They do not promote wound closure; in fact they may delay it and promote decay beneath the coating. Photograph by James Robbins.

Photo 8.24. Water sprouts are produced by adventitious buds on limbs, often as the result of heavy pruning. Some species such as crabapple are very prone to sprouting. Water sprouts and root suckers (sprouts occurring from rootstocks of grafted trees) can be reduced by avoiding heavy pruning and using cultivars that have been produced on their own roots, rather than grafted on a seedling rootstock. Sprout-control products containing NAA are available for after pruning application.

Hensen-Tracy (*Journal of Arboriculture*, 2002) found orange shellac or Lac Balsam, with or without Binab, had little or no consistent effect on wound closure by Norway maple, honeylocust, eastern white pine (*Pinus strobus*), or eastern hemlock (*Tsuga canadensis*).

Topping

Unsuspecting clients are too frequently conned, by less than reputable "tree surgeons," into having their tree topped. *Topping* is the indiscriminate cutting of major limbs to stubs without regard to their location. It is an ill-fated attempt to control the size or shorten large-growing trees. Topping ruins the form of the tree and results in the development of a vigorous, upright thicket of water sprouts. The branches formed by the new shoots are weakly attached and break readily in storms. In addition, the large, unprotected surfaces of the stubbed branches are vulnerable to decay.

The results of topping are loss of function for the tree in the landscape and drastic reduction of its life span. Future problems and maintenance costs resulting from topping are increased and the value of the property is lowered.

Growth of large-growing or notoriously weak-wooded trees can be controlled and their height reduced with proper arboricultural techniques. Selective thinning of large or high branches or drop crouching (removal of branches at laterals) may not be within the realm of all grounds managers. High work requires specialized lifts, equipment, climbing techniques, and knowledge. Large tree operations are best subcontracted to certified and experienced professional arborists.

Photo 8.26. This sycamore (*Platanus occidentalis*) has been *pollarded*. Pollarding is not topping. It is a training system in which the shoots are cut back to the same point each year. An enlarged knob develops at the branch ends. The tree pictured is in Williamsburg, VA; pollarding was common during the colonial period. Trees have been maintained at the same height by pollarding for hundreds of years in Europe. Pollarding is labor intensive and potentially injurious to the tree. Photograph by James Robbins.

Photo 8.25. Indiscriminate topping of trees ruins their natural form and produces a large amount of growth that is poorly attached and more prone to loss from wind or snow than the original. NEVER TOP TREES.

Photo 8.27. High work and drop crotching of trees to reduce height must only be attempted by a trained, certified arborist. The operation pictured is a *take down* or removal. The tree is taken down in small sections to avert damage to people and property below. Photograph by James Robbins.

Fastigiate, Columnar, and Upright Forms

Fastigiate, columnar, and upright trees and shrubs are narrowly upright in silhouette. Such forms occur in many species, including arborvitae, birch, chamaecyparis (*Chamaecyparis* spp.), crabapple, hawthorn (*Crataegus* spp.), hornbeam, juniper, maple, pine, oak, yew, and others. Upright and fastigiate are used in formal, home, and commercial landscapes, and as screening plants. Branches of these forms turn sharply upward and grow parallel with little or no horizontal development. Some columnar plants maintain a dominant main trunk with stubby, twiggy side branches.

True fastigiate, columnar, and upright forms seldom need pruning. Remove occasional branches that grow laterally. When shaping and thinning, always prune to a bud on the *inside* of the plant. This is the opposite of normally accepted pruning practices. In the case of upright-growing forms, direct growth inward, rather than outward. Specimens may require an infrequent thinning; remove branches at their origin and cut some small branches at various heights.

Weeping Specimens

Another specialized group of plants used in landscapes have *decumbent* or weeping forms. Young weeping trees gradually build height by arching shoots that develop somewhat above the trunk. These grow into heavier branches that eventually support another layer of central arches. If an upright shoot appears, it should be removed or the weeping habit will be lost. Allow weeping branches to grow to the ground. Trimming the branches to a uniform height above the ground, an artificial hemline, destroys the effect of the plant.

Weeping trees sometimes spread too wide. In this case, remove outreaching branches at a crotch. Encourage closer-to-the center branches to develop by pruning away young branchlets at an inside bud.

Large Conifers

Most *large conifers* such as pine, spruce (*Picea* spp.) and fir (*Abies* spp.) have a strong excurrent growth (central leader) habit, especially when

Photo 8.28. Upright species seldom require pruning. When they do, remove the limb entirely or prune back to an upward or inward facing bud. Photograph by James Robbins.

Photo 8.29. Prune weeping cultivars and species to maintain their arching form. Remove upward growing branches; allow the weeping branches to grow to the ground. Photograph by James Robbins.

168

Photo 8.30. Pines produce whorls of branches marking the point at which the annual growth began and ended. Except for a few species, pines do not produce buds along the entire stem. Cutting back mature limbs of pines will results in non-growing stubs, unless they are removed to the trunk. Photograph by James Robbins.

Photo 8.31. Pinch the candles of pine when the new needles are approximately one-fourth inch in length. The distance between the whorls of branches will be reduced and a new bud will form to retain the excurrent form. Photograph by James Robbins.

young. Large-growing conifers require little training unless an atypical effect is desired. Conifers are pruned to increase the density or thickness between branches, to shape young plants, and reduce the size of older trees.

Pines produce definite whorls of branches marking the point at which the annual or seasonal growth began. Most pines do not normally produce buds along the entire stem. Therefore, if the annual growth is cut back after growth has matured, the cut terminal will remain a non-growing stub.

In vigorous trees, branch whorls are sometimes spaced further apart on the main trunk than desired. The density of the tree, the space between new whorls, is increased by pinching or cutting off part of the new growth (candle) after it has approached full length and the needles have begun to elongate. Pinching is preferred since cutting with shears causes the needles to develop brown tips. The amount of growth suppression is directly related to the severity of the pinch. The tree will set a new terminal bud, retain the excurrent form, and the distance between the next whorl is reduced.

Pinching candles will also control the size of mugo pines (*Pinus mugo*). Misshapen or lopsided mugo pines can be repaired over time by pinching the candles on the taller side more severely than those on the shorter side.

Spruce and *fir* also produce a customary whorl of branches that marks annual growth. These species, however, form some buds between annual whorls. Some of the buds remain dormant indefinitely but others form twigs or side branches. Because of these lateral buds, spruce, and fir may be pruned at any time of the year. Prune back to a bud, which will break dormancy and continue to grow upward or outward. Do not cut back further than the previous year's growth as the buds beyond that point may not break dormancy.

If the terminal bud of pine, spruce, or fir is destroyed, then the plant will try to replace the leader with two or more shoots from the whorl of buds just below the destroyed leader. All but one of these shoots should be removed to retain the excurrent habit. The remaining shoot may require staking to a more upright position for a season.

Palms

Palms are pruned to remove old and unsightly fronds, or individual leaves, and fruiting clusters. Dead fronds, called the boot or thatch, of Mexican fan palm (*Washingtonia robusta*) and others, can harbor insects and rodents, or be a fire hazard. Fallen leaves and fruit are a nuisance and dangerous to passers-by and property.

A palm normally maintains only a certain number of fronds, depending on species and growing condition. As new leaves develop from the terminal, the older leaves abscise as they senesce. The degree to which the fronds abscise, or drop from the tree, varies with species. Some palms are considered *self-cleaning*, as their dead leaves readily drop naturally. Royal palm (*Roystonea regia*) and coconut palm (*Cocos nucifera*) are self-cleaning. Self-cleaning palms require little pruning maintenance, unless they are growing in an area where falling fronds will cause damage or be a danger to people. Royal palm fronds can weigh 70 to 80 pounds each and can cause considerable damage when dropping. Other palms are *non-self-cleaning*, such as queen palm (*Syagrus romanzoffianum*), Mexican fan palm, desert fan palm (*Washingtonia filifera*), and date palms (*Phoenix dactylifera*).

Many palms have small fruits; however, some, such as coconut palm, produce and drop large fruits that can be a danger to people and property. The fruit of coconut palm is removed when it is immature two to three times a year if it is growing in the vicinity of people. In Hawaii, Florida, and parts of Texas, *hurricane pruning* is commonly performed. Hurricane pruning is the same as any other palm pruning, but it is done just before hurricane season, usually June through October. Although palms are very wind-resistant, violent storms can rip leaves off. Fruits become dangerous missiles in high winds.

Palms in high maintenance landscapes are pruned twice a year, spring and fall. Species such as coconut palms that produce large, hazardous fruit, or that frequently drop old fronds in high traffic areas are pruned three times per year. If semi-annual pruning is not within the budget, then palms should be pruned once a year, in the spring.

Palms are monocots. Wounds in the trunk do not callus, so climbing spurs should be avoided.

Photo 8.32. A coconut palm pruned properly to remove lower fronds and fruits. The fruit becomes a lethal weapon if it drops on people or objects.

Many old coconut palms that have been climbed by arborists with spurs three times every year for decades, however, do not show any ill effects from the experience. Continuous spiking, however, is unsightly and can open the tree to disease invasion. The best way to prune a palm is using a bucket truck.

When pruning a single-stem palm, remove the flowers and all stages of maturing fruit. Remove one-third to one-half of the lower leaves in their entirety. Think of the entire top of a palm tree as a clock. Remove the lower leaves from eight o'clock to four o'clock if pruning two or three times per year. Remove the leaves from nine o'clock to three o'clock if pruning once per year.

Removing too many fronds of any palm produces what are termed feather dusters. Feather dusters are unsightly and negatively affect the palm. Over pruning at the growing point limits the amount of energy produced through photosynthesis to maintain the terminal. Excessive pruning also results in palm decline and pencil pointing (narrowing of the trunk).

Leaves can be removed with a machete, heavy knife, or chainsaw. Chainsaws are useful for pruning palms, especially date palms (*Phoenix* spp.) or armored palms (those with spikes), but there is a danger of transmitting Fusarium wilt. Palm fronds can also be very tough on chainsaws.

Take care to not damage the trunk when removing leaves or fruit. The wounds do not callus. Palms grow only from the terminal. Never remove or damage the terminal growing point.

Multi-stemmed palms form new shoots below ground; so entire stems can be removed. There is little need to prune multi-stem palms unless individual stems are too close to a building or internal growth is too thick. Some palms are *monocarpic*, that is the old stems die after fruiting. Remove the dead stems after fruiting.

Wound Closure and Treatment

Wounds, from natural or man-made causes, provide entrance for decay organisms into a tree. The traditional concept of wound closure was developed in the 1800s. Decay fungi were theorized to move unchecked through the stem or trunk because wood is primarily dead, unresponsive tissue. Research by Dr. Alex Shigo and others have conclusively demonstrated that woody plants actively resist the spread of infectious microorganisms throughout the plant through *compartmentalization*. The model for tree response to external wounds has been dubbed CODIT, Compartmentalization Of Decay In Trees.

A bark penetrating injury to a plant is contained with a two-step process. The first response after a wound to a tree is the accumulation of plant produced *anti-microbial substances* at the edge of the injury. This active plant reaction is not completely understood, and species differ in anti-microbial production. Phenolic and other compounds develop in deciduous species, and terpenes are produced in conifers. These chemicals have anti-microbial capabilities. This reaction zone is not static; new zones form in advance of the movement of infection organisms.

The second response of the tree is to produce *physical barriers* to decay. In addition to an active reaction zone, vertical movement of decay organisms is physically hindered by plugging of the vascular tissue by tyloses and accumulation of plant products. This vertical barrier is the weakest of the four physical barriers to decay found in trees and explains why decay will spread up and down (usually down) in trees.

The second physical barrier to movement of decay in a tree is last intact annual growth ring, which compartmentalizes inward movement of decay organisms. Annual rings result from the change in cell size and density as growth slows each year. There may also be production or accumulation of anti-microbial compounds in this area.

Radial spread (around the stem) of decay is held in check by ray cells, the third physical barrier. Ray cells transport

Photo 8.33. Properly pruned wounds close quickly. This limb removal wound is covered with *woundwood*.

Photo 8.34. Woundwood ridge formed on thornless honeylocust. The woundwood is formed from callus produced by meristematic tissue at the edge of the wound. The age of some wounds can be determined by the number of woundwood ribs; these form annually. Photograph by James Robbins

sugars, water, and nutrients across the stem. There may also be some phytochemicals involved in containment.

The fourth and strongest barrier to movement of decay is formed by production of *wound wood* over the wound. Wound wood, produced by callus, prevents movement of the organisms into tissue formed later. Although tree wounds are often said to heal, formation of callus by the plant is not analogous to healing of wounds by animals or humans. Plants wounds do not heal in the sense of regeneration or restoration of tissue. They close over defects and compartmentalize them in layers of new tissue.

Compartmentalization has been observed, although sometimes unknowingly, by anyone who has felled a partially hollow tree. Staining of the wood from infection or hollowing of the tree can sometimes be seen contained or compartmentalized into pie-shaped wedges or distinct zones surrounded by healthy tissue.

The ability to compartmentalize varies greatly among species and between individuals within a species. A tree must have the genetic ability to resist invasion by decay organisms. A tree's response to wounding is also controlled to some degree by environment and tree vigor. The more vigorous a plant's growth, the stronger and more effective the containment of decay.

Treating wounds. Despite the best intentions, wounds caused by equipment, vandals (two- and four-legged), or accidents occur to landscape trees.

If bark wounds to trunks or limbs are discovered soon after the incident, then the bark can be successfully re-attached. The bark must be torn cleanly and the cambium moist and not discolored. The bark can be held in place by small nails, with rubber or plastic strips, or twine. Asphalt-based or other wound dressings should not be applied. Remove the ties in about three weeks; nails can remain in place without harm.

An alternate procedure prescribed in one source is to wrap about two inches of moist, clean sphagnum peat moss over the bark after nailing. The area is then covered with white polyethylene that can be sealed against the trunk at the top and bottom with tape. The poultice is removed in two or three weeks.

If the cambium is injured or the wound is old, the damaged area should be cleaned and dead or loose bark removed from the edges. Avoid cutting into healthy tissue. Some sources recommend *tracing* the wound, which is cutting back to healthy tissue to form an oval or ellipse. It does not seem prudent to enlarge an existing damaged area. Jagged or damaged bark and cambium should be removed, but give careful consideration before enlarging the wound for the sake of cosmetics.

Research by Dr. Dan Neely, Illinois Natural History Survey, resulted in some interesting discoveries in plant responses to wounds. He studied the effect of wound shape, direction, time of year, and species on wound closure. Wounds shaped as circles, squares, "D's," and ellipses were deliberately imposed on several tree species. Square wounds, because of their geometry, were wider than the others and closed slightly more slowly than the others. The squares formed an ellipse during closure. There was no difference in rate of closure among the other shapes studied.

The aspect or *compass direction* of a wound had no effect on the rate of closure. This is in deference to some who claim wounds with southern or western exposure close more slowly because of increased temperatures. This allegory is not supported by research.

Dr. Neely found that late winter and early spring wounds closed more rapidly than late summer or early fall wounds. The delay may be due to desiccation and to initiation of the growth cycle. Mercer found no effect of season on callus development by beech (*Fagus* spp.). Such findings serve as a basis for developing pruning schedules.

Neely showed that wound closure rate was species dependent and somewhat based on the rate and amount of radial growth. Mercer also found that callus growth varied with species, but was more rapid for young, vigorous trees, or those receiving fertilizer applications. Drs. Martin and Sydnor, Ohio State University, found green ash and sweet gum (*Liquidambar styraciflua*) closed wounds more quickly than 'Bradford' Callery pear and river birch (*Betula nigra*). Wound closure was more closely correlated to species than to common growth parameters. The researchers suggested the possibility of selecting trees for urban use based, at least in part, on their response to mechanical damage.

Bibliography

1. Abrahamson, S. 1982. The right tools make pruning a snap. *Grounds Maintenance* 17(4):24.

2. Anonymous. 1988. Pruning and trimming ornamental trees and shrubs. *Arbor Age* 8(9):12.

3. Anonymous. 1989. Safety in pruning palms. *Arbor Age* 9(9):41.

4. Anonymous. 1990. Retaining natural tree shape critical to pruning. *Lawn & Landscape Maintenance* 11(5):62.

5. Anonymous. 1990. Tree trimming equipment. *Arbor Age* 10(9):12.

6. Anonymous. 1992. Pruning tools. *Arbor Age* 12(9):38.

7. Anonymous. 1993. Strategies for maintaining trees. *Lawn & Landscape Management* 15(5):32.

8. Baumgardt, J. 1985. Custom-tailored pruning. *Grounds Maintenance* 20(4):58.

9. Brennan, E. 1996. The tree-pruning guidelines. *Arborist News* 6(4):29.

10. Britton, J. *et al.* 1995. *Tree-Pruning Guidelines*. International Society of Arboriculture, Savoy, IL.

11. Chapman, D. 1982. Pruning: A key to integrated plant management. *Weeds, Trees, and Turf* 21(1):52.

12. Code, C. 1988. Tree pruning & staking. *ALA* 9(9):24.

13. Costello, L. 2001. Training young trees for structure and form. *Arborist News* 10(2):25.

14. Doughty, S. 1990. Pruning properly. *American Nurseryman* 172(1):103.

15. Evans, P. and J. Klett. 1984. The effects of dormant pruning treatments on leaf shoot and root production from bare-root *Malus sargentii*. *Journal of Arboriculture* 10:298.

16. Feucht, J. and J. Butler. 1988. *Landscape Management*. Van Nostrand Reinhold Co., NY.

17. Fizzell, J. 1984. How to increase your skill at pruning. *Landscape Contractor* 25(10):8.

18. Flemmer, W., III. 1989. Correcting pruning mistakes. *Grounds Maintenance* 24(6):10.

19. Foster, R. 2002. Pruning shrubs for health and beauty. *Tree Care Industry* 13(4):22.

20. Gadd, D. 1989. Effective management of tree pruning. *Golf Course Management* 57:28.

21. Gilman, E. 1997. *An Illustrated Guide to Pruning*. Delmar, Albany, NY.

22. Gilman E. and R. Black. 1990. *Pruning Landscape Trees and Shrubs*. Univ. Florida Coop. Ext. Pub. 853.

23. Gilman, E. and S. Lilly. 2002. Principles, objectives, and pruning types. *Arborist News* 11(3):17.

24. Hagan, B. 1994. Tree pruning: Refreshing vital techniques. *Arbor Age* 14(1):10.

25. Harris, R. 1992. *Arboriculture*. 2nd edition. Prentice-Hall, Englewood Cliffs, NJ.

26. Harris, R. 1994. Clarifying certain pruning terminology: thinning, heading, pollarding. *Journal of Arboriculture* 20(1):50.

27. Harris, R. 1995. Pruning standards & guidelines. *Arborist News* 4(5):34.

28. Hensley, D. 1979. Pruning-why, when and how. *Journal of Arboriculture* 5(10):239.

29. Hensley, D. 1983. Tree wound studies reveal interesting results. *American Nurseryman* 157(8):98.

30. Hensley, D. 1996. Pruning is common practice for directing tree growth and performance. *T&O Service Tech* 1(1):52.

31. Hensley, D., R. McNiel, and M. Hotze. 1979. *Pruning Landscape Trees*. Univ. Kentucky Coop. Ext. Ser. Pub. KY102.

32. Hensley, D, S. Wiest, and L. McGillivary. 1994. *Reduction of Underline Pruning Costs in the Urban Environment*. Final Report KRD-269. Kansas Electric Utilities Research Program, Topeka, KS.

33. Hensley, D. and J. Yogi. 1996. Growth regulation of some tropical species. *Journal of Arboriculture*. 22(5):244.

34. Hendricksen, J. 1988. *American National Standard for Tree Care Operations*. American National Standards Institute, Inc. New York, NY.

35. Howard, B. 2003. Palm shaving. *Environmental Horticulture Issues* 12(2):2.

36. Hudler, G. and S. Jensen-Tracy. 2002. Lac Balsam as a treatment to hasten wound closure and minimize discoloration and decay. *Journal of Arboriculture* 28(6):264.

37. Iles, J. 1989. The case against tree topping. *Grounds Maintenance* 24(6):51.

38. Johnson, T. 2003. How to write pruning specifications using the A300 standards. *Tree Care Industry* 14(10):44.

39. Kemmerer, H. 1983. Pruning for design. *Grounds Maintenance* 18(4):64.

40. Klett, J. *et al*. 1989. Routine pruning may not be warranted. *American Nurseryman* 169(3):99.

41. Lilly, S. and G. Kempter. 2002. Putting the revised A300 standards to work for you. *Tree Care Industry* 13(4):36.

42. Martin, J. and T. Sydnor. 1987. Difference in wound closure rates in 12 tree species. *HortScience* 22:442.

43. Meade, G. and D. Hensley. 1998. *Pruning Landscape Trees and Shrubs*. Univ. Hawaii Coop. Ext. Serv. Pub. L-8.

44. Mercer, P.C. 1983. Callus growth and the effect of wound dressings. *Annals of Applied Biology* 103:527.

45. McNiel, R. and D. Hensley. 1980. Determining the damage from tree wounds and decay. *American Nurseryman* 151(11):15.

46. Neely, D. 1979. Tree wounds and wound closure. *Journal of Arboriculture* 5:135.

47. Neely, D. 1989. Tree wounds and how they heal. *Grounds Maintenance* 24(11):40.

48. Ossenbruggen, S. 1985. A properly placed cut crucial to healthy pruning. *American Nurseryman* 161(6): 132.

49. Ossenbruggen, S. 1985. Tree wounds: to paint or not to paint? *Grounds Maintenance* 20(6):46.

50. Phillips, R. 1993. Hand tools. *Arbor Age* 13(7):9.

51. Santamour, F., Jr. 1986. Wound compartmentalization in tree cultivars: addendum. *Journal of Arboriculture* 12(9):227.

52. Shigo, A. 1982. Tree health. *Journal of Arboriculture* 8:311.

53. Shigo, A. 1986. *A New Tree Biology*. Shigo and Trees, Associate. Durham, NH.

54. Shigo, A. 1989. *Tree Pruning. A Worldwide Photo Guide*. Shigo and Trees, Associate. Durham, NH.

55. Shigo, A. 1991. *Modern Arboriculture*. Shigo and Trees, Associate. Durham, NH.

56. Shigo, A. and H. Marx. 1977. *Compartmentalization of Decay in Trees*. USDA Forest Service Bulletin 405.

57. Shigo, A. and W. Shortle. 1983. Wound dressings: results of studies over 13 years. *Journal of Arboriculture* 9:317.

58. Stamen, T. and J. Chambers. 1990. A hard look at future tree pruning standards. *Arbor Age* 10(1):42.

59. Thornton, L. 1996. Topiary. *Nursery Management & Production* 12(9):30.

60. Troy, T. 1991. Tree pruning: start young to avoid problems later. *Lawn & Landscape Maintenance* 12(4):42.

61. Trusty, S. and S. Trusty. 1992. Pruning with a purpose. *Lawn & Landscape Maintenance* 13(2):60.

62. Vidic, T. 1992. Tree pruning essentials. *Lawn & Landscape Maintenance* 13(12):50.

63. Young, T. 1998. Prune to the standard. *Grounds Maintenance* 33(9):15.

Chapter 9
Water Management

Water is essential for plant establishment and growth. Water is the most frequently limiting factor to growth encountered in landscape management. *Too little* water reduces photosynthesis, mineral uptake, and transport of nutrients and results in death of landscape plants. *Too much* water can also lead to plant death because the roots must have oxygen to function. *Not too little, not too much— just right.*

In the majority of the nation, especially the arid and semi-arid regions, irrigation is a constant need and a major responsibility of the landscape manager. Even in the more humid, high rainfall areas of the country, supplemental irrigation is necessary for quality landscapes.

The availability of water or ability to irrigate a landscape sets the pace for the rest of the management, and determines the quality of the landscape. The full utilization of the fertilizer applied cannot be achieved if water is limiting. Likewise, rain and irrigation determine the number and frequency of mowings. It is impossible to maintain quality turf, sensitive ornamentals, seasonal color, or newly planted landscapes in most areas of the country without supplemental irrigation.

Irrigation programs

How water is applied, *how much* is applied, and *how often* it is applied are the key factors in landscape irrigation. The soils and climate

Photo 9.1. Water determines the quality of the landscape and sets the pace for landscape management.

throughout the world are highly variable, requiring different irrigation programs for turfgrass and landscapes. A good irrigation program applies enough water to replenish the root zone, conserves water, and reduces the potential for leaching of nitrates and pesticides. Irrigation programs must account for the equipment available, climate, soil conditions, plant needs, and other considerations, such as water rationing.

Soil factors. The soil is the reservoir of water for landscape plants. The soil water reserve is regulated by soil texture and structure, compaction, moisture supply, and soil depth. Clay soils hold water very well. Heavy and compacted soils often hold too much water and too little air for

Table 9.1.

Estimated runoff volume from a 24-hour, seven-inch rain event

Land Use	Runoff amount (inches)
Woodland	2.2
Turf – golf course	2.7
Row crop – terraced contour	3.7
Row crop – straight row	4.7

Source: USDA Natural Resources Conservation Service.

many landscape plants. Clay soils can become very hard when they dry, and may crack. Irrigation must be applied slowly or in short cycles to clay soils or compacted sites to prevent run off.

Coarse textured or sandy soil has a low water holding capacity necessitating more frequent irrigation. Water can be applied more rapidly to coarse textured soils. Water penetrates deeply but not very widely in sand. The ideal soil is a mixture of sand, clay, and silt, known as *loam*.

Many landscapes have shallow soils over a hard or compacted layer or rock. Soils less than a foot deep cannot hold a large amount of water and easily become waterlogged. Shallow soils must be watered more frequently, with a lesser amount of water applied during each watering to avoid run-off.

The topography and the cover of the site affect water infiltration and run-off. Steep slopes result in rapid run-off and reduced infiltration. Irrigation schedules must be shortened and more frequent to compensate. Soil covered with turfgrass or mulch increases water infiltration into the soil and reduces run-off.

Plant factors. Water is lost from *plants* by transpiration. Transpiration moves nutrients and other material from the root to the leaves and cools the plant. Plant available water is also lost through evaporation from the soil. These combined losses are termed *evapotranspiration* or *ET*. Evapotranspiration rate is determined by light, relative humidity, temperature, wind, and season.

Plant type, size, and population also influence water loss. *Large plants* lose more water than smaller plants, depending on their shape and sun exposure. Single plants use more water than individuals do in a grouping because of greater exposure to sun and wind. Plants in a mass, however, provide more competition for the available moisture. Plants vary in size, shape, and extent of the root system, the water reservoir potential of the plant, and leaf and branch arrangement and size.

Newly planted landscapes and turf require more frequent watering than established plants. The water collection area for the root systems is severely limited during the first weeks or months after planting.

Table 9.2.

Effective rooting depths for various landscape plants

Plant type	Effective root depth (inches)
Bedding plants	6 - 8
Groundcovers	6 - 10
Shrubs	6 - 24
Trees and palms	12 - 40
Turfgrasses	4 - 8

Determining When and How Much to Irrigate

Specific irrigation recommendations are difficult to make because of plant and soil factors, but also because of differences in equipment, expertise, and philosophy. Just because it is Wednesday is not a good reason to irrigate. The *objective* of any irrigation program is to balance plant performance and water use. Apply water to supplement rainfall in such a way to avoid run-off and insure wetting of the upper six to 10 inches of the root zone. This may require one to two inches of water per week applied in one or more applications.

Manager experience

Most irrigation regimes are determined by the experience and expertise of the manager. This requires experience, knowledge, and observation. Most plants present some signal when too little water is available.

- Wilting, especially of the new growth, is the most obvious water stress signal.

- Shiny leaves take on a dull appearance.

- Some species, such as bluegrass (*Poa* spp.) develop a bluish color.

- Other turfgrasses and landscape species may develop an uneven color.

- Some landscape managers indicate that turf under water stress has a gray tint when looked at with blue blocker sunglasses.

- If you walk on grass and can look back and see your footprints, it is time to water.

- Wilting of impatiens is sometimes used as a signal that watering is needed. These annuals are sensitive to water stress and wilt before other plants show drought symptoms.

The moisture content of the soil can be estimated by feel. Take a soil sample with a probe or trowel at a depth of four to six inches. Roll or squeeze a small sample of soil into a ball. If the soil will not mold into a ball, it is too dry to supply adequate water to the plants. If the ball formed will not crumble when rubbed with the thumb, the soil is too wet. If the soil can be molded into a ball that crumbles when rubbed, the moisture content is about right for plants. This highly unscientific method is influenced by soil texture; sandy soils will crumble even when wet.

Tensiometers

Properly installed tensiometers provide accurate readings of plant available soil moisture, and when used properly, will aid water management. Tensiometers measure the soil moisture status that directly relates to the plant's ability to extract water from the soil.

A *tensiometer* consists of a porous ceramic tip connected by a tube to a vacuum gauge. All of the components are filled with water. The ceramic tip is permeable to water and salts.

Tensiometers are placed in the landscape with the ceramic tip firmly in contact with the soil in the plant root zone. Water in the sealed tube moves through the porous tip to equilibrate with the soil water, creating a partial vacuum that is read by the vacuum gauge. This vacuum is an indication of the energy that is necessary for a plant to extract water from the soil. This is commonly referred to as *soil-water tension*. Tensiometers do not directly measure the soil water content. As the soil dries, the water potential decreases (the soil-water tension increases) and the vacuum gauge reading increases. Conversely, an increase in soil water from irrigation or rain decreases the soil-water tension and lowers the reading. Thus, a tensiometer is able to record fluctuations in the soil water potential in the landscape.

The reading is accurate as long as air does not enter the tube. Air expands and contracts with pressure changes resulting in inaccurate measurements. Even if the instrument does not have any leaks, air dissolved in the water will accumulate

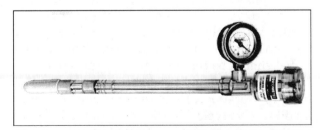

Photo 9.2. Correlating irrigation with tensiometer readings saves water. Image provided courtesy of Irrometer Company Inc., Riverside, CA

during normal operation. When a significant amount of air enters the tube, it must be removed by refilling the tensiometer with water to restore reliable operation.

Units of measure. Water potential, or soil-water tension, is measured in *centibars* or *kilopascals*, depending on the gauge maker. The vacuum gauge dial measures from 0 to 100 centibars or kilopascals (100 centibars = 100 kilopascals = 1 bar = 1 atmosphere). One centibar is equal to one kilopascal. The operational range for the instrument is between 0 and 85 centibars. Above 85 centibars, the column in the plexiglass tube will form water vapor bubbles and cease to function. The measurable range represents only a fraction of the soil-water tension range that is normally considered available for plant growth. Some plants will survive to a water tension of 1500 centibars. However, the soil water available to turfgrass and many landscape plants before they experience drought symptoms occurs between 30 and 70 centibars.

Research in Florida has shown that irrigation should be scheduled when soil water tension reaches 10 to 20 cb in sandy soil. The exact value depends on the specific site and soil. The Irrometer Company has introduced the model "LT" Irrometer, sometimes referred to as a "Florida tensiometer" that has a full-scale gauge reading from 0 to 40 cb. The compressed scale is ideal for irrigation scheduling in sandy soils.

Site Selection. A tensiometer measures soil water in only a small volume of soil immediately surrounding the ceramic tip. The instrument must be placed in the active root zone of the crop or plants for which irrigations are being scheduled.

Some sites contain several types of soil with different water holding characteristics, so several measurements may be necessary to adequately access the water status of a large property. For small sites, or those with uniform soils, one or a few tensiometers may be adequate. The site selected should be representative of the surrounding conditions. Avoid isolated low or wet areas or high, dry locations. Place the tensiometer where it will receive typical irrigation or rainfall. Tensiometer readings are not affected by salts in the soil or by brackish or effluent irrigation.

The price of tensiometers varies with their length and manufacturer. Normally, a six-inch size is adequate for turfgrass and 12-inch lengths are adequate for landscape plants. For turf, groundcovers, or bedding plants, place the tensiometer in the center of the root zone, but at least four to six inches below the surface.

For deeper-rooted plants, such as shrubs, trees, or palms in beds, consider two tensiometers. One is placed at a shallower depth, such as eight to 12 inches and the second about six to 12 inches deeper. When multiple tensiometers are used, typical irrigation is scheduled to replenish the upper part of the root zone monitored with the shallower instrument. The deeper tensiometer indicates when less frequent, larger irrigations are needed to replenish the entire root zone.

Installation. Tensiometers must be installed correctly. The instrument must have good contact with surrounding soil so water can move away from and into them efficiently. Read and follow the manufacturer directions for preparation and installation. When purchasing tensiometers for the first time, also buy the small hand vacuum pump available. This is necessary to test the instruments and to service them.

Tensiometers are installed in cored holes. Coring tools are available or a 7/8-inch outside diameter (O.D.) steel pipe can be used to make the hole. Do not push or hammer the tensiometer directly into the soil. Push the tensiometer into the access hole to the proper depth. The gauge should be two to three inches above the soil surface. If a rock or other obstacle is encountered, move to another location. Do not make holes deeper than the tip or inaccurate readings may result. The tip must be in contact with the soil on all sides. Tamp the soil around the instrument to assure good soil contact and to prevent surface water from running down around the tube.

After installation, several hours will be required for the tensiometer to come to equilibrium with soil moisture and provide accurate readings.

Tensiometers are delicate instruments and should be protected before and after installation. Handle them carefully and protect from maintenance equipment and vandalism.

Servicing tensiometers. Tensiometers must be serviced periodically to continue providing accurate readings. Air bubbles will accumulate under normal use. If the area becomes drier than one bar, the tube will be drained and the water column will be broken, requiring refilling.

Inspect the water level in the tube during each reading. If more than ¼ inch of air has accumulated beneath the cap, remove the cap and refill the tube with water.

Scheduling irrigation with tensiometers. Tensiometers are useful in that they give a continuous indication of soil water status. This information must be calibrated to the landscape. Tensiometers do not indicate how much water should be applied. The landscape manager must make this decision.

The decision to irrigate is made when the average tensiometer reading exceeds a given critical value. The specific values depend on soil types, the plants or crops involved, the desired quality, and the budget. To determine the critical value for the specific location, calibrate the tensiometer reading against drought stress symptoms. Irrigate the site well and then shut off the irrigation system. Observe the drought symptoms on the turf or plants in the landscape where the tensiometers are located. Note the reading on the tensiometer when the symptoms first become visible. The critical value for irrigation for the landscape is before the point when drought symptoms are observed. For instance, if the drought symptoms appear when the tensiometer indicates a reading of 60 centibars or kilopascals, the irrigation should be applied when the reading is 50 or 55 centibars.

The amount of water to be applied must be determined by the manager based on the irrigation system and infiltration characteristics of the soil. The depth of irrigation water to be applied should be adequate to restore the root zone to field capacity.

Automating tensiometers. Tensiometers are available that can be used to switch on an irrigation system or pump when the gauge reaches a preset reading. The irrigation system will operate for a preset period. The tensiometer reading will change as the water from the irrigation cycle percolates into the root zone and moves into the tensiometer. The irrigation system will not run again until the gauge again reaches the preset critical value.

Electrical resistance meters

Soil moisture can be measured as the *electrical resistance* between electrodes embedded in gypsum, nylon, or fiberglass blocks. Electricity has less resistance flowing through a substrate as the moisture content increases. The porous blocks absorb moisture and equilibrate with the surrounding soil moisture. Soil moisture readings are made with a calibrated resistance meter (ohmmeter). As the water content of the porous block increases, resistance decreases correlating to the soil matric potential and soil moisture level.

Resistance measurements for soil moisture are most accurate between 100 and 1,500 cb, but they

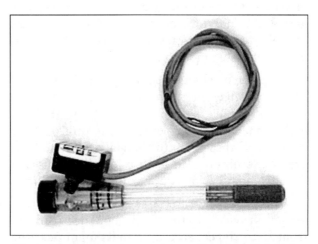

Photo 9.3. Tensiometers can be used to automate irrigation systems. The tensiometer signals the controller to begin irrigating at a pre-selected soil water tension. Image provided courtesy of Irrometer Company Inc., Riverside, CA

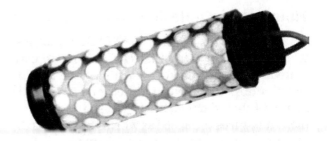

Photo 9.4. Soil moisture can be measured as the electrical resistance between electrodes embedded in gypsum, nylon, or fiberglass blocks. Image provided courtesy of Irrometer Company Inc., Riverside, CA

179

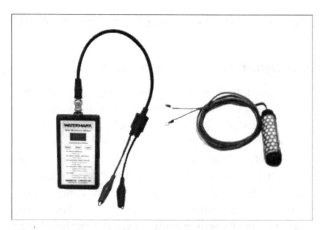

Photo 9.5. Electrical resistance sensors are buried and read with a resistance meter or directly wired into irrigation controllers. Image provided courtesy of Irrometer Company Inc., Riverside, CA

are not as sensitive as a tensiometer to tensions less than 100 cb. The majority of plant available moisture, as discussed earlier, occurs between 30 and 80 cb. Therefore, electrical resistance devices have limited adaptation to turfgrass and landscape irrigation determination.

Gypsum blocks are inexpensive and can be left in place over winter. Gypsum blocks deteriorate with time more so than other materials. The higher the soil water content, the quicker gypsum blocks dissolve into the soil solution. They are not recommended for use in saline soils and salts from irrigation water will affect readings.

Watermark™, a granular matrix soil moisture sensor, provides accurate soil moisture readings from 10 to 200 cb, according to its manufacturer, the Irrometer Company. This low maintenance, low cost sensor will not dissolve in the soil. The sensor is read with a meter or directly wired into irrigation controllers.

Time domain reflectometry

Time domain reflectometry (TDR) is a new technique in the trade that can be used to estimate soil moisture content. An electromagnetic wave is directed down parallel guides (usually stainless steel rods) placed in the soil. An instrument measures the speed at which the pulse travels to the end of the guides and returns.

This technique is based on the dielectric constant of water, which is higher than the value for mineral soils. The presence of water slows the speed of the electromagnetic wave slightly. Salin-

ity can influence readings, although new techniques are under development to overcome this problem. The primary drawback of TDR is cost.

Measuring foliage temperature

Exposed leaves of plants with sufficient soil moisture have temperatures equal to or slightly below air temperature. As soil moisture becomes limiting, transpiration, and thus evaporative cooling, is reduced and leaf temperatures increase. Landscape plants in dry soil have leaf temperatures from 10 to 25° F above ambient temperatures.

Using an *infrared thermometer*, the temperature of exposed and unexposed leaves can be measured and compared to the air temperature. These instruments resemble a police radar gun and are pointed at the object in question.

The cost of infrared thermometers has dropped dramatically, making this technique feasible for wider use. Research in turfgrass management indicated that irrigation frequency was reduced when irrigation was based on leaf temperatures, compared to irrigation on queue from a tensiometer. In a few years, evaluating surface temperature may provide an efficient method of determining irrigation needs and plant stress.

Evapotranspiration (ET)/water budgets

Irrigation can be planned and scheduled, or *budgeted*, if the water-holding capacity of the soil is known and evapotranspiration (ET) reports are available. The amount of water lost daily through ET is reported in many regions. *ET rates* are adjusted for different landscape compositions and microclimatic differences. In theory, the specific amount of water lost can be replaced at appropriate intervals. Replacing only the water lost daily provides maximum conservation of water. Irrigation using ET rates requires reasonable records but is used by golf courses and other turfgrass intensive sites.

Developing irrigation programs for landscape plants using water budgets is more complex. Landscapes offer more diversity of species within a single-value irrigation zone. Planting densities affect irrigation requirements and vary in sections of a landscape. There are also complex combinations of canopy coverage beneath trees and shrubs in a developed landscape. There has been a great

Table 9.3.

Evapotranspiration rates

Evapotranspiration is expressed in inches of water per day. The following are some average moisture losses for various conditions.

Average Environment	Inches of water per day
Cool, humid environment	0.10 – 0.15
Cool, dry environment	0.15 – 0.25
Warm, humid environment	0.15 – 0.20
Warm, dry environment	0.20 – 0.25
Hot, humid environment (think Florida)	0.20 – 0.30
Hot, Dry environment (think Arizona)	0.30 – 0.40

deal of research, especially in California, to determine the water use coefficients of landscape plants and plant combinations. The K_L method [University of California Cooperative Extension Service] considers environmental factors, species differences, and plant densities to estimate the amount of water a given landscape needs to maintain acceptable quality. This water budget model can be used to estimate water for new and existing landscape projects. Mathematical models require adjustment and refinement to compensate for local conditions. Models will become more accurate and use will increase as additional knowledge is gained about plant water use.

Water Quality

The quality of irrigation water used for landscapes varies from excellent to very poor. Water quality has become a much more serious issue as many new large turfgrass facilities and landscapes are encouraged or required to use poor quality, recycled, treated effluent, or brackish water for irrigation. Irrigation water quality has always been an issue in western states.

Undesirable elements and compounds are left in the soil profile as water evaporates. Repeated applications of poor quality water can eventually raise the concentration of these materials to toxic levels and negatively impact soil physical properties.

Testing irrigation water is frequently overlooked, but it is as important as soil tests for determining the plant palette for a site, management operations to alleviate the affects of poor quality water, and for problem solving. The basic criteria for evaluating water quality for landscape and turfgrass irrigation include:

- pH;

- Salinity (total soluble salt content);

- Sodium hazard (proportion of sodium (Na^+) relative to other cations);

- Bicarbonate concentration (HCO_3^-) relative to that of calcium (Ca^{++}) and magnesium (Mg^{++});

- Concentration of elements toxic to turfgrass and landscape plants; and

- Nutrient content.

Irrigation water pH

The *pH of irrigation water* gives some basic information about irrigation water quality. Water with a neutral or slightly acidic pH (7.0 or less) probably has little sodium or bicarbonate problem. However, acidic water, below pH 5.5, can contain high levels of some ions that are harmful to plants. Alkaline water, especially pH 8.0 or above, is common in the West and Southwest and leads to potential sodium, salinity, and other problems.

Management options - pH. Liming materials are used to increase the soil's pH if the irrigation water is abnormally low. High pH water is corrected by application of sulfur or sulfur-containing materials to the site and through use of acidifying fertilizers. The type and amount of amendment application for pH modification should be determined based on soil tests.

Salinity

Salinity of irrigation water is reported as *Total Dissolved Salts* (TDS) in parts per million (ppm), or as *Electrical Conductivity* (EC), reported most commonly as millimhos per centimeter (mmhos cm^{-1}). EC is also reported as micromhos per centimeter (μmhos cm^{-1}) or decisiemens per meter (dS m^{-1}).

$$1 \text{ mmhos cm}^{-1} = 1000 \text{ }\mu\text{mhos cm}^{-1} = 1 \text{ dS m}^{-1}$$

TDS (ppm) is calculated from EC (mmhos cm^{-1}) by multiplying by 640. EC (mmhos cm^{-1}) is calculated from TDS (ppm) by dividing by 640.

$$TDS = EC (640)$$

$$EC = \frac{TDS}{640}$$

Salts in the irrigation water can accumulate in the soil resulting in *physiological drought*. Even though the site is well watered, the plants wilt because they cannot absorb sufficient water to replace that lost through transpiration. The degree of the problem depends on the sensitivity of the plant to salts and the concentration of salts accumulated in the soil.

Many landscape plants are more sensitive to salts in irrigation water applied to the foliage than to salts in the soil, or from soil applied water. Salt toxicity in broadleaf trees and shrubs is first expressed as stunting of growth and yellowing of foliage. Burning (necrosis) of the leaf margins and defoliation usually follow. Plants are killed in severe cases.

Management options - Salinity. Irrigation with high salinity water, regardless of source, may require one or more changes in turfgrass and landscape management. Obstructions to normal soil drainage such as hard pans, clay pans, or other problems causing poor drainage, should be solved. Sandy soils tolerate poor-quality water better than clay soils. Soils that do not drain well accumulate salts and cannot be leached – the poorer the drainage, the better quality of water required.

One solution is to blend poor quality water with less salty or potable sources, if available. The two waters are mixed in a reservoir or mixing chamber before irrigating. Although there is some variation due to the types of salts and environmental conditions, the water quality is usually improved in direct proportion to the ratio of the waters mixed. If equal portions of a water with an EC of 5 dS m^{-1} are mixed with water with an EC of 1 dS m^{-1}, the resulting blend should have an EC of about 3 dS m^{-1}.

Additional water is applied to leach excess salts that accumulate due to evaporation past the root zone. The amount of additional irrigation water or *leaching fraction* (LF) is calculated using the following formula:

$$LF = \frac{ECw}{5(ECe)-ECw}$$

- *ECw* is the electrical conductivity of the irrigation water to be applied.

Table 9.4.
Guidelines for salinity hazard in landscape irrigation water

Salinity hazard to landscape plants	Total dissolved salt content	
	ppm	EC (millimhos/cm)
No salinity hazard or use restriction.	<450	0.7
Some salinity hazard to sensitive landscape plants.	450 - 1000	0.7-1.5
Salinity hazard to moderately sensitive ornamentals and careful management required to reduce salt build up.	1000 - 3000	1.5-3.0
Irrigation should be used for salt-tolerant ornamentals in well-drained soil with careful management to reduce build up.	>3000	>3.0

- *ECe* is the electrical conductivity of the soil water tolerated by the turf or landscape plants being grown.

For example, if the turf or landscape plants have a tolerance of water with a salinity of 3 dS m^{-1} and the irrigation water used has a salinity of 2 dS m^{-1}, the leaching fraction required would be 0.15. The normal watering requirement should be increased by an additional 15 percent for each irrigation event to prevent salts in the irrigation water from accumulating.

$$LF = \frac{2}{5(3)-2} = .15$$

Plant selection. Many turfgrass species have demonstrated moderate to high salt tolerance, however, many landscape species have proven to be far more sensitive. Grasses accumulate salts in the leaf tips and these are regularly removed during mowing. Landscape plants vary widely in their salt and specific ion tolerance. Many landscape plants can tolerate medium to high salt irrigation water if the water is applied directly to the soil as opposed to application of nonpotable water directly to the foliage. Research has shown that species selection at planting is the most important strategy to avoid the negative effects of irrigating with nonpotable water. Select

Table 9.5.
Estimated salt tolerances of common turfgrasses

Common Name	Botanical name	Warm or Cool Season
Tolerant (10 dS/m)		
Alkaligrass	*Puccinellia spp.*	Cool season
Bermudagrass (common and improved)	*Cynodon dactylon*	Warm season
Seashore paspalum	*Paspalum vaginatum*	Warm season
St. Augustinegrass	*Stenotaphrum secundatum*	Warm season
Moderately Tolerant (6-10 dS/m)		
Creeping Bentgrass	*Agrostis palustris*	Cool season
Fairway wheatgrass	*Agropyron cristatum*	Cool season
Perennial ryegrass	*Lolium perenne*	Cool season
Slender creeping red fescue	*Festuca rubra spp. trichopylla*	Cool season
Tall Fescue	*Festuca arundinacea*	Cool season
Western wheatgrass	*Agropyron smithii*	Cool season
Blue gama	*Bouteloua gracilis*	Warm season
Buffalograss	*Buchloe dactyloides*	Warm season
Zoysiagrass	*Zoysia spp.*	Warm season
Moderately Sensitive (3-6 dS/m)		
Annual ryegrass	*Lolium multiflorum*	Cool season
Chewings fescue	*Festuca rubra spp. commutata*	Cool season
Creeping bentgrass	*Agrostis palustris*	Cool season
Creeping red fescue	*Festuca rubra spp. rubra*	Cool season
Hard fescue	*Festuca longifolia*	Cool season
Bahiagrass	*Paspalum notatum*	Warm season
Sensitive (<3 dS/m)		
Annual bluegrass	*Poa annua*	Cool season
Colonial bentgrass	*Agrostis tenuis*	Cool season
Kentucky bluegrass	*Poa pratensis*	Cool season
Rough bluegrass	*Poa trivialis*	Cool season
Centipedegrass	*Eremochloa ophiuroides*	Warm season

Adapted from: USGA, Waste Water Reuse for Golf Course Irrigation.

or replace dead or sensitive plants with more tolerant species; lists will vary with region.

Landscape managers suggest pruning lower limbs of salt sensitive trees and shrubs to prevent direct contact with the foliage. Adjust spray heads so that foliage or shrubs and trees are not in the direct path.

Science may increase the tolerance of sensitive landscape species in the future. Researchers at the University of Toronto have isolated a gene that confers salt tolerance in plants. We may someday be able to genetically modify landscape plants to better tolerate poor quality irrigation, except, of course, in Europe.

Sodium hazard

High levels of *sodium* (Na^+) in irrigation water can accumulate and become toxic to grasses and landscape plants. However, the greatest concern to landscape and turf managers is sodium's indirect effect on soil structure and permeability. Reclaimed and brackish water, and many regular irrigation sources in the West, have elevated sodium levels.

Irrigation with water high in sodium causes *deflocculation* (loss of aggregation) of the clay particles in the soil and severely reduces aeration, water infiltration, percolation, permeability, and root growth.

The sodium hazard of irrigation water is expressed as the *Sodium Absorption Ratio* (SAR). It is the ratio of the concentration of sodium to calcium and magnesium. SAR is calculated using this formula.

$$SAR = \frac{Na}{\sqrt{\dfrac{Ca + Mg}{2}}}$$

The values for sodium (Na), calcium (Ca) and magnesium (Mg) are given in miliequivalents per liter (meq L^{-1}). Some water analyses report the SAR. If the water quality report does not give the SAR, it can be calculated reasonably easily.

Some water analyses report concentrations of these elements in miliequivalents so you only need to plug in the numbers. If the values are in parts per million (ppm), then the conversion is:

$$meq\ L^{-1} \times equivalent\ weight = ppm$$

$$meq\ L^{-1} = \frac{ppm}{equivalent\ weight\ of\ ion}$$

The equivalent weight for:

Na = 23

Ca = 20

Mg = 12.2

Water with a SAR above nine can cause severe permeability problems when applied to clay soils over time. Permeability is less of a problem with sandy soils so they will tolerate irrigation water with a SAR of nine or greater.

Management options - sodium hazard. High sodium irrigation water can be blended with water of lower sodium content in a reservoir or mixing chamber as described earlier. Overcoming sodium hazards from poor water quality, however, usually requires additional management considerations.

Gypsum (calcium sulfate) can be applied to soils low in calcium to increase the amount of calcium directly. Sulfur or sulfur containing materials are applied to soils high in calcium to make the calcium more soluble and lower the SAR. Once present in the soil and available, calcium replaces sodium on clay and organic matter particles thus preventing deflocculation. Excess sodium is flushed from the root system by periodic leaching. Regular and frequent aerification of turfgrass also helps to combat sodium hazard.

Bicarbonate concentration

Some irrigation water in the West, Southwest, and from reclaimed sources, can contain high levels of *bicarbonate* (HCO_3^-). Bicarbonate is not directly toxic to plants, but it affects soil permeability and influences pH. High bicarbonate levels can cause iron chlorosis symptoms in landscape plants. The bicarbonate in irrigation water combines with calcium and magnesium to form calcium/magnesium carbonates. Removal of these elements increases the SAR due to the increase in the proportion of Na ions to Ca and Mg.

Management options - bicarbonate. In addition to blending low quality irrigation water, some turfgrass managers inject sulfuric or phosphoric acid into the water. Acid injection, however, requires specialized equipment and precise

Table 9.6.

Potential for chlorine (Cl) damage to landscape species from irrigation water

Concentration		
Milliequivalents per liter (meq/L)	**ppm**	**Potential effect of chlorine on landscape plants**
< 2	< 70	Safe for all plants.
2 - 4	70 - 140	Sensitive species may show injury.
4 - 10	140 - 350	Moderately tolerant species may show injury.
> 10	> 350	May result in severe problems.

Adapted from Irrigation Water Quality Criteria, 2001, Colorado State Coop. Ext. Pub. 506.

measurements. Acid injection is used when levels of bicarbonate in the water are very high and drastic measures are required.

Gypsum is applied to sites with low soil calcium, and sulfur or sulfur-containing materials are applied to soils with higher calcium levels. Use of acidifying fertilizers in normal landscape and turfgrass management is advisable.

Toxic elements

Sodium (Na), chlorine (Cl) and Boron (B) are the most common *toxic elements* in irrigation water of concern to landscape managers. Like sodium, boron and chlorine from marginal irrigation sources can accumulate to toxic levels in the soil and cause injury to sensitive plants.

Chlorine is not particularly toxic to turfgrasses, but many landscape species are sensitive. Sodium and chloride concentrations are particularly important if irrigation is supplied by a sprinkler. Plants absorb both ions through the foliage. Toxicity due to foliage absorption occurs at lower concentrations than through soil absorption, especially under high evapotranspiration. All three ions result in leaf chlorosis and marginal necrosis (burning). Boron toxicity symptoms may also appear as small black spots near the leaf margin. There is little help available to develop a list of tolerant landscape species.

Water high in chlorides reduces phosphorous availability to plants and can reduce the concentration of organic acids in plants. Boron is often a problem in reclaimed irrigation water and can be a problem for grasses, as well as a broad host of landscape species.

Some reclaimed water may contain heavy metals (copper, nickel, zinc, or cadmium). It has been recommended that irrigation water contain no more than:

0.01 ppm cadmium;

0.2 ppm copper;

0.2 ppm nickel; or

2.0 ppm zinc.

Table 9.7.

Potential for boron (B) damage to landscape species from irrigation water.

Concentration (ppm)	Potential effect of boron on landscape plants
< 0.5	Safe for all plants.
0.5-1.0	Sensitive species may show injury.
1.0-2.0	Use for only moderately tolerant species.
2.0-4.0	Use only for tolerant species.

Adapted from Irrigation Water Quality Criteria, 2001, Colorado State Coop. Ext. Pub. 506.

Most reclaimed water receiving secondary treatment meets these standards.

Management options - toxic ions. If toxic ions are present in the source water, then it can be blended with better quality water to reduce their concentration. Irrigating more frequently also dilutes the ions in the soil solution and helps to leach them out of the root zone. Periodic leaching by adding additional water helps flush the ions out of the root zone, but boron is difficult to leach.

Nutrient content

Reclaimed water and treated effluent contain variable amounts of plant nutrients, depending on the source. Nitrogen, phosphorus, sulfur, and potassium are the primary nutrients in reclaimed water and all are beneficial to turf and landscape plants. The economic value of these nutrients can be substantial to managers of large turf areas.

Even if the nutrient quantities in reclaimed water are low, they are applied on a regular basis and used efficiently by turfgrass and landscape plants. Published reports indicate that turf and other landscape plants may obtain all or most of their required phosphorus and potassium from regular irrigation with some reclaimed sources. A large part of the nitrogen requirement can also be met from reclaimed irrigation water. Most reclaimed or treated effluent sources contain sufficient micronutrients for landscape plant needs. Managers using irrigation water containing plant nutrients should deliberately reduce the amount of nitrogen applied through fertilization.

Irrigation with Nonpotable Water

Many new large turfgrass sites and some landscapes have the opportunity, or may be required, to irrigate with gray water, treated effluent, reuse, wastewater, reclaimed/recycled water, or other reduced quality sources of water. Nonpotable (not drinkable) irrigation sources are especially important in chronically water poor areas. Nonpotable water has been used in California and Arizona for decades. Municipalities often offer carrots to landscape managers to switch to treated

---

Table 9.8.
Approved landscape uses of recycled water in California

The State of California and California landscape contractors have the greatest experience and some of the most stringent rules governing use of recycled water in landscapes.

Definitions for table:
Disinfected tertiary recycled water: near drinkable; all bacteria, viruses and other organisms have been killed.
Disinfected secondary recycled-2.2 water: one step below the above; 2.2 bacteria per 100 ml.
Disinfected secondary recycled-23 water: slightly less chlorine used, thus slightly more bacteria present.
Undisinfected secondary recycled water: cleaned, but not disinfected.

Use	Disinfected tertiary recycled water	Disinfected secondary recycled-2.2 water	Disinfected secondary recycled-23 water	Undisinfected secondary recycled water
Decorative fountains	Allowed	Not allowed	Not allowed	Not allowed
Parks and playgrounds	Allowed	Not allowed	Not allowed	Not allowed
School yards	Allowed	Not allowed	Not allowed	Not allowed
Residential landscapes	Allowed	Not allowed	Not allowed	Not allowed
Unrestricted access golf courses	Allowed	Not allowed	Not allowed	Not allowed
Restricted access golf courses	Allowed	Allowed	Allowed	Not allowed
Restricted recreational lakes and ponds	Allowed	Allowed	Not allowed	Not allowed
Highway landscapes	Allowed	Allowed	Allowed	Not allowed
Cemeteries	Allowed	Allowed	Allowed	Not allowed
Landscape lakes and ponds	Allowed	Allowed	Allowed	Not allowed
Cleaning roads/sidewalks	Allowed	Allowed	Allowed	Not allowed

Adapted from WaterReuse Association of California, March 1997.

effluent or recycled water. The water is often provided free or at a substantial discount. Texas allows for county property tax exemptions for improvements made to commercial and residential landscape systems so they can handle treated effluent.

Irrigation system and management factors. Using lower quality irrigation water requires adjustments to irrigation and turf/landscape management.

Irrigation system design requires special considerations if low quality or recycled irrigation sources are planned. Application uniformity is critical to minimize wet and dry areas. Designers sometimes use fewer irrigation heads per zone when planning for nonpotable sources. Low volume heads are appropriate, and it is critical that application rate match soil infiltration rates. Irrigation times with nonpotable water may also be restricted. Using nonpotable water mandates reliable backflow prevention devices.

Irrigation with recycled water or treated effluent through sub-surface irrigation is sometimes desirable. Neighbors do not see water dispersal and chances of wind-driven drift are eliminated.

Differences in the actual irrigation systems using effluent are minor compared to those using drinkable water. The color of the pipe, the heads and other parts of the system is different, usually purple, to denote that the system is nonpotable. Posting of warning signs is typically required.

Drought stress occurs at higher soil moisture as water quality declines because the salts increase the osmotic potential. When using poor-quality water, increase irrigation frequency to maintain a moist soil. As the soil dries, the salts in the soil solution concentrate, and plant damage is more likely to occur.

Some effluent is treated with very high rates of chlorine, often five to 10 times that of drinking water. This can result in damage to brass and some plastic valves. Valves, emitters and nozzles will require regular cleaning.

Basin irrigation

Water can be applied to basins constructed around individual plants, beds, or entire land-scapes, by fixed bubblers, hoses, or tanks. The area must be reasonably flat. Infiltration characteristics of the soil must be such that the water moves into the root zone before it evaporates. Basin irrigation is used for newly planted trees in many places, and entire landscapes in the Southwest. Mulches reduce evaporation between waterings.

Sprinkler Irrigation

Sprinklers are the most common method of applying water to landscape turfgrass and plantings. The uniformity and effectiveness of the system depend upon its design and installation. Irrigation system design must accommodate varying water pressures, wind conditions, and topography. Soil type, infiltration rates, and soil covering determine application rates. Some estimate that conventional spray heads are only 55 to 65 percent efficient. Proper design, installation, and maintenance, determine the utility of the system and the quality of the landscape. Irrigation design and installation professions are licensed or certified in many states, and for good reason.

When designing and operating an irrigation system for turfgrass, ensure that woody and herbaceous ornamentals will not be over-watered. Turfgrass will be irrigated more frequently than woody ornamentals. Woody and herbaceous beds should be zoned for separate control. The plant beds should be constructed so water from the turf area does not drain into them.

Automated systems that water for set periods on given days are particularly useful where site or soil conditions limit infiltration or on contracted

Photo 9.6. Basin irrigation for a street tree planting.

Table 9.9.

Common sprinkler irrigation mistakes and problems

Here are some common problems, in no particular order, to watch out for when evaluating a new contract or taking over management of a site. Many of these are easy and inexpensive to remedy.

- Different types of irrigation heads (rotors, sprays, bubblers, or drip) operating on the same irrigation zone. This results in differential and non-uniform wetting.
- Rotor or spray heads that do not have head-to-head coverage. Areas between heads do not receive adequate water and become noticeable under stress.
- Shrub beds and planter boxes irrigated for the same time as turf areas. Shrubs and planters require different amounts of water at different intervals than turf, and will suffer if irrigated with the same frequency and amount.
- Over-spray of walks, streets and drives because of improper adjustment or alignment of spray, impact, or rotor heads.
- Impact or spray heads on risers within six feet of areas where people will be. Fixed risers around walks, paths, drives, and play areas drastically increase the potential for accidents and liability.
- Systems without rain shut-offs. These inexpensive devices increase irrigation efficiency by 10 to 15 percent by turning the system off during rain.

properties. Adding *rain sensors* that prevent operation of, or turn off the irrigation system in the event of rain, further sophisticate automated systems. Other refinements include the addition of *freeze sensor*s that prevent operation when the outside temperature is below a set point (e.g., 45° F.). Some landscape supervisors still prefer to control the rate and frequency of water application manually.

Irrigation can be initiated by tensiometers, as discussed earlier. Using tensiometers increases moisture conservation and makes the system more responsive to soil moisture levels. Computer controlled systems are available and can give managers precise control, especially when coupled with measurement of environmental parameters.

The landscape manager or contractor must *control the irrigation scheduling*. The quality and pace of other landscape operations, such as mowing, are in large part established by the irrigation schedule.

Drip or Trickle Systems

Drip or trickle irrigation has become a popular and practical addition to landscape sites, especially in areas where water conservation is paramount. Relatively new technology to many landscape contractors, drip irrigation was used in the

Photo 9.7. and photo 9.8. Sprinklers are the most common type of irrigation for managed turfgrass and landscapes. Images provided courtesy of Rain Bird Corporation.

Table 9.10.
Advantages to drip irrigation

- **Water conservation** – savings can range from 10 to 60 percent of sprinkler system.
- **Unlimited operating hours** - no need to worry about spraying passersby or over spray.
- **Efficiency** – require less water than sprinkler systems, unaffected by wind or water evaporation issues, operate at low pressures, and soil erosion not a problem.
- **Cost** – less than sprinkler irrigation for plant beds according to many designers.

Hanging Gardens of Babylon where porous containers were hung over the garden to slowly drip over time. Drip irrigation was re-discovered and refined in Israel and adapted to cropping in that arid climate. Drip irrigation was first adapted to landscapes in the West and Southwest and has become a mainstay for landscape managers.

Drip irrigation applies water slowly for long periods to only a portion of the root zone. Drip irrigation operates at very low pressures, (10 to 50 pounds per square inch (psi)). It allows for precise, controlled applications of water that save water and labor, and produce quality plant growth.

Several different delivery systems are available.

- *Drip tapes* or *drip lines* are thin-walled polyethylene, or similar material, hoses with periodic holes (every 12 inches more or less) for water to drip or ooze out. Drip tapes and lines are primarily used in vegetable production, but have application in annual and perennial flowers or groundcovers beds. The tapes are more applicable to trees and shrubs in nursery rows than to woody landscape plantings.

- *Line source* systems disperse water all along its length. Soaker hoses are line source systems. Drip irrigated groundcovers often use line-source irrigation products.

- Most commonly, landscape drip irrigation systems deliver water via *emitters* inserted in the lateral or on the end of small plastic tubes. Emitters can be selected to apply water at rates as low as 0.5 gallons per hour (gph) and up to two or more gph. The number of and volume of emitters that serve an individual plant can be adjusted as its water needs increase with the season and growth.

Drip irrigation requires a good filtration system to reduce maintenance and ensure proper operation. Pressure regulating valves or pressure

Photo 9.9. Drip lines have periodic holes (every 12 inches, more or less) for water to drip or ooze out. Drip lines are primarily used in vegetable production, but have application in annual and perennial flowers or groundcovers beds. Image provided courtesy of Irrometer Company Inc., Riverside, CA

Photo 9.10. Drip irrigation emitter. Image provided courtesy of Rain Bird Corporation.

compensating emitters will be necessary. A drip system can be automated with timers, tensiometers, and other moisture sensors. Drip can be added as part of an overall site irrigation plan. Design and installation information for trickle irrigation is widely available from manufacturers and other sources.

Drip systems dramatically increase water conservation and supply the plant with a more constant moisture level compared to overhead systems. The cost of drip irrigation systems is often less than that of a sprinkler system, and drip systems offer greater flexibility. A Northern California landscape architect estimated sprinkler systems installation at $.90 to $1.25 per square foot (1990 dollars) and installation cost for drip system was estimated at $.60 to $.75 per square foot.

Laterals and emitters can be added or removed as necessary. Laterals and main lines can be buried and concealed, and emitters can be buried if necessary for aesthetics. Operation of the system is more difficult to monitor if the emitter discharge is underground. Above ground systems are subject to vandalism, fire, and chewing by animals.

The most common problem for drip irrigation is plugging of lines or emitters by soil particles, water deposits, bacterial slimes, and algae. Drip systems are more difficult to monitor since there is no spray; each emitter much be checked individually. Self-cleaning emitters are available, but more expensive. These emitters require less maintenance, but are not foolproof.

Clogging by mineral deposits from the water or algae can be compensated for by acid and chlorine injection. Cleaning emitters and periodically flushing the system are simpler and less expensive solutions, according to some managers. Other common mistakes with drip irrigation include failure to install adequate numbers of emitters per plant or locating them too close to tree trunks.

Drip systems are sometimes considered temporary irrigation systems, except in confined areas. The plant's water requirements need not eventually outgrow the potential supply with good planning and provisions for expansion. The number of emitters can be increased and the emitters changed to a higher volume discharge as plants grow and their needs increase. Research has indicated that 50 to 65 percent of the plant's root system needs to be wetted to supply adequate mois-

Photo 9.11. Conventional irrigation for shrub beds can be converted to drip irrigation. The device above replaces a spray head; the lines go to drip emitters or micro-sprays. Image provided courtesy of Rain Bird Corporation.

ture. Dr. Jimmy Tipton, University of Arizona, effectively irrigated mature trees with drip irrigation.

Many irrigation manufacturers have developed equipment to allow conversion of spray systems to drip. Devices can be attached to risers in shrub beds that reduce pressure and separate flow of water into individual drip lines.

Microsprays

Mini-sprinklers, or *microsprays*, are the low volume likeness of overhead sprinkler irrigation. Water is applied slowly - typical flow rates range from four to 10 gph - and uniformly to the root zone as with drip irrigation. The wetted zone, however, is expanded by the sprinklers to a more practical range for landscape applications. The wetting diameter ranges from six inches to 25 feet. Microsprays allow coverage of larger areas with few emitters while still reaping the benefits of other low volume systems.

The shape of the zone can be circular or angular. The heads are placed on plastic risers of varying length and connected to the lateral by ¼-inch tubing. Microsprinklers are now available in retractable models, much like conventional spray heads. Adapters are also available to retrofit most manufacturer spray heads to a microspray. Microsprays can be easily repositioned as plants grow and they are easily removed for replanting or at season's end.

These small sprinklers have been quite successful in flower beds, where faster application rate is necessary to maintain healthy plants during warmer months. They also have utility for landscape beds and groundcovers but are not generally acceptable for use in turfgrass. They work well near pedestrian ways, in median strips, and in other locations where over-spray and run-off are undesirable.

Sub-surface Irrigation

Sub-surface drip irrigation has been evolving for the past 20 or so years and is finding broader audiences and applications. Irrigating turfgrass, groundcovers, or shrub beds underground eliminates problems associated with wind and over spray and maximizes water use efficiency. It has also proven to be an ideal way to irrigate with recycled water in sensitive areas.

Sub-surface irrigation systems depend on capillary action to bring water from discharge points to plant roots. Distribution of an underground irrigation supply is severely limited by soil texture, structure, compaction, and water quality. Because of the dependence on capillarity, the depth and distance between underground drip systems is critical. The new generation of subsurface irrigation techniques and products has proven to be effective.

General Landscape Irrigation Recommendations

A single, all encompassing irrigation schedule cannot be specified because of vast differences in sites, soils, turf and landscape species, management practices, growing season, climate, and requirements of the client. Careful irrigation scheduling, however, is critical for turfgrass and landscape quality.

The worst possible irrigation program is to water turf or a landscape bed daily for five to 10 minutes. Regular, frequent, shallow irrigation of established turf causes the grass plants to be shallow rooted. Shrubs and trees receiving inadequate amounts of water are trained to develop surface roots. Deep, infrequent watering encourages the growth of deep roots, making plants more drought tolerant. It also lessens the likelihood of salt buildup.

Photo 9.12. Mini-sprinklers are the low volume equivalent of overhead sprinkler irrigation. These small sprinklers have been quite successful in color, groundcover, and shrub beds, where faster application rate is necessary to maintain healthy plants during warmer months. Image provided courtesy of Rain Bird Corporation.

Photo 9.13. Irrigating turfgrass, groundcovers, or shrub beds with a subsurface irrigation system eliminates problems associated with wind and overspray and maximizes water use efficiency. Subsurface irrigation is an excellent way to irrigate with recycled water in sensitive areas. Image provided courtesy of Rain Bird Corporation.

If rainfall or irrigation for turf or landscape plantings for the week is less than one inch under normal conditions, consider applying water to bring the total for the week to one inch. If rainfall is an inch or more, irrigation may not be needed that week. More water is required for rapidly draining soils and during environmental extremes. Apply enough water to soak the soil to a depth of six to eight inches or more but do not over-water.

Apply irrigation at a rate that minimizes run-off. Determine the maximum amount of water that can be applied before run-off occurs and calculate the appropriate run time for the automatic irrigation controller for each zone. Water *more frequently* if the soil type texture is coarse, for south- or west-facing slopes, plantings on berms or mounds, where competition for water is severe, in areas bordering pavement, and those newly planted or intensely managed landscapes. If the soil is poorly drained or heavy clay, water *less frequently*.

Photo 9.14. Portable irrigation systems increase water efficiency where underground systems are unavailable. Traveling irrigation systems are effective for large turf sites and athletic fields.

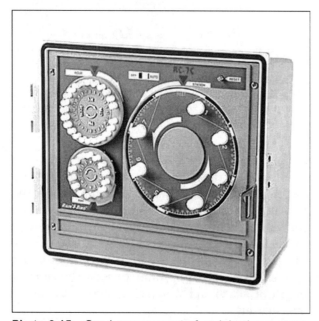

Photo 9.15. Good management of an irrigation program means that controller is regularly adjusted to reflect changes in the season, weather conditions, plant growth, and to compensate for soil factors. Image provided courtesy of Rain Bird Corporation

Monitor the soil water supply and irrigate based upon actual need. This requires use of tensiometers or other sensors. When scheduling irrigation for mixed plantings, water to meet the needs of the least tolerant species. If the surrounding lawn or landscape is irrigated regularly, trees will not need additional water. Established trees have extensive root systems that harvest water from a large area. Most established trees have deep roots that can obtain enough moisture without additional irrigation. They are able to tolerate less frequent applications of water and some drought with no visual or growth effects.

Sprinklers are best used early in the morning. Water pressure is greater, there is minimal wind, operation will not interfere with other site activities, and the foliage dries quickly. Evaporation in hot, windy areas is reduced.

Newly planted material must be watered more frequently because of its smaller root zone. The sole source of water for container-grown plants is limited to the container soil until new roots grow into the surrounding soil. Newly planted container-grown plants require frequent monitoring and irrigation.

Design or amend the irrigation system to reflect the exposure and microclimate of the plants (north versus south sites, sun versus shade, and wind). This may mean entirely different irrigation equipment in some sections of the landscape and many more separate controls.

Schedule regular system inspections. Overhead systems should be checked weekly, preferably right after mowing. Inspect and clean filters frequently, especially if the system uses nonpotable water. Flush drip lines twice per year. Inspections and repairs will be discussed in detail later.

If the landscape is irrigated with hoses and portable sprinklers, variations in the distribution pattern are minimized if settings are made so they are equal to the radius covered by the sprinkler. This produces an overlapping pattern similar to that used in in-ground systems.

Irrigation System Maintenance

Irrigation installation and maintenance are two of the fastest growing services for the landscape industry. Most full-service landscape man-

Table 9.11.

Revenue from irrigation services for landscape firms

Irrigation system installation and maintenance are profit centers for many landscape management firms. Ninety-eight percent of the firms surveyed performed installation and all maintained irrigation systems. Irrigation design largely remains a service of landscape architects and designers.

	Percent of landscape firms responding to survey		
	Irrigation Services		
Percent of revenue	Design	Installation	Maintenance
0	68	2	0
1-20	31	9	30
21-40	1	13	32
41-60	0	31	19
61-80	0	31	9
81-100	0	14	10

Data adapted from Lawn and Landscape, 2001. 22(10):l2.

agement contractors offer irrigation system checks and repairs as part of their service. Irrigation can also add a new dimension to the company. Quality service is an excellent way to obtain consideration for later installation contracts by the same client or general contractor.

Irrigation system checks and evaluations are usually billed as a flat-fee or fixed-fee. Irrigation checks or monitoring may be conducted weekly, bi-weekly, or monthly, depending on the client, and the budget. The frequency of inspections and the amount of service depend on the age of the system, how well it was designed and installed, its level of use, and traffic.

If the contractor is using a production rate estimating system, then irrigation labor is billed at a higher rate than general labor. The higher rate is because of the expertise required by irrigation technicians and cost of inventory and equipment necessary. Irrigation technicians require licensing or certification in some areas.

Irrigation maintenance and service require knowledge of irrigation equipment, installation, and troubleshooting. An inventory of irrigation products and parts is necessary. Special equipment required includes a voltage meter, wire tracer, and a small manual pump. Trenchers can be rented or leased. Licenses and permits may also be required. Licensed electricians are sometimes required to install or repair low voltage controller wiring.

Most distributors conduct seminars on basic irrigation design, installation, marketing, and service. Videos are available for training or refresher programs. Irrigation distributors are a valuable source of information and knowledge.

Irrigation system evaluation

The most common maintenance procedure is what is termed a *check*, or *walk-through*, while the system is operating. Set the controller to a minimum time (two, three, or five minutes) per zone so that the system can be checked efficiently. Some systems have remote control devices that advance the controller and speed the procedure. Emitters of drip irrigation systems are checked to make sure they are not plugged; the filter should also be checked and cleaned as necessary.

Irrigation servicing adjusts irrigation programs and station times as necessary. All regions of the country operate with a spring, summer, and fall schedule reflecting plant water requirements. The number of days of operation and the run time increase as water needs increase during the summer. Winter irrigation is done in the Deep South, Southwest, California, and Hawaii.

Schedule a walk through following mowing to catch any damage from the machinery. Commercial irrigation systems should be checked at least every other week. Since commercial sites are often irrigated at night, problems may go unnoticed. Residential systems require the least maintenance

Table 9.12.
Irrigation system maintenance checklist

Controller

✓ **Physical Inspection**
- *Wiring* should be neatly routed and properly connected.
- *Cabinet* – Check door seal, clean up debris, and seal openings.
- Replace *battery* per manufacturer's recommendation.
- *Check program timer* for accuracy (day/date, and time), this is the number one source of problems for automatic systems.
- *Check advanced settings:*
  - Rain sensor override or bypass.
  - Event day on/off.
  - Program cycles.
- *Check common wires.*
- *Check grounding.* Earth ground should be 5 ohms or less.
- *Check rain sensor.* Clean and adjust external sensor and enable controller to react to the sensor.

✓ **System Test**
- *Run each station* with a test program or a remote control unit to manually activate each station.
- *If a zone fails to activate:*
  - *Check supply line.* Is the water turned on? Bleed the valve to see if line is pressurized.
  - *Check field wires.*
    - A good circuit will have 20-60 ohms of resistance with power off.
      - Remove common wire before testing resistance.
  - *Check valve.*
    - If valve is receiving power, check internal exhaust port for blockage.
    - Replace diaphragm assembly if necessary.

✓ **Check Spray Heads**
- *Pop up heads* that do not pop up or operate poorly may be the result of a broken riser or fitting.
- *Spray arc* should be uniform to prevent dry spots.
  - If not, *clean filter and nozzle* and replace if needed.
- *Check spray radius:*
  - Set to keep water off of buildings, cars, etc.
  - *Misting* is the result of excessive pressure.
    - Adjust flow control on valve or pressure regulator, or change heads to those that will operate under available pressure.
- *Check for obstructions.*
- *Check nozzles* to be sure all in the zone match and replace as necessary.
- *Check rotor heads:*
  - Set *arc and radius* for coverage and avoid over spray on walks, etc.
    - Change heads if excessive adjustment is required.
  - Poor *rotation* of rotor heads often means a clogged filter.

✓ **Drip Irrigation**
- *Clean and flush* drip systems annually
- *Check pressure regulators* for leaks.
- *Check emitters* for flow where possible.

✓ **Lines and laterals**
- *Watch for leaks or breaks in pipe or valves.*

Photo 9.16 and photo 9.17. Regular maintenance of the irrigation system to repair leaks, damaged heads, and to adjust for overspray, is critical to obtain maximum water use and conservation. Photograph by James Robbins.

from the contractor's point of view. Problems are usually spotted and reported by the client. Irrigation systems using marginal water quality or with frequent problems require more frequent cleaning.

Winterization. In the northern states, (usually USDA Zone 7 and north) irrigation systems are *winterized* annually. Systems in more southerly areas, USDA Zones 8 and 9 (minimum temperatures 10 to 30° F) require freeze sensors and draining pumps and above-ground components. Zone 10 and warmer do not require winterizing. They will have a winter watering schedule.

The water in the system is evacuated with pressure for full winterization. Tow-behind air compressors can be rented in most localities. Adequate air volume and proper air pressure are important. The recommended minimum air compressor volume is 60 cubic feet per minute (CFM) for the average residential system and 125 CFM for larger commercial systems with two-inch mains. For systems with four-inch or larger pipe, use a 250 CFM compressor. It requires a lot of air to push out a large column of water. Undersized compressors will not provide enough air to completely blow out a large system. Blow the system out with 60 to 80 psi; higher pressures can damage the piping and equipment.

Shut off the irrigation supply valve before blowing the system. Always have one zone *on* while the compressor is operating. Slowly introduce air to the system to prevent water hammer that can damage the irrigation system or its com-

ponents. Air is compressible and can build up pressure sufficient to cause many problems if not handled correctly.

Activate the zone furthest from the water source and continue to run through the zones until the water from the sprinklers is a fine mist. On average, this will take about five minutes per zone. Flush each zone twice.

In addition to blowing out the system, shut it off, unplug the controller, and remove the battery. If the controller is located outside or installed in a moist area, it may be advisable to leave the controller plugged-in. The heat generated by the transformer helps keep the cabinet dry. Set all watering times to zero. Remove or inactivate any sensors.

The average residential system will require 30 to 45 minutes to winterize. Large commercial systems may require an entire day or longer.

Spring start up. Part of irrigation servicing is turning the irrigation system on every spring. The water supply is turned on and the controller activated. Walk through the system to check for damage to heads during the winter. The system should be re-checked after any major repairs.

Re-set all sprinklers and valve boxes to the proper grade. Check the controller, batteries and fuses, reset contacts, and clean the controller box. Check the backflow preventer connections and make sure rain shut-offs and other sensors are operating.

195

Water Conservation

Although estimates vary, outdoor water use for managed landscapes can account for as much as 50 percent of household water use. The percentage jumps even higher in Southern California, Arizona, New Mexico, Utah, Texas, Nevada, and Florida. Many governing agencies and water authorities view irrigation systems as water wasters. Water rates will continue to increase and impact landscape budgets and the public. Conservation of water by the green industry cannot wait. Water supply, quality, and use have become critical throughout the nation. There is a flurry of interest in new products that promise assistance in conserving water, whether they work or not. Western states have become leaders in realistic water conservation. The rest of the nation must learn from their efforts to conserve this limited, precious, and increasingly expensive resource.

General techniques to conserve water

The better the design, installation, and continued management of the landscape and irrigation system, the more efficient the water use. The average residence with a well-managed automatic irrigation system will use 40 to 60 percent less water than one with an average manual watering system.

When watering, water well and infrequently. Try to fill the entire root zone profile, whether the target is turfgrass or trees, but do not overwater. Light frequent waterings encourage shallow rooting and greater water stress later.

One school of thought suggests mowing as low as the particular turf will handle during seasonal water stress. This supposedly reduces the transpiring leaf surface. Another school points out that low mowing of turf encourages shallow rooting. They correctly suggest raising the mowing height for cool-season grasses during the summer. Higher mowing heights increase rooting depth and water reserve. The taller grass blades shade the soil and reduce evaporation.

Zone irrigation systems according to sun, shade, turf, and plant areas. Though more costly, the practice allows separate control of watering and increased efficiency. Use automatic irrigation controllers with sensors that shut off during natural rain. New Jersey, Minnesota, and Florida require use of rain shut-offs on all new irrigation systems. Water between midnight and 8:00 am when water loss through evaporation is lowest.

Xeriscapes

Nowhere is the emphasis on water conservation as critical as it is in the West and the Southwest. Mandatory conservation programs are often controversial, hard to implement, and often rejected by the public. Out of this concern, the *Xeriscape* concept was initiated by the Denver Water Department in 1981. Xeriscape™ is a coined and trademarked word combining the Latin *xeri-*, for dry, and *scape*, from landscape. Xeriscape has come to represent a positive, creative approach for water conservation without the sacrifice of beauty.

Xeriscape concepts include and build upon: *Education* of the public in water conserving measures; *Demonstration* of water conservation principles; and *Cooperation* between industry, citizens, and government. Currently xeriscape programs are being promoted in Arizona, California, Colorado, Florida, Georgia, Hawaii, Kansas, Oklahoma, Texas and several other states. Training programs have been directed to the public and green industry professionals. Several botanic gardens and municipalities have initiated demonstration projects. These numbers will grow as the concept gains further attention, legitimacy supported by research, and acceptance from landscape designers, architects, nurserymen, and landscape managers.

Photo 9.18. Water conservation landscapes demonstrating low water-use plants and irrigation technology are popular additions to botanic gardens, arboretums, and for water department landscapes. Greater numbers of residential and commercial landscapes are adapting water conservation techniques. Photograph courtesy of James Robbins.

The basic premise behind the concept is to save water. Water savings between 30 and 60 percent can be achieved by implementing Xeriscape elements without sacrifice of landscape aesthetics.

The Xeriscape program has not developed any new or novel approaches to water conservation. Many current landscape norms in semi-arid regions have been adapted. Most Xeriscape concepts are solid, age-old horticultural principles that, when combined, provide maximum water savings. The real solution to water conservation requires much more than just a plant list, and Xeriscape has provided a positive forum for change.

Xeriscape is based upon seven elements or water conservation guidelines: 1) follow good design principles; 2) appropriate use of turf; 3) efficient irrigation; 4) soil improvements; 5) mulches; 6) lower water-demand plants; and 7) appropriate maintenance.

Proper design and planning. Planning is the most important step in creative water conservation. The planning process is no different from that of conventional landscapes. Designers consider the activity and desires of the owner, the site, and use design principles to develop a final concept. Special note is made of microclimates and the design takes advantage of these features. The time and capital expenditures for installation and maintenance are thoroughly considered and reflected in the final plan.

Mixing plants of different water needs is the most water inefficient way to design any landscape. Too many people, including landscape professionals, feel that if they use low-water demand plants among other ornamentals in the landscape,

then they will reduce the need to irrigate. (Wouldn't it be nice?) The landscape bed is irrigated to meet the needs of the least drought tolerant species included in the composition. If mixed with conventional water-use plants, there is no savings realized from drought-resistant species. They may even suffer from over-watering.

Hydrozoning is the key to water conservation. Hydrozoning groups plants according to their water needs or irrigation scheduling preferences. The plantings can be irrigated effectively and efficiently.

A water efficient landscape does not require that all plants be drought tolerant. High-water use plants are efficiently used in a water conserving landscape by grouping them together in high visual impact areas and managing them appropriately. Higher water use plants are used in high visibility, high impact, or critical areas where the increased use of water is justified.

Medium-water use plants should likewise be grouped together so they may be irrigated efficiently. Low-water use plants can be used in appropriate areas. Low-water use plants may be very effective as screens and barriers, and in lower-management areas. Many drought tolerant plants offer outstanding aesthetic attributes and warrant use as specimens or accents. Low water-use species should be grouped together so that irrigation can be reduced drastically.

Appropriate use of turf. The majority of the water used to support a traditional landscape goes to sustain the *turf*. Recommendations to eliminate or limit turf to conserve water have sparked controversy. Some municipalities have restricted

---

Table 9.13.
Examples of hydrozones for water conserving landscapes

Designers and managers in Denver work with three defined *water zones* or *hydrozones* to develop water-conserving landscapes. The following zones are the amounts of water, in inches of water, required for a sandy loam soil in midsummer during a rainless period.

- ***High-water use zone***: Area uses 18 to 20 gallons of water per square foot for a 20-week growing season. Without rainfall, apply 0.5-inch of water three times per week.
- ***Moderate-water use zone***: Area uses approximately 10 gallons of water per square foot through a 20-week growing season. Without rainfall, the plants require 0.75-inch of water once a week.
- ***Low-water use zone***: Area uses 3 gallons or less water per square foot during a 20-week growing season. Without rainfall, irrigate with 0.5-inch of water every other week.

use of turf and encouraged specific turfgrasses in new landscapes. Turf can be managed to reduce its water requirements without reducing its quality through proper selection, irrigation techniques and scheduling, and proper management. Many woody plants actually use more water than turfgrasses.

Turfgrass has a definite and important place in commercial and residential landscapes. Base selection and management of grass on sound scientific and design strategies. Locate grass where it provides functional benefits. Turfgrass is used for recreation and entertainment. In some areas, however, turf serves no function and little purpose, except to be maintained. In these instances, grass could be replaced with less water demanding materials such as groundcovers, low water-use plants, a meadow, mulch, or hard surface.

Select appropriate low water use turfgrasses for moderate- and low-irrigation landscapes. Studies have quantified the water use rates of most turfgrasses. There are significant differences in water use rates between turf species. Bermudagrass possesses significantly more drought tolerance than bluegrass, for instance. There are also wide differences in drought tolerance and resistance among commercially available cultivars within a grass species. Consult the local Cooperative Extension Service for regionally specific recommendations.

Efficient irrigation. If *irrigation* is to be installed, then design water saving measures into the system. Design the system to accommodate the microclimates. Northern and eastern exposures require less water, while slopes should be irrigated more slowly to reduce run-off. The lawn must be zoned separately from landscape plantings so that both can be irrigated individually and efficiently. Drip irrigation aids water conservation in shrub and tree plantings, but it is not a cure-all for conserving water.

Monitoring and managing the irrigation system properly reduces water use from 10 to 25 percent. Monitor and independently schedule different water-use zones of the landscape. Zone high demand areas and other plantings separately from low water demand areas. Check irrigation systems to eliminate leakage from damaged heads, excessive overlap, overthrow onto hard surfaces, and clogged emitters.

Photo 9.19. Rain sensors turn off the irrigation system during precipitation and save water. They can also save irrate calls from the client. Rain sensors are required by law on irrigation systems in some cities. Image provided courtesy of Rain Bird Corporation.

Apply water according to need of the individual plant zones, not according to a rigid schedule or time clock. Monitoring the water needs of the plants and irrigating manually, or on the basis of soil moisture measuring devices, saves a great deal of water. Deep infrequent waterings encourage deep roots and drought tolerance.

Soil improvement. *Soil improvement* before planting improves water infiltration and retention. The exact nature of amendments, if necessary, depends on the site. Soil structure and aggregation are the keys to proper soil water relations. Organic matter has the greatest positive effect on soil structure, aggregation, and water holding capacity, of any amendment that can be incorporated into the soil or planting bed. Ignore the claims of the magic powders.

Mulches. *Mulches* reduce water loss by reducing evaporation. In addition, mulches reduce weed competition, slow erosion, and regulate soil temperatures. Mulches are also aesthetically pleasing. Mulch material may be either organic (bark and wood chips) or inorganic (rocks and gravel). Either type of mulch should be applied to a depth of three to four inches. Organic mulches improve soil structure over time, but will require periodic replenishment as they decompose. Inorganic mulches do not decompose, but will require periodic raking and refreshing.

However, excessive layers (over six inches) of organic mulch on a bed may result in anaerobic decomposition of the material. The products of anaerobic respiration are alcohols and aldehydes; both are harmful to plant roots. The greatest problems occur when too much mulch is applied to soggy sites, or where there is an overabundance of irrigation. The problem is alleviated with careful management.

Low water-demand plants. Using plants with reduced water requirements is typically the first reaction to water conservation; but they are only one tool in the box. Research in Colorado, California, Arizona, and elsewhere has identified many low water-use plants.

Few trees and shrubs, however, have actually been quantitatively assessed for water-use rates. Many low-water use plant lists have assumed that plants capable of surviving in arid regions are low water users. The physiological mechanisms by which plants control water-use rates and resist drought vary considerably among and within species. Many arid area plants are actually water spenders and compensate for losing large amounts of water with extensive root systems. Individual selection must consider site-specific conditions, the intent of the design, and aesthetics. Future research will further quantify water use rates by plants under landscape conditions.

Unique tags to bring low water use plants to the consumer's attention have resulted from combined efforts between garden centers, nursery trade associations, water conservation groups, and other marketing organizations. The number of drought tolerant species available for landscape use is increasing as they gain popularity and acceptance.

Appropriate maintenance. Correct landscape management techniques and timing are important to maintain the water conservation features of a landscape. Proper fertilization, pest control, pruning, and irrigation system maintenance, enhance water conservation. A well-designed, well-managed, water-conserving landscape consisting of well-adapted plants can reduce maintenance by up to 50 percent or more.

Other management factors must reflect the water conservation mode of the landscape. Reduce nitrogen rates of turf and woody plants. High fertilization rates result in excessive turf and woody plant growth that cannot be supported by the water budget. Mow at a somewhat higher cut. Be diligent in mulching beds and controlling weeds.

Antitranspirants

Antitranspirants, or antidesiccants, are chemicals that reduce transpiration. Although antitranspirants are most useful at transplanting, they have been used to reduce water requirements and plant loss during drought. Antitranspirants have also been applied to reduce irrigation in semi-arid areas, protect from aerial salt damage, and to protect conifers from winter burn with varying success. Film-forming materials have been around since the early 1960s. Antitranspirants may reduce transpiration by:

1. *Film Coverings*. Film-forming wax, latex, or plastic covering sprayed onto leaves block the stomata and thus reduce water loss. Film-forming antitranspirants are the most common types found in the green industry. They are useful as transplant aids.

2. *Reflective Materials*. Application of reflective materials to a plant leaf reduces absorption of light and leaf temperatures, thereby reducing transpiration. Reflective materials are light colored or silvery films. Although effective, the color change may not be acceptable for landscape use. Reflective coverings also reduce photosynthesis and plant growth.

3. *Physiological Means*. Research has sought chemicals that restrict the opening of the stomata without coating the leaf. Some materials identified are potentially environmentally damaging or incredibly expensive. Some day there may be abscisic acid (ABA) derivatives or other materials that reduce plant water loss during excessive stress periods, without affecting growth or breaking the budget.

Film-forming antitranspirants. The effectiveness of the film-forming antidesiccants varies with species, stage of development, and atmospheric conditions. The duration of the reduction in water loss varies with individual products, environmental conditions, application accuracy and coverage, and the amount of new foliage produced after application.

Films, regardless of brand, provide only limited protection. Under the best conditions, the manager can anticipate reduced transpiration from only a few days up to possibly 14 days. Cracks in the film resulting from leaf growth, movement by the wind, incomplete application, expansion of the leaf, and the environment, soon result in near normal water loss rates.

Antitranspirants have been helpful in transplanting plants in full leaf. When transplanting during the off-season, a few days respite from water loss may be critical to the plant's success. Antidesiccants have also reduced water loss during shipping of bareroot nursery plants.

Film-forming materials are sometimes applied to conifers to reduce winter burn or drying. These materials have not shown any consistent practical protection against winter burn in several studies.

Wetting Agents

Wetting agents are surfactants that reduce the attraction of water molecules for each other. This allows the water to spread more evenly over hydrophobic surfaces, to move more rapidly through small pores, and to more effectively cross boundary layers. Wetting agents enhance the ability of water to moisten solid substances; they make water wetter. Wetting agents vary considerably in their effects on different soils. For general use, landscape managers should look for a non-ionic, non-phytotoxic material with high residual activity and a high concentration of active ingredients. Many different wetting agents are available in liquid or granular formulations under several trade names.

Wetting agents have enhanced water penetration through thatch and into soil. Golf courses frequently use these products to combat dry spot on greens. The net result is a more efficient, uniform use of natural or applied water. Run-off is also reduced because of increased infiltration.

Wetting agents are not cure-alls for turf, thatch, or drought problems. Wetting agents do not reduce compaction, do not affect plant water-use rates, and cannot replace basic cultural practices. They are one of several practices available for use in improving water penetration and movement into hydrophobic (water repelling) soils, thatch, and localized dry spots.

Wetting agents are effective in correcting these conditions for one or two weeks after application. They are too expensive for general maintenance use. The majority of soils where turfgrasses are grown are hydrophilic (wettable).

The benefits of wetting agents on normal, wettable soils have not been consistently documented by research. There are few reasons, according to some turfgrass experts, to believe any significant benefits would occur.

Water-Holding Compounds

Hydrophilic gels are known as hydrogels, moisture holding compounds, cross-linked polymers, super-sluppers, and other jargon and trade names. These water-holding materials absorb many times (30 to 1,500 depending on the product) their weight in water and then release it as the environment becomes dry. There are three types of absorbent polymers in the trade. The first is *starch-graft copolymers*. Soil bacteria and fungi rapidly decompose the starch materials. Their life span in the soil varies from a few days to a few months.

Further refinements in absorbent compounds resulted in development of synthetic *cross-linked polyacrylamides* (polyacrylates) and *acrylamide-acrylate co-polymers*. Synthetic polymers usually remain active for one year or more, according to manufacturers. Most of the gels presently being considered for use in agriculture are acrylamide-acrylate co-polymers.

Manufacturers suggest hydrogels may increase available water, improve media aeration, reduce compaction, improve drainage, increase plant survival and growth, enhance germination and survival rates, and provide safer athletic playing surfaces. These properties would be very advantageous in plant production and landscape management. Water-holding compounds are used for gel seeding of vegetable seeds and as packing material for shipping bareroot nursery plants.

Interest in these materials in the landscape industry has waxed and waned during the past 25 plus years since their introduction into the agronomic and horticultural markets. Unfortunately, managers seeking information about the effectiveness of hydrophilic polymers encounter conflicting facts from sales representatives and horticulturists alike. It is up to the manager to digest the available information and make an informed decision. These materials are expensive and present certain advantages and disadvantages.

Research on the use of hydrogels as a media amendment in plant production, landscape, and turfgrass management has increased, but remains conflicting. The studies differ widely in products, plants, procedures, and test conditions. The quality of their performance also varies widely. Results from any given study cannot be universally extrapolated to every plant species, material, or situation.

Incorporation of gels at the manufacturer's suggested rate does sometimes appear to be advantageous in improving plant water status for some species under limited moisture conditions. There is some research indicating that addition of some gel products to container medium has reduced water stress and increased time to wilt. Other plants and reports, however, have shown no advantage; in fact, some indicate damage from use of the materials.

Even though testimonials acclaim the products, no published research I am aware of has indicated any positive effect on plant survival or growth resulting from sprinkling small quantities of hydrogels in the bottom of planting holes, adding them to the planting backfill, or from watering-in the plant with gel containing water. Published research showed no benefit to plant water relations from dipping plants in hydrogel. The gels may cause the roots to cling together, actually reducing the potential water to absorbing area for several days. Researchers at Texas A&M found no statistical difference in soil moisture levels when a hydrophilic polymer was incorporated at 0, 25, 50, 70, or 100 pounds per 1,000 sq. ft.

There remains insufficient information to predict which, or if, plant species may be aided by the use of gels. Similarly, the effect of various environmental conditions on hydrogels is beginning to be published in reliable research journals.

One interesting study evaluated the amount of water actually absorbed by one product [*Soil Science News and Views*, 1989. 10(7):3]. The manufacturer indicated the product could absorb 500 times its weight in water. The maximum amount of distilled water it absorbed after six hours was slightly over 350 percent of its weight. This was less than promoted, but still significant.

The researcher soaked the material in a solution of 0.01 molar $CaCl_2$, which is similar in salt content to an average soil solution. This reduced the amount of water absorbed by 90 percent.

Other studies reported that fertilizer salts and overall salinity of the soil solution dramatically reduced absorption by hydrophilic gels. Divalent ions such as Ca^{++} and Mg^{++} inhibit cross lining and lock the polymer in place, restricting expansion and reducing water absorption by 90 percent. Monovalent ions, K^+ and NH_4^+, reduced hydration of several gels by 80 percent.

The role of hydrophilic gels in turfgrass management has received a great deal of recent interest. Many trade magazine articles have been published about the water conserving and irrigation reducing potential of co-polymer gels. The calculated increase in water stored in the soil by one author was 0.25 inches of water from 320 pounds of soil-incorporated hydrogel. This was equivalent to one day of water for a summer ET for the region. Unfortunately, this increase in water holding was *calculated*, rather than *measured*. A sales representative calculated that it required 1,300 pounds per acre of his product to store water equaling a four-day supply for turfgrass. Again, this publication referred to potential water savings on paper, not in the field.

Research has been less positive. Butler and Fry [*HortScience* 1989. 24(1):79] extrapolated from greenhouse studies that 80x rates (7,000 pounds/A) would be needed to enhance field establishment of tall fescue. Researchers at Colorado State University were unable to reduce irrigation on bluegrass or tall fescue with incorporation of gels into the soil, even at 80 pounds per 1,000 square feet. Karlick (1995) found neither the presence of polymers nor the rate used had any affect on establishment or quality of bermudagrass or tall fescue under adequate or reduced irrigation. Fertilizer ion and salinity concentration of irrigation water and the soil solution would negatively affect water holding capacity of hydrophilic gels in turf.

While hydrophilic gels may have an advantage in a few limited situations, they are not a panacea. Gels cannot substitute for good management. Each manager must determine if these effects are real or truly economical in their situation. Much of the published literature from promoters represents testimonials, rather than hard scientific facts. A glowing testimonial, in most instances, should not be taken as the gospel. *Caveat Emptor.*

Bibliography

1. Anderson, G. 1999. Drip irrigation technology. *Irrigation & Green Industry* 2(5):14.

2. Anonymous. 1989. Water absorbents increase transplant survival. *Lawn & Landscape Maintenance* 10(8):44.

3. Anonymous. 1990. The role of polymers in water management. *Golf and Sports Turf* 6(6):11.

4. Anonymous. 1990. "Micro" irrigation: an alternative low volume watering method. *Lawn & Landscape Maintenance* 11(10):10.

5. Anonymous. 1992. Use wetting agent, cultural procedure to reduce dry spots. *Landscape Manager* 31(11):31.

6. Anonymous. 1992. Trees or turf? *Grounds Maintenance* 27(10):13.

7. Anonymous. 1993. National xeriscape council disbands. *Landscape and Irrigation* 12(6):37.

8. Anonymous. 1993. *Guidelines for the Treatment and Use of Reclaimed Water.* Hawaii State Department of Health Wastewater Branch, Honolulu, HI.

9. Anonymous. 1996. *Managing Lawns and Gardens to Protect Water Quality.* North Carolina State Univ. Coop. Ext. Ser. Pub. AG 439-21.

10. Anonymous. 1997. Research update. *Grounds Maintenance* 32(7):1.

11. Arnold, M., *et al.* 2003. Irrigating landscape bedding plants and cut flowers with recycled nursery runoff and constructed wetland treated water. *Journal of Environmental Horticulture* 21(2):89.

12. Arpin, R., *et al.* 1985. Plant Lists. In: *Mile High and Dry Xeriscape Symposium.* Denver Water Dept., Denver, CO.

13. Ball, K. 1998. Just add (a little) water. *American Nurseryman* 187(7):42.

14. Barker, B. 2000. Testing the waters. *Southwest Trees and Turf* 5(11):7.

15. Beard, J. 1973. *Turfgrass: Science and Culture.* Prentice-Hall, Inc., Englewood Cliffs, NJ.

16. Belt, J. and J. Fortier. 2002. The seven deadly drip sins. *Southwest Trees & Turf* 7(5):1.

17. Bilderback, T. and M. Powell. 1996. *Efficient Irrigation.* North Carolina State Univ. Coop. Ext. Ser. Pub. AG-508-6.

18. Billeau, L. 1988. Landscape the xeriscape way to mulching. *National Xeriscape News* Mar/Apr:3.

19. Bisconer, I. 1988. Successful drip irrigation. *Grounds Maintenance* 23(7):3.

20. Black, R. and D. Rogers. 1989. *Soil Moisture Measurements.* Kansas State Univ. Coop. Ext. Ser. Bul. L-795.

21. Borland, D. 1986. Xeriscape. *Nursery Manager* 2(3):82.

22. Borland, J. and G. Weinstein. 1989. Mulch: is it always beneficial? *Grounds Maintenance* 24(2):10.

23. Bowman, D., R. Evans, and J. Paul. 1990. Fertilizer salts reduce hydration of polyacrylamide gels and affect physical properties of gel-amended container media. *Journal American Society for Horticultural Science* 115(3):382.

24. Carleton, B. 2001. Wednesday is not a good reason to irrigate. *Southwest Trees & Turf* 6(8):5.

25. Carpenter, P., T. Walker, and F. Lanphear. 1975. *Plants in the Landscape.* W.H. Freeman and Co., San Francisco, CA.

26. Carrow, R. 1985. Getting back to basics. *Weeds, Trees, and Turf* 24(7):44.

27. Christians, N. 1999. Why inject acid into irrigation water? *Golf Course Management* 67(6):52.

28. Cline, H. 1993. Turf vs. ornamentals: which uses more water? *Western Turf Management* 4(7):12.

29. Cline, H. 1993. Soil amendments can provide many benefits. *Western Turf Management* 4(8):21.

30. Cohen, S., *et al.* 1997. Water pollution minimal from monitored courses. *Golf Course Management* 65(11):54.

31. Costello, L., N. Natheney, and J. Clark. 1991. *Estimating Water Requirements of Landscape Plantings.* Univ. California Coop. Ext. Ser. Leaflet 21494.

32. Cox, R. and J. Klett. 1984. Evaluation of some indigenous western plants for xeric landscapes. *HortScience* 19(6):856.

33. Deputy, J. 2000. *Guidelines for Professional Turf and Groundcover Management.* Univ. Hawaii Coop. Ext. Ser. Pub. L11.

34. Devitt, D. and R. Morris.1999. Soil moisture sense I. *Southwest Trees & Turf* 4(10):7.

35. Devitt, D. and R. Morris. 1999. Soil moisture sense II. *Southwest Trees & Turf* 4(11):4.

36. Devitt, D., R. Morris, and D. Neuman. 2003. Impact of water treatment on foliar damage of landscape trees sprinkle irrigated with re-use water. *Journal of Environmental Horticulture* 21(2):82.

37. DeYoung, J. 1991. Low-volume drip. *Lawn & Landscape Maintenance* 12(5):28.

38. Dunn, G. 1989. Test with a product having alleged value for increasing plant available water in soil. *Turfgrass Topics* 10(3):3.

39. Dyer, A. 1999. High and dry. *Lawn & Landscape Maintenance* 20(7):92.

40. Evans, J. 1992. Selling the benefits of irrigation. *Lawn & Landscape Maintenance* 13(4):32.

41. Evans, R., I. Sisto, and D. Brown. 1989. *The Effectiveness of Hydrogels in Container Plant Production is Reduced by Fertilizer Salts.* University of California Coop. Ext. Ser. Flower and Nursery Report 5.

42. Follett, R. and P. Soltanpour. 2001. *Irrigation Water Quality.* Colorado State Univ. Coop. Ext. Ser. Pub. 0.506.

43. Fonteno, W. and T. Bilderback. 1993. Impact of hydrogel on physical properties of coarse-structured horticultural substrates. *Journal American Society for Horticultural Science* 118(2)217.

44. Foster, W. and G. Keever. 1990. Water absorption of hydrophylic polymers (hydrogels) reduced by media amendments. *Journal of Environmental Horticulture* 8(3):113.

45. France, V. and D. Welch. 1987. Landscaping the xeriscape way to limiting turf areas. *National Xeriscape News* Sept./Oct.:3.

46. Frank, L. 1997. The economics of water use. *Lawn & Landscape* 18(7):62.

47. Fry, J. and J. Butler. 1989. Water management during tall fescue establishment. *HortScience* 24(1):79.

48. Gibeault, V. *et al.* 1991. *Managing Turfgrass During Drought.* Univ. California Coop. Ext. Ser. Leaflet 21499.

49. Gibson, H. 1988. Irrigation training schools. *Grounds Maintenance* 23(11):28.

50. Gibson, H. 1990. Irrigation with wetting agents. *Grounds Maintenance* 25(7):22.

51. Gillis, P. 1999. Incorporating drip irrigation into the landscape. *IA.* 7(6)38.

52. Green, C. 2001. Irrigation innovations. *Lawn & Landscape* 22(6):84.

53. Greenleaf, C. 2000. Getting hip to drip. *Lawn & Landscape* 21(6):28.

54. Harris, R. 1983. *Arboriculture.* Prentice-Hall, Inc., Englewood Cliffs, NJ.

55. Hartin, J. and L. Frank. 1993. Hydrozoning: An innovative way to reduce water waste. *Landscape and Irrigation* 17(7):50.

56. Henderson, J. and D. Hensley. 1986. Hydrophilic gels can influence nutrient retention in media. *American Nurseryman* 162(9):107.

57. Henderson, J. and D. Hensley. 1986. Efficacy of a hydrophilic gel as a transplant aid. *HortScience* 21:991.

58. Henderson, J. and D. Hensley. 1987. Do hydrophilic gels improve germination and survival? *American Nurseryman* 166(4):189.

59. Henderson, J. and F. Davies. 1987. Effect of a hydrophilic gel on water relations, growth, nutrition of landscape roses. *HortScience* 22:114.

60. Hensley, D. 1989. Mulching by the side of the road. *Nursery Manager* 5(5):76.

61. Hensley, D. 1990. Creative landscaping for water conservation. *Nursery Manager* 6(9):83.

62. Hensley, D. 1990. Gels may improve water availability in some cases. *Nursery Manager* 6(11):65.

63. Hensley, D. 1991. Make the most of mulches. *Nursery Manager* 7(3)96.

64. Hensley, D. 1992. Xeriscape: Creative landscaping to conserve water. *Horticulture Digest* 97(Oct.):5.

65. Hensley, D. 1993. How to save money, water by using drip irrigation. *Nursery Manager* 9(7):104.

66. Hensley, D. 1993. Irrigating to conserve water. *Hawaii Landscape* 7(3):14.

67. Hensley, D. 1994. Drip irrigation saves water, money, and plants. *Hawaii Landscape* 8(1):10.

68. Hensley, D. 1994. Take a hard look at water-holding compounds. *Horticulture Digest* 99 (Mar.):11.

69. Hensley, D. 1995. Landscaping: Irrigation to conserve water. *Hawaii Landscape* 9(3):10.

70. Hensley, D. and J. Deputy. 1999. *Using Tensiometers for Measuring Soil Water and Scheduling Irrigation*. Univ. of Hawaii Coop. Ser. Ext. Pub. L 10.

71. Hensley, D., J. Deputy, and J. Tavares. 1999. *Watering Lawns*. Univ. of Hawaii Coop. Ext. Ser. Pub. TM-7.

72. Hensley, D. and C. Fackler. 1984. Do water holding compounds help in transplanting? *American Nurseryman* 159(3)93.

73. Hensley, D. and V. Meade. *Watering Trees*. Univ. of Hawaii Coop. Ext. Ser. Pub. L-2.

74. Hume, J. 1999. The basics of freeze protection. *IA* 7(5)28.

75. Hummel, R. Effect of antitranspirant sprays on water relations of container-grown woody and herbaceous plants. *The Digger* June:48.

76. Karlick, J. 1995. Effects of pre-plant incorporation of polymers on turfgrasses. *California Turfgrass Culture* 45(3):19.

77. Klett, J. and R. Cox. 1986. Xeric landscapes need well-chosen plants. *American Nurseryman* 63(10):58.

78. Latta, M. 1988. Landscaping the xeriscape way to use of lower water-demand plants. *National Xeriscape News* May/June:2.

79. Lee, J. 2002. Have you ever seen the rain? *Southwest Trees & Turf* 7(5):1.

80. Lehmann, D., W. Cline, and D. Hensley. 1991. Making the most of mulches. *Nursery Manager* 7(3):96.

81. Lenie, D. 1999. Weathering the winter. *Grounds Maintenance* 34(10)18.

82. Lynch, B. and B. Vinchesi. 1989. Regular maintenance prevents need for urgent repair service. *Lawn and Landscape Maintenance* 10(7):20.

83. Kauck, D. 1986. Water-absorbing compounds: what can they do for you? *Greenhouse Grower* 4(11):54.

84. Keesen, L. 2001. Turf irrigation to the basics. *Southwest Trees & Turf* 6(1):1.

85. Koski, T. 1997. How wetting agents apply. *sportsTURF* 12(120:18.

86. Knopf, J. 1991. Xeriscaping. *Grounds Maintenance* 26(2)78.

87. Knowles, S. 1990. Choosing an irrigation system. *Landscape Management* 29(3):80.

88. Knutson, T. 1998. Know your water when switching to a non-drinkable municipal source. *Landscape and Irrigation* 22(1):46.

89. McGuirk, S. 2001. Retrofit to drip. *Grounds Maintenance* 36(6):44.

90. MacNair, J. 1993. Estimating water use and irrigation schedules for ornamental landscapes. *Landscape and Irrigation* 17(4)40.

91. Major, M. 1990. Misconceptions contribute to slow wetting agent acceptance. *Lawn and Landscape Maintenance* 11(5):56.

92. Maloney, K. and J. Wright. 1993. Subsurface irrigation: the solution when overspray brings criticism. *Landscape and Irrigation* 17(5):84.

93. Marcellino, M. 1989. Stop water shortages for evaporating your landscapes. *ALA/Maintenance* 10(6):28.

94. Martin, D. 1991. Using infrared thermometers. *Grounds Maintenance* 26(8):54.

95. Matheny, N., and J. Clark. 1999. Managing landscape using recycled water. *Arborists News* 8(6):37.

96. Milford, M. 1988. Landscaping the xeriscape way to soil amendments. *National Xeriscape News* Jan./Feb.:3.

97. Miyamoto, S., R. Galceran, and R. Garcia. 1997. Landscape irrigation with salty water. *Grounds Maintenance* 32(11):22.

98. Ninemire, S. 1997. Effluent water has positive potential. *Grounds Maintenance* 32(5):20.

99. Nolde, B. 1998. Reclaimed water; hold the salt please. *California Fairways* 7(3):20.

100. Nolde, B. 1998. Shades of gray. *Landscape & Irrigation* 22(8):31.

101. Nus, J. 1993. Water-absorbing polymers. *Golf Course Management* Special International Edition:54.

102. Pellett, H., R. Hummel, and L. Mainquist. 1980. Relationship of fall watering practice to winter injury of conifers. *Journal of Arboriculture* 6(6):146.

103. Pirone, P., J. Hartman, M. Sall, and T. Pirone. 1988. *Tree Maintenance*. Oxford University Press, New York, NY.

104. Polhemus, D. 1992. Soil polymers for turf areas: A technical review. *sportsTURF* 8(6):14.

105. Pollard, E. 1992. Protecting irrigation systems through winterization. *Landscape and Irrigation* 16(10):74.

106. Powell M. and T. Disy. 1996. *Wise Water Use in Landscaping*. North Carolina State Univ. Coop. Ext. Ser. Pub. AG 5081.

107. Pryor, W., Jr. 1991. Designing a water conserving landscape on a large site. *Lawn & Landscape Maintenance* 12(2):20.

108. Riccardi, T. 1989. Tricks of the irrigation trade. *Grounds Maintenance* 24(11):26.

109. Rogers, D., L. Stone, and R. Black. 1989. *Tensiometer Use in Scheduling Irrigation*. Kansas State Univ. Coop. Ext. Ser. Bul. L-796.

110. Sarsfield, A.C. 1985. Drip and minis in the commercial landscape. *Grounds Maintenance* 20(10):34.

111. Severson, L. and B. Mart. 1989. Is there such a thing as solid H$_2$O. *Arbor Age* Aug.:12.

112. Shurtleff, M. 1993. Trees and drought. *Grounds Maintenance* 28(4):49.

113. Sloan, M. and D. Hensley. 1987. Xeriscape: Creative landscaping for water conservation. *Grounds Management Forum* 11(2):6.

114. Smajstria, A. and D. Harrison. 1998. *Tensiometers for Soil Moisture Measurement and Irrigation Scheduling*. Univ. of Florida Coop. Ext. Ser. Circular 487.

115. Snyder, R. *et al.* 1991. *Turfgrass Irrigation Scheduling*. Univ. California Coop. Ext. Ser. Leaflet 21492.

116. Solomon, K. and G. Jorgensen. 1992. Subsurface drip irrigation. *Grounds Maintenance* 27(19):24.

117. Spaid, T. and D. Hensley. 1986. Mulch selection guide. *Nursery Manager* 2(3):113.

118. Steinegger, D., R. Gaussoin and G. Horst. 1996. *Evaluating Your Landscape Irrigation System*. Univ. of Nebraska Coop. Ext. Ser. Pub. G93-1181-A.

119. Swearengin, R. 1987. Water savings flow with efficient irrigation, good practices. *National Xeriscape News* Nov/Dec:1.

120. Terry, A. 2000. Recycled water - be aware, not afraid. *Southwest Trees and Turf* 5(12):1.

121. Thomson, S. and B. Ross. 1996. *Using Soil Moisture Sensors for Making Irrigation Management Decisions in Virginia.* Virginia Coop. Ext. Ser. Publication No. 442-024.

122. Tobey, S. 1999. Drip irrigation options. *Southwest Trees & Turf* 4(12):4.

123. USGA. 1994. *Wastewater Reuse for Golf Course Irrigation.* Lewis Publishers, Chelsea, MI.

124. Vinchesi, B. 1994. Winterizing irrigation systems can avoid pipe stress. *Lawn & Landscape Maintenance* 11(10):33.

125. Vinchesi, B. and B. Lynch. 1990. Water purveyors: friends or foes? *Lawn & Landscape Maintenance* 15(4):52.

126. Waller, R. 2000. Irrigation insurance. *Turf* Nov:7.

127. Welch, D. 1988. Landscaping the xeriscape way to appropriate maintenance. *National Xeriscape News* Sept/Oct:1.

128. Welch, D. 1991. Xeriscape guidelines and turfgrass use. *Grounds Maintenance* 26(2):79.

129. Westrick, D. 1989. N.J. irrigation contractors fight to install low voltage wiring. *Lawn and Landscape Maintenance* 10(9):12.

130. Wickham, D. 1999. Common irrigation errors. *Lawn and Landscape Maintenance* 20(10):54.

131. Wisniewski, N. 2000. Programming irrigation controllers. *Lawn and Landscape Maintenance* 21(1):102.

132. Zupancic, J. 1999. Reclaimed water: challenges of irrigation use. *Grounds Maintenance* 34(3):33.

Chapter 10
Fertilizing the Landscape

David Hensley and James Robbins[1]

Fertilization of landscape plants is the most discussed topic in landscape management. Fertilizer is applied regularly and in copious quantities. The timing and rates vary with region, climate, species, and recommendations of individual authors and managers.

Some grounds managers believe that fertilizer possesses mystical quality, curing all ills; *"When in doubt, fertilize."* Fertilizer maintains the health and vigor of woody and herbaceous plants. Research has equated proper levels of plant nutrients with reduction in winter bark splitting of trees, reduced severity of drought damage, and increased insect and disease resistance. Aesthetically, proper nutrition will increase the size and number of fruits and flowers, as well as the size, color intensity, and amount of foliage.

Fertilization is not a panacea. It will not take care of all of the problems encountered by the plant or landscape manager. No amount of added nutrients can make up for lack of water, poor drainage, or other limiting site factors. Excessive fertilization, especially nitrogen, increases some problems. Fireblight is more severe when there is excessive succulent new growth. Excessive nitrogen can lead to increased density of shade trees and understory plants may suffer from reduced sunlight. Nutrient runoff is a genuine problem, one in which every landscape professional must be concerned.

Landscape plants rely on man to provide the majority of their nutrients. They do not have the advantage of century-old, humus-rich, forest soils. Landscape sites are frequently stripped of topsoil or filled with poor quality material. Landscape sites are often low in critical nutrients. Landscape plants do not have the advantage of natural nutrient recycling; leaves and grass clippings are often collected before their nutrients can be returned to the soil. Fertilization is a routine, but very important part of the management of every landscape site. In 1999, there were 24,977,896 tons of nitrogen fertilizers consumed in the United States for all uses, according to the Fertilizer Institute. The volume of fertilizer used grows annually.

The Essential Elements

Sixteen essential elements are necessary for plant growth. An element is classified as *essential* if: the plant fails to complete its life cycle in its absence; the action of the element in the plant is specific (it cannot be replaced by another element); and it has a direct effect on the plant (as opposed to indirect, such as repelling animals or insects).

---

[1] Dr. James Robbins is an Extension Specialist in landscape and ornamental horticulture with the University of Arkansas Cooperative Extension Service.

The essential nutrients are divided into *Macro* elements: carbon (C); hydrogen (H); oxygen (O); nitrogen (N); phosphorus (P); potassium (K); calcium (Ca); magnesium (Mg); sulfur (S); and *Micro* elements: iron (Fe); manganese (Mn); zinc (Zn); boron (B); copper (Cu); molybdenum (Mo); and chlorine (Cl). Recent work has indicated that nickel (Ni) may also be an essential element. Classification as macro- or micronutrients does not refer to their importance, but to the relative amounts required by plants.

Carbon (C), hydrogen (H), and oxygen (O) are obtained from air and water; they are not manageable, nor can they be added as a fertilizer. Nitrogen, phosphorus, and potassium are referred to as the *fertilizer elements* for obvious reasons. Iron (Fe) is frequently referred to as a *border element*; it is classified as a macronutrient by some sources and a minor element by others. Iron is required in a greater amount than other micronutrients and deficiency problems are frequently encountered.

Macronutrient: Nitrogen

Nitrogen is the most important fertilizer element, the most frequently limiting nutrient in landscape soils, and of the greatest concern to landscape managers. Nitrogen is supplied to plants through decomposition of organic matter, nitrogen fixation by soil microbes and some higher plants, and the addition of fertilizers. Nitrogen is rendered unavailable to plants due to absorption by weeds and other non-target plants, utilization or denitrification by soil organisms, volatilization, and leaching.

Addition of nitrogen results in the greatest response in growth. There is no additive or synergistic effect when nitrogen is applied in association with other nutrients.

Specifications and recommendations. Landscape managers must be sensitive to plant health and environmental quality issues. A mineral nutrition program for a landscape begins with soils tests and foliar nutrient analyses, and a stated goal. The goal(s) for a fertilization program may be to overcome visible or detected nutrition deficiencies, increase plant size, maintain an acceptable aesthetic level for the landscape, or increase the vitality of the plant or landscape. Different fertility programs are needed to reach these goals. Higher soil fertility is required for growth, while lower fertility levels will meet maintenance objectives.

Nitrogen is the most common nutrient applied to any landscape site. It will be applied at least annually and most likely several times during the year for the benefit of the turf. Turf fertilization is discussed in detail in Chapter 12.

Nitrogen fertilizer rates for turfgrass and woody plants should be specified and recommended as *pounds of nitrogen*, rather than pounds of a specific fertilizer. Fertilizer type does not appear to be important in nitrogen nutrition of trees and probably other woody plants. This allows the contractor freedom of choice in fertilizer material based on price and the considerations discussed earlier. If a slow-release material is required, the percent nitrogen necessary as slow-release or water-insoluble nitrogen (WIN) should be specified. For instance, *"The fertilizer shall contain at least 60 percent slow-release nitrogen"*.

If other fertilizer nutrients are necessary or required, these can be specified in pounds of element (e.g. Two pounds phosphorus per 1,000 square feet) or their inclusion can be indicated as a specified ratio. For instance, *"Two pounds of nitrogen per 1,000 square feet shall be applied as a 3:1:1 fertilizer."* This indicates that one-third pound of P_2O_5 and K_2O will be applied for each pound of nitrogen. This recommendation might be used where phosphorus and potassium levels are marginal. Allowing the contractor some freedom to choose specific products for the fertilization program usually results in a better price for the client.

Calculating of fertilizer rates. The number of pounds necessary of any fertilizer to yield the required rate of nitrogen or other element specified is easily calculated. Divide the pounds of nitrogen required by the percent of nitrogen in the fertilizer analysis.

For Example...

You wish to apply 2 pounds of nitrogen (N) per 1,000 square feet as urea. Urea (45-0-0) is 45 percent (0.45) N. Therefore, 2 (pounds of N desired) divided by 0.45 (% N in urea) equals 4.4 pounds of product.

Nine (9) pounds of ammonium nitrate (33-0-0) is required to apply 3 pounds of N, (3 ÷ 0.33 = 9).

208

Ten pounds of superphosphate (0-20-0) is required to apply 2 pounds of P_2O_5 per 1,000 square feet (2 ÷ 0.20 = 10).

And on, and on, nothing magical, no need for a computer. Fertilizer rates can be calculated in the dust on the hood of the pickup.

Nitrogen Fertilization of Trees

Rates: surface area method. An all-purpose recommendation for most soils and moderate rates of tree growth is two to four pounds of nitrogen per 1,000 square feet of crown area. Thirty to 50 percent of the nitrogen should be in a slow-release form. The crown area is generally considered the *dripline* or edge of the canopy (or slightly beyond). This is not an enchanted area; the roots of trees are known to extend beyond the dripline in all directions.

Dr. Ed Gilman, University of Florida, found that more than 50 percent of the roots of several trees extend beyond the crown, as much as three times the crown radius for some species. Measurements of sugar maple (*Acer saccharum*) indicated that the root area was 1.75 times greater than the radius of the crown. The root area of tuliptree (*Liriodendron tulipifera*) was 2.5 times greater than the crown radius. The root area and crown area of pin oak (*Quercus palustris*) were about the same. Sandy soils are more conducive to larger root systems than fine-textured soils.

The general figure most frequently discussed is that the roots extend twice the radius of the crown. Another is that the roots extend outward a distance approximately equal to the height of the tree. The extent of a tree's roots varies by species and soil type.

Regardless, the dripline makes a convenient area to measure. It is easy for most employees to find and is a concept the client understands. If fertilizer is applied within the dripline of the tree, there are more than enough active roots to adsorb the material. Some arboriculture texts recommend calculation of nitrogen rates based on the estimated root zone (two times the crown radius) and application of the material to the same area. This figure may involve the entire front yard of some residential proprieties. Application of fertilizer beyond the dripline has not been shown to be advantageous to the plant.

Experimentally, trees have responded to a variety of nitrogen rates. Whitcomb, in Oklahoma, found maximum growth with four pounds of nitrogen per 1,000 square feet. Good growth was achieved by Neely, in Illinois, with six pounds nitrogen per 1,000 square feet. In Ohio, Dr. Elton Smith found maximum growth of trees in a nursery from three to six pounds of nitrogen per 1,000 square feet per year applied in three applications. The majority of these and other studies, however, involved nursery production and did not consider turf response. The quality of turf in a maintained landscape is of equal importance to that of the trees and shrubs.

The two to four pound rate recommended in this discussion provides a guideline for reasonable growth within the figures used experimentally. Soils with high levels of organic matter may need less nitrogen. Sandy soil, especially in high rainfall areas, will require more. As a rule, evergreens need lower levels of nitrogen than deciduous trees. Rates for trees in turfgrass should be adjusted to consider the amount of nitrogen supplied during turf fertilizations.

Most established trees growing in managed landscapes where turf and shrubs are fertilized with a reasonable nitrogen fertility program would not require additional nitrogen. If additional N is required (i.e. specified in the maintenance contract, required to correct a specific problem, or to promote additional tree growth) it should be applied in two or more applications (usually spring *and* fall) or possibly as a deep root application to not burn the turf. Never surface apply more than two pounds of nitrogen per 1,000 square feet per application beneath trees in turf.

Rates: caliper method. There are various formulas for computing the amount of nitrogen needed to fertilize a tree based upon trunk diameter or caliper at *dbh* (diameter breast height or 4 1/2 feet). Arborists have historically used caliper calculations. In most managed landscapes, however, the contractor or grounds manager is dealing with several trees of different sizes, turf, shrubs, herbaceous perennials, annuals, and bulbs. It is more efficient to calculate nitrogen rates on a square foot of surface area basis, rather than measuring each tree individually.

A common recommendation is one-half pound nitrogen per inch dbh. Work by Dr. Jim Robbins, while at Kansas State University, found that rates based on crown area of open-grown trees typically provided more nitrogen than did rates based on trunk diameter for a wide variety of species.

Special situations. Trees in *confined areas*, such as parking lot islands, street trees, or planters, have restricted root systems and limited clear surface area. In these situations, base nitrogen fertilization rates on accessible *root area*, not crown spread. Normal rates of nitrogen applied to the few feet of surface not covered by pavement will result in high salt accumulation problems, damage to the roots, and top growth in excess of that which can be supported by the roots. In root-confined situations, the nitrogen applied should be on the low side of recommended rates and this should be divided into split applications made several times per year as surface applications, foliar sprays, or other alternative methods. A novel approach to fertilize and irrigate trees with restricted surface access is to use liquid soil injection using a water lance. A competent professional must evaluate each case individually.

Upright, columnar, or fastigiate trees should be fertilized based on estimated root spread rather than upon their actual crown area. Calculate the area of the root zone using a radius equal to the tree's height for rate and application purposes.

Be aware of potential problems for turf growth and vigor under trees, especially when higher nitrogen rates are required. Some sources recommend reduction of nitrogen rates to turf under dense stands of trees because of the change in morphology and physiology of the grass plant resulting from the reduced light.

Over-fertilization of trees can cause over-stimulation of foliage, exposing understory plants to heavy shade and the associated growth responses and problems. Soil and water pollution problems may result. Be careful with recommendations and application methods; keep the environment in mind. Higher rates of nitrogen for the tree's benefit should be applied as a deep (six to 12 inches) root or soil injection application in these situations.

Timing. Timing of nitrogen and other nutrient applications for maximum benefit varies with research study and location. For deciduous trees, higher nitrogen use efficiency is realized if nitrogen is applied slightly before or at budbreak, than during the leafless, dormant season. Several researchers have found fall better than or equal to spring application. Researchers generally agree that nitrogen application should be timed so there is nitrogen available for the new flush of growth in the spring. Timing is not as important for soil applications of phosphorus, or most other nutrients, including micronutrients.

In general, preferred application time for trees and shrubs in the Midwest and North is in early spring at or before budbreak or in October to November. Soil temperatures in the fall are favorable for root activity and nutrient absorption; roots are active as long as soil temperatures remain above 40°F. Moisture conditions are conducive for work and movement of the material into the root zone. Fall is also a preferred time for application since that is when the majority of nitrogen is applied in cool-season turf programs. A study by Smiley and Shirazi (2003) showed no biologically significant reduction in cold hardiness of five tree species due to fertilizer treatment applied in September and October in North Carolina.

Early spring, two to four weeks before bud break, appears to be equal in benefit to fall application. Some authors have speculated that loss from leaching would be less for spring applications and, therefore, more nitrogen is available for plant absorption.

In regions with milder conditions, growth begins earlier in the spring and continues later in the fall. Nitrogen applications in late winter or early spring are appropriate. In areas of high rainfall or coarse-textured soils, a second, midsummer application may be beneficial. In subtropical and tropical areas, fertilize in advance of major flushes of growth.

In all cases where winter damage is a possibility, late summer and early heavy fall applications of nitrogen to trees should be avoided. These can result in a late flush of growth that may fail to acclimate (develop cold hardiness) before the severe autumn freezes.

Split applications of fertilizer, late fall and spring, may be considered. Split applications to trees are more costly since the site must be visited twice. Some research has reported growth increases with spilt applications in nurseries. If high nitrogen rates are used, split applications should be made to preserve the turf. Never apply more than two pounds readily available nitrogen per 1,000 square feet per broadcast application for trees growing in turfgrass. Higher nitrogen rates can be used with soil injection methods.

Shrubs

A rate of two to four pounds of nitrogen per 1,000 square feet of bed area is the most common figure used in the trade. A four-pound application is not excessive in shrub beds where there is no turf or groundcover. To avoid burning the foliage if groundcovers are present, consider applying lower rates, or blowing or washing granules from the leaves. Rhododendrons, azaleas, and other Ericaceous species have shallow roots that are injured by higher rates of quickly available nitrogen. For these plants, use lower rates or split applications. In addition, Ericaceous species should be fertilized using an acid-type material to help maintain an acidic soil reaction.

Needle evergreens, such as pine, fir, and spruce, respond to lower fertilization rates than deciduous species. Research has shown that rates above a certain minimum do not necessarily translate to increased growth. There is no need to try to segregate them, however, as the additional nitrogen used for deciduous species will not harm evergreens.

Frequency. Frequency of fertilization depends on the *type* and *age* of the tree or shrub, the *objective* of the fertility program, *soil conditions*, *maintenance level*, and the *budget*. Most trees and shrubs will respond to annual applications of nitrogen. Neely found growth increases from fertilization persisted only one to two years after application. *Nutrient deficiencies* require successive applications until the problem is corrected. Soil and foliage tests will tell the manager the effectiveness of the fertilizer program. Foliar applications of micronutrients are required annually to alleviate the deficiency symptoms.

Fertilize recently established landscapes annually until the plants reach sufficient size. Established woody landscape plants require less fertilization, only enough to retain good color and reasonable vigor. Fertilize these on a biennial basis, although annual fertilization will not cause

any plant problems. Again, *a good turf fertilization program may supply all of the nitrogen necessary for established woody landscape plants.*

Older, mature trees, especially in lower maintenance situations, such as parks, can be fertilized less frequently. Application of nitrogen every three to four years is usually adequate. These recommendations will vary with specific circumstances.

Fertilization at planting

There are as many different recommendations for fertilizing trees and shrubs at planting as there are trees planted. Research has not helped solve this dilemma. In fact, some published reports have added to the controversy. Recommendations vary from none to 0.1 pound of nitrogen mixed in the backfill or applied to the surface after planting. One researcher reported no response of bareroot landscape trees to soil nitrogen levels during the first three years after planting.

Other research [*Journal of Arboriculture* 1988. 14:204] found that container-grown magnolia (*Magnolia grandiflora*) grew more if a small amount of fertilizer was added at planting. This increase in growth occurred regardless of where the fertilizer was placed (in the bottom of the hole, in the backfill, or on the surface after planting). Also, the increase in growth was evident three years after planting and fertilizer application. Container-grown plants are more likely to utilize and respond to nitrogen added at planting than are bareroot plants or possibly balled and burlapped plants. Container-grown material is transplanted with a full compliment of roots, whereas the root systems of bareroot and balled and burlapped stock are severely reduced (up to 90 percent, depending upon plant size) at harvest.

Consider incorporating fertilizer when planting in low fertility soils or where subsequent fertilizer applications are unlikely, such as roadsides, or other low budget landscapes. If the contract calls for application of fertilizer at planting, the decision has already been made. Regardless, use low levels of a low salt-index nitrogen fertilizer, with phosphorus and potassium included, if needed. Slow-release fertilizers have low salt levels, and provide a source of nitrogen for several months, but are expensive. The material may be buried beneath the plant's root system or ball, mixed thoroughly into the backfill, or applied to the surface immediately after planting.

Bring shrub and turfgrass areas to recommended soil test levels before planting. Nitrogen is usually incorporated during bed or soil preparation, but the application should not exceed two pounds nitrogen per 1,000 square feet.

Phosphorus, and sometimes potassium, are revered for stimulating root growth if included in the planting hole. Phosphorus and potassium should be brought up to proper levels based on soil tests before planting, since these elements are not readily mobile in the soil. Mixing them into the planting hole incorporates the nutrients into the root zone. Addition of phosphorus or potassium to the planting hole in soils where these elements are not limiting has no effect on top or root growth of woody landscape plants. The use of high-phosphate, vitamin-fortified, root enhancers or stimulators has as much effect on root growth as snake oil for growing hair. Marketing is still more powerful than science, or common sense.

Phosphorus

Most soils contain adequate *phosphorus* for trees and shrubs. Woody plants, by means of mycorrhizae, are able to exploit larger volumes of soil for phosphorus than annual crops and turfgrass. Phosphorus may be limiting or unavailable at soil pH above 7.0 where it can complex with calcium. This is often found in tropical soils and some coastal sandy soils. At low soil pH, phosphorus may precipitate out of the soil solution as iron and aluminum phosphates. The amount and availability of phosphorus to landscape plants can be estimated by soil tests indicating the amount of phosphorus in the soil and the soil pH. Foliar analysis determines the amount of phosphorus in the plant.

Routine addition of phosphorus-containing fertilizers has shown no benefit or growth response to woody plants unless phosphorus is limiting in the soil. Sources proclaim enhanced root development of woody plants, especially in urban and other difficult sites, if additional phosphorus is added at planting and during annual fertilization. There is no experimental evidence, however, that addition of phosphorus in non-deficient situations increases root growth in woody plants. There is evidence, however, that high phosphate

starter fertilizers aid establishment of vegetable and other herbaceous transplants.

Phosphorus does not move readily in the soil; broadcasting concentrates it near the surface. This may be fine for turfgrass but may limit availability of supplied phosphorus to deeper-feeding trees and shrubs. For efficiency, amend the soil based on a soil test before planting. Deep root applications place nutrient sources in the zone of the majority of feeder roots of established trees. Excessive levels of phosphorus will not harm woody species, but overuse of phosphorus containing fertilizers contributes to water pollution.

Potassium

Most landscape soils contain adequate *potassium* for plant growth. Deficiencies have been reported in areas of Florida, Hawaii, and other localized situations. Soil tests can confirm visual symptoms. Foliar analysis may be misleading since potassium is readily mobile in the plant and is also leached from leaves by rain and irrigation.

Potassium is not mobile in soil. It is best incorporated in planting areas before plant establishment or applied to existing trees and shrubs by deep root applications or soil injection methods. Surface applications can be effective if rooting is shallow and on sandy soils when turf is not present.

Potassium possesses amazing benefits for plants according to some authors, such as increasing drought resistance, reducing winter damage and disease severity, and enhancing flower color. There is no published research to verify these attributes within woody plants or that potassium affects plant responses any more than other elements. Addition of potassium will not promote a growth response in woody plants unless it is deficient. Large amounts of potassium may cause magnesium deficiency, especially in acid and sandy soils.

Calcium

Calcium is seldom restricting in most soils. It may be limiting in acid soils, sandy soils in high rainfall regions, acidic peat soils, and soils derived from serpentine rock. Calcium can be added as agricultural or dolomitic limestone to acid soils and as gypsum to alkaline sites. It should only be applied on the basis of a soil test. As with phosphorus and potassium, calcium is most efficiently supplied by incorporation before planting.

Magnesium

Magnesium can be leached from acidic sandy soils and tied-up in unavailable forms in calcareous soils, but is sufficient for growth of landscape plants in most soils. Add dolomitic limestone as a magnesium source for acid sites and Epsom salts ($MgSO_4 \cdot 7H_2O$) in neutral or alkaline soils. As with the other nutrients, except nitrogen, it is most expedient to correct magnesium deficiencies before planting, and only on the basis of a soil test.

Sulfur

Irrigation water, precipitation, decomposing organic matter, by-products in fertilizers, some fungicides, and air pollution supply enough sulfur to meet the needs for normal growth of landscape plants.

Iron

Iron is the most common micronutrient problem and probably the second most common nutrient deficiency occurring in landscape plants. Iron deficiency may be due to low iron content in the soil, but more commonly it is the result of unavailability due to high (alkaline) soil pH. Iron deficiency symptoms, *interveinal chlorosis* (yellowing between green veins), occur most frequently in cold, wet soils, during periods of drought, or in situations where the root system has sustained damage. Plant species vary widely in the ability to scavenge iron from the soil and their susceptibility to iron chlorosis. Pin oak (*Quercus palustris*) and Ericaceous species are notable in their susceptibility.

Horticulturists have attempted to correct iron deficiency for over 100 years with every iron compound conceivable in every manner imaginable. Even today, there is considerable research underway in this area.

In most cases, an iron chlorosis problem is a result of soil conditions that limit the availability of iron to the plant. Generally the soil has sufficient amounts of iron, but it is found in an unavailable form.

A number of remedies are available for this serious problem. These include use of iron-effi-

Photo 10.1. Iron is the most common micronutrient problem for landscape plants. Many species such as pin oak and azaleas are prone to iron problems in alkaline soil.

cient (iron-resistant) cultivars or species, application of iron compounds, or acidification of the soil.

Use of iron-efficient cultivars or species. This approach works very well in field crops like soybeans; however, this approach is so far nonexistent with ornamentals. In theory it is a worthwhile area for someone to pursue. When planting in soils or conditions that lend themselves to an iron chlorosis problem, avoid ornamental species that are most susceptible. These include: pin oak (*Quercus palustrus*), silver maple (*Acer saccharinum*), azalea (*Rhododendron* spp.), chrysanthemum (*Chrysanthemum* spp.), sweetgum (*Liquidambar styraciflua*), spiraea (*Spiraea* spp.), birch (*Betula* spp., especially river birch, *B. nigra*), hibiscus (*Hibiscus* spp.), crabapple (*Malus,* spp.), plums (*Prunus* spp.), gardenia (*Gardenia* spp.), bermudagrass (*Cynadon dactylon*), ixora (*Ixora* spp.), bougainvillea (*Bougainvillea* spp.) and many others.

Soil acidification. Soil acidification with sulfur or aluminum sulfate in small planting areas is feasible; however, this solution is not economical or permanent for large sites. A large amount of material will be required and the soil must be amended deeply (at least 12 to 18 inches). Specific rates follow in the section on *Soil Reaction*.

Constant leaching of alkaline material in limestone-based soils increases the pH of acidified soils over time. The problem is aggravated when the site is irrigated with alkaline water. The duration of soil acidification projects increases if substantial amounts of organic matter are incorporated.

Application of iron compounds. A number of iron containing materials can be applied to plants either to the soil or foliage. These materials fall into five categories: inorganic sources (e.g. ferrous sulfate), synthetic iron chelates (e.g. FeEDDHA), organic complexes (e.g. iron lignosulfonates), mine tailings (e.g. Ironite®), and industrial by-products (e.g. Iron-Sul®). Each one of these iron sources has its merits and detractions. These various sources also lend themselves better to certain application methods than to other methods.

Iron compounds can be applied to the soil surface, sprayed onto plant foliage, injected into tree trunks, or injected into the soil. Application of large amounts of *iron sulfate* to the soil surface has provided mixed results. The pH change is temporary and the iron is immobilized in a short period of time. Several authors have reported reasonably long-term, semi-permanent success in treating iron chlorosis by deep root application of iron sulfate/sulfur mixes. Mixtures of 1:1 or 3:1 sulfur:iron sulfate have relieved iron chlorosis for several years. Theoretically, sulfur reduces the pH in localized areas around the deep root application hole making the iron in the iron sulfate more available.

Surface application of *iron chelates* to soil is less affected by soil pH. Chelates do, however, vary in their relative stability at high soil pH. FeEDDHA is more stable over a wide range of soil pH than is FeEDTA. Since the material is mobile in the soil, the treatment must be repeated periodically. Iron chelates can be included in liquid soil injection mixes and have been reported effective for two or more years. Iron chelates are typically more expensive than other iron materials.

Spray applications of iron sulfate or iron chelates to the foliage have given irregular response with different species (effective with oak to ineffective with citrus). Foliar applications are effective for only a single season. Since iron is not mobile in the plant, new foliage emerging after an application will be chlorotic. Other disadvantages include problems in coverage, staining of walks, cars, and buildings, foliar residue, and potential foliar burn under certain conditions. Foliar applications correct only the symptoms, not the problem, but may be useful in conjunction with other, longer-term treatments.

Organic iron salts have been *injected* or *implanted* into tree trunks since 1930 and this process can correct iron deficiency for up to three or more years. Several systems are commercially available. Gelatin capsules of ferric ammonium citrate, ferric citrate, or other organic salts are inserted into holes drilled into the trunk. Pressurized injection is also used commercially. The Mauget® system offers iron and other micronutrient injection treatments.

Another injection system, Medi-ject®, uses iron sulfate with water as a carrier, gravity-fed into holes drilled in the lower trunk or root flare. I have observed several trees treated with the Medi-ject® system in Kansas; these were free of iron chlorosis symptoms for four to six years and grew normally after treatment. Tree injections will be further discussed under application techniques.

Manganese

Manganese (Mn) is one of the more commonly deficient micronutrients, second only to iron. As with iron, deficiency may be due to low manganese levels in the soil, or unavailability of existing supplies due to soil pH. At pH values above 6.5, manganese is converted to a low solubility form and sensitive plants will show deficiency symptoms. Symptoms are difficult to distinguish from those of iron (interveinal chlorosis) and the two are often mistaken for each other. Red maple (*Acer rubrum*), citrus, several species of palm, apple, cherry, and many other species are especially troubled by manganese deficiency. Symptoms are more likely under drought conditions.

Acidification of alkaline soils will usually correct the deficiency; however, the potential problems and economics make this an unattractive alternative. Manganese sulfate has been used as a soil treatment but manganese chelate may be more successful. Foliar sprays provide annual relief of the symptoms, and trunk injections have been successful.

Zinc

Zinc (Zn) deficiency is most common on heavily graded areas and in alkaline and calcareous soils of the western United States. Zinc deficiency is also a problem in Florida and other areas along the Gulf Coast. Zinc deficiencies are aggravated by heavy or long-term use of high-phosphate fertilizers. Leaves of zinc deficient plants are yellow and small, and internodes may be shortened.

Surface application or soil injections of zinc sulfate are more successful in soils with a pH below 6.0. Zinc chelates have been more successful in other situations. Annual foliar applications can be used. Trunk injections of zinc solutions are effective for up to three years. Some people have resorted to driving zinc coated nails into the trunks of trees, but there have been no reports on the success of this treatment.

Boron

Plants require extremely small amounts of *boron* for normal growth. The range between deficiency and excess for boron is very narrow. Foliar analysis of fruit trees showed a normal level of boron between 20 and 80 ppm. Levels below 20 ppm are deficient. Toxic levels vary widely with species ranging from 80 to 500 ppm.

Boron deficiency symptoms are aggravated by drought, irrigation water low in boron but high in calcium, and by heavy applications of lime. Boron deficiency is corrected by soil or foliar application of borax. Soil application during summer or fall produces a growth response the following spring.

Other nutrient deficiencies

Any nutrient can occur in insufficient quantities for plant growth due to supply or other factors mitigating uptake. Deficiencies of molybdenum (Mo) and copper (Cu) are rare and isolated. Problems with boron, copper, and molybdenum are isolated and managers should consult local authorities. Chlorine (Cl) and nickel (Ni) have not been reported in deficient levels under field conditions.

Fertilization Practices

Fertilizer recommendations are cloaked in secrecy and tradition. Wide variations exist in amounts, timing, materials, and other facets of current fertilization techniques. Many grounds managers and landscape maintenance contractors have basic misunderstandings of soils, nutrients, and plant growth. Landscape fertilization programs are complicated by different plant types, sizes, and nutrient requirements of plants growing in immediate proximity.

The manager must be sure the *plant symptoms* are due to a nutrient deficiency or toxicity before applying corrective fertilizers. Pesticides, drought, excessive moisture, temperature, soil and air pollutants, compaction, and physical injury mimic foliage discoloration, chlorosis, and other classic nutrient deficiency symptoms.

The plant's *location* impacts the fertility program and plant response. Plants growing in low-stress pastoral settings, such as many home backyards, require less crucial attention to nutrition than plants growing in parking lots or urban situations.

The physical properties of the *soil* influence the amount of nutrients held, and to an extent, their availability. Be cognizant of the influence of soil texture, soil structure, and soil depth on nutrient retention, and availability.

Not all plants respond to fertilizers in the same way. Faster growing species respond more rapidly and dramatically than slower growing species. The number of preformed initials in the buds determines growth of deciduous and evergreen species, such as oaks and pines. The first year after fertilization they may show improved leaf color, but will not show increased growth until the following season.

The greatest growth response of landscape plants results from *nitrogen* (N); there will be no response to added phosphorus (P) or potassium (K) unless the soil is deficient in these elements. There is no additive or synergistic effect if either phosphorus or potassium is included with nitrogen in a fertilizer program. Rely on a soil test to indicate whether P or K is required.

Some *plants* have specific nutritional problems. As discussed earlier, pin oak (*Quercus palustris*), sweet gum (*Liquidambar styraciflua*), birch, and azalea and rhododendrons develop iron chlorosis in alkaline conditions, while red maple frequently suffers from manganese deficiency.

The manager must also consider the strategy or reason for applying fertilizer. The goal with young trees may be to increase their growth rate. With mature trees, however, fertilizer is applied to maintain foliage color and health. Growth rate is less important.

Palms

Palms are among the most common landscape trees in subtropical and tropical regions. Palms present special nutritional problems for landscape managers. Palms suffer quickly from insufficient or inappropriate fertilization. They are slow growing plants so they take longer to recover from nutrient disorders. Nitrogen, magnesium, manganese, and potassium are the most frequently encountered nutrient deficiencies. Soil nutrient deficits are best corrected prior to planting.

Controlled-release nitrogen forms are preferred to rapidly available sources. Fertilizers should be formulated to release for long periods at higher temperatures, since palms occur in subtropical and tropical regions.

The fertilizer ratio of 3:1:3 is recommended by several palm experts. The materials should also contain magnesium at one-third the rate of potassium. Micronutrients should also be included. *Palm specials*, produced by several fertilizer formulators, are available with these general specifications. Consult the fertilizer label and local Extension Services for rates. Broadcast materials beneath the crown (palm roots are not wide spreading); do not place fertilizer against the stem or where newly emerging roots can be injured.

A good guide on palm nutrition is available through the University of Florida: <<http://edis.ifas.ufl.edu/BODY_EP052>>.

Determining Deficiencies or Toxicities

Grounds managers have a number of tools at their disposal to determine deficiencies or toxicities of plant nutrients and to monitor nutritional programs.

Visual analysis. Many experienced managers can adequately gauge the nutritional needs of plants by appearance. Appearance cannot reveal intricate problems, but deficiencies of nitrogen, iron, manganese, and magnesium produce recognizable foliage symptoms. Table 10.1 lists common deficiency symptoms for landscape plants.

Shoot growth and *leaf size* are common indices of the nutritional status in trees and shrubs. If a young, moderately fast growing shade tree has twig growth of less than nine to 12 inches per year, it will respond to application of additional nitrogen. Mature trees producing less than six inches of new growth per year will also respond. These growth rates vary with species and site.

Problems associated with using visual symptoms are obvious. A slight deficiency may reduce growth without noticeable foliar symptoms. Once symptoms appear, plant growth has been impaired. Although some nutrient deficiencies produce distinct traits, others are generalized and it is impossible to determine the specific cause of the problem based solely upon visual observations. Also, it is often difficult to separate deficiency symptoms from those produced by pesticides, compaction, air and soil pollution, and biotic factors.

Soil Analysis. *Soil tests* are inexpensive guides to soil nutrient and pH levels. Soil tests indicate levels of phosphorus (P), potassium (K), and pH. Some testing labs will also include calcium (Ca), magnesium (Mg), lime requirement (based on a buffer pH test), and local problem elements, such as iron (Fe), or zinc (Zn). Additional tests are usually available upon request and for a price. Nitrogen is seldom determined because soil levels change rapidly. Some tests determine soil organic matter content and use this to make recommendations for nitrogen additions; this is common for home garden and agronomic crop reports.

Sampling procedures. Soil tests are of the greatest value when establishing a landscape. Deficiencies can be determined and corrected before planting. After planting, soil tests should be taken every three to five years, more frequently if the site has a history of nutritional problems, or if it contains excessive cuts or fills.

Professionals sample the area with a soil core probe, but a hand trowel or shovel can be used to remove samples from a larger hole. Take five to 10 cores per area and remove the turf and debris from the core. Mix these separate cores or subsamples to yield a final sample of about a pint. Generally, samples will be taken from the upper six to 10 inches of soil. A few sources suggest sampling two to four feet deep for trees, but there is minimal opportunity to change the nutrient status at this depth. The majority (90 percent according to some research) of the feeding roots of trees and shrubs are concentrated in the upper six to 18 inches of soil. For turf or annual flowers,

Table 10.1.
Nutrient element deficiency symptoms of woody plants

Nutrient	Symptoms
Nitrogen (N)	Small, pale young leaves. Uniform yellowing beginning with older leaves. Abscission of older leaves may occur.
Phosphorus (P)	Small, dark-green leaves with bronze to purple tinge. Older leaves are affected first.
Potassium (K)	Marginal burn of leaf tips and edges of older leaves; growth slows. Partial, interveinal chlorosis of recently matured leaves, beginning at tips, followed by necrosis.
Calcium (Ca)	Death of terminal buds; tip dieback, and chlorosis of young leaves. Browning of root tips; root injury often first apparent sign.
Magnesium (Mg)	Marginal chlorosis of older leaves then interveinal chlorosis and upward curling along leaf margins.
Iron (Fe)	Interveinal chlorosis of young leaves; veins usually remain distinct green.
Manganese (Mn)	Interveinal chlorosis, usually beginning at margins and progressing toward midribs, followed by necrotic spots between the veins.
Zinc (Zn)	Whorls of small, stiff, and mottled leaves near the tip of current season's growth. Bud formation reduced and interveinal chlorosis occurs. Citrus especially sensitive.
Sulfur (S)	Uniform yellowing of young leaves, but older foliage usually not affected. New growth is small and spindly.
Boron (B)	Terminal growth dies; lateral growth that develops is sparse. Leaves are small, thick, misshapen, and brittle.
Copper (Cu)	Terminal growth dies, preceded by rosetting. Leaf symptoms are not usually present as with Fe, Zn, or Mn. Veins lighter than blades.
Molybdenum (Mo)	Stunting and general lack of vigor; leaves cupped and distorted. Interveinal chlorosis preceded by marginal chlorosis, beginning with older leaves.

Adapted from: E. Smith. 1986. *Fertilizing Landscape and Field Grown Nursery Crops.* Ohio State University Cooperative Extension Service Bulletin 650, and H. Mathers. 1999. Uncommon deficiencies of woody ornamentals. *NMPro* 10(3):62.

the depth of the soil cores can be limited to six inches.

Sample atypical areas separately. Cuts or fills will have a different soil nutritional status and potential needs. Separate excessive slopes, open flat areas, and areas that are distinctly different. Be reasonable. Twelve different fertility programs cannot be easily developed for the same site. However, the manager should be cognizant of where problem areas are located.

Air dry moist samples at room temperature before sending them to the lab. Soil test services are available through most county Cooperative Extension offices and private laboratories. The Extension Service is less expensive than private labs, but the turn around is longer. The wait is even longer during planting season when the university or county lab will be backlogged with farm samples. Unfortunately, most soil analysis labs are geared to agronomic crops and not landscape plants. Private and some public labs have developed specific tests and recommendations programmed for turf, and a few have recommendations for established woody species.

Interpreting soil test results. Soil test results should be interpreted by someone with experience in evaluating laboratory data in relation to plants and soils in the given region. The test results reflect *soil levels.* Just because the nutrient level appears adequate does not mean that it is available to the plant. This is especially true for minor nutrients. The soil pH will be a helpful key in determining availability.

The soil nutrient levels in Table 10.3 serve as general *guidelines.* Levels below a medium range are deficient and corrective action should be taken. Levels in the medium ranges will probably not result in deficiency symptoms, but may limit growth. Corrective measures are advisable if the soil nutrient level is in the lower portion of the

Table 10.2.
General symptoms of nutrient toxicities for specific elements
Further examination and soil and foliar analyses should be conducted before definitive actions are taken.

Nutrient Element	Symptoms
Nitrogen (N)	In some plants (e.g. azalea), excess nitrates result in iron deficiency symptoms (interveinal chlorosis) because of poor iron metabolism. Toxicity results in injury and death of the root system. Yellowing or bleaching of new foliage may occur.
Phosphorus (P)	Very rare. Responses variable, including symptoms mimicking iron or zinc deficiency. Chlorosis of the older foliage may appear. Chlorotic areas are irregular as contrasted to regular symptoms of potassium and magnesium deficiencies.
Calcium (Ca)	Excessive Ca adversely affects availability of other essential elements, so symptoms can vary.
Boron (B)	Marginal chlorosis in older leaves, followed by necrosis at tips of the serrations or irregularities along the leaf margin. Abscission of the foliage usually follows.
Manganese (Mn)	Chlorosis and yellowing of new foliage with marginal cupping. Small, irregular, scattered, brown patches can occur. Apical dominance can be lost and auxiliary shoots can proliferate. May appear because of the increase of free Mn in highly acid conditions or because of poor aeration.
Chlorine (Cl)	Burning of leaf tips or margins, bronzing, premature yellowing and abscission.
Zinc (Zn)	Light-green, transparent water-soaked areas occur along veins of leaflets and leaves. Leaves turn yellow to brown and drop.
Aluminum (Al)	Death of the plant is usually preceded by variable chlorosis and necrosis of the foliage. Usually results from highly acid conditions. Pink hydrangea flowers become blue when aluminum is present.

Adapted from: *Soil Testing and Fertilizer Applications for Nursery Management and Production.* University of Minnesota Agricultural Extension Service Bulletin AG-BU-2830, and H. Mathers. 1999. Common toxicities of woody ornamentals. *NMPro* 10(3):62.

medium range. Application of nitrogen to the landscape as complete fertilizer may be helpful if the levels of P and/or K are in the upper portion of the medium range. A soil nutrient level above the medium range indicates the soil does not require, and will not respond to, the additional nutrient.

Soil test results are reported in *pounds per acre* for the macronutrients and *parts per million* (ppm) for micronutrients. One part per million equals around two pounds per acre at plow depth (six to eight inches). Soil test results for phosphorus and potassium, and more importantly their recommendations, may be described as *nutrient elements* (P or K) or as the fertilizer elements (P_2O_5 and K_2O) per acre or other given unit area.

Convert recommendations in P to P_2O_5 and K to K_2O to calculate amounts of specific fertilizers necessary. The conversion from the elemental to the fertilizer form (and vice versa) is:

$$P = P_2O_5 \times 0.44$$
$$P_2O_5 = P \times 2.3$$

$$K = K_2O \times 0.83$$
$$K_2O = K \times 1.2$$

For Example...

If a soil test indicated that a site contained 20 pounds of P per acre, and the manager wished to increase this to 80 pounds phosphorus (P) per acre, how much P_2O_5 would be required?

80 pounds P - 20 pounds P = 60 pounds P required.

60 pounds P x 2.3 = 138 pounds of P_2O_5 required.

To apply 100 pounds of potassium (K) per acre would require:

100 x 1.2 = 120 pounds of K_2O

Table 10.3.
Ranges for soil test values for most landscape plants

Soil levels	P (#/A)	K (#/A)	Mg (#/A)	Zn (#/A)
Very high	100+		>500	>18
High	80 – 100	> 400	250 – 500	6 – 18
Medium	40 – 80	200 – 400	100 – 250	3 – 6
Low	20 – 40	100 – 200	50 – 100	1 – 3
Very low	<20	<100	<50	<1

Table 10.4.
Desired soil test levels of calcium (Ca), based on soil texture, and soil pH for most landscape plants

Soil texture	Pounds Ca/A
Sandy	800 - 1000
Sandy/silty loams	1000 - 3000
Clay loams	3000 - 4500
Clays	>4500
Soil pH:	5.0-7.5

Table 10.5.
Soluble salt levels affect landscape plant

Soluble salts:	
< 2.0 millimhos /cm:	No growth problems
2.0-4.0 millimhos /cm:	Expect injury to plants
4.0-8.0 millimhos /cm:	Widespread injury to landscape plants

Foliar or Tissue Analyses

Foliage, tissue, or leaf analyses determine the mineral element content within a plant. It is an important tool for establishing and maintaining a proper nutrition program and for diagnosing suspected mineral deficiencies or excesses. Foliar analysis can be used over a wide range of soils and climatic conditions. It should be used in coordination with soil tests to develop a better nutritional picture of the site. Foliage can be analyzed at university laboratories through the local Cooperative Extension office, or by private laboratories. Each laboratory has specific sampling procedures, but the following suggestions apply:

1. Samples should be taken between mid-June and mid-September (mid-growing season) from the most recently matured leaves. These occur midway on the current season's growth. If sampling for problem diagnosis, be sure to sample both affected and healthy plants for a comparison. Collect soil samples in the same area for analysis.

2. Take 30 to 100 leaves from deciduous species or 50 terminal cuttings from narrow-leafed evergreens. Do not collect diseased, injured, or dead foliage.

3. If necessary, wash samples with a 0.1 percent detergent solution to remove dust and residues. Rinse thoroughly and dry the samples. Send samples to the testing laboratory in the mailer supplied. Follow the directions specified by the testing laboratory.

4. Obtain professional assistance in interpreting the results of tissue tests.

Interpreting foliar analysis results. Table 10.6 serves as a *guideline* for foliar levels of various elements typically found in normal and deficient woody species. This information was collected after extensive evaluation of healthy and abnormal plants. Consult with the Cooperative Extension Service or other local experts for specific regional information or peculiarities.

Fertilizers

The fertilizers used to maintain or correct the soil or plant nutritional levels vary in content, application method, and cost. Fertilizer selection should be based on more than just price. The specific use, application equipment and firm's operation, as well as price, affect fertilizer selection. Consider the following when selecting or purchasing fertilizers.

a. *Analysis or grade* is the percentage (%) by package weight of N-P_2O_5-K_2O in the material. A 20-10-5 fertilizer contains 20 percent N, 10 percent P_2O_5, and 5 percent K_2O. Fertilizer is sold as the oxides of phosphorus and potassium, not the amount of actual element available. The conversion from elemental to oxide (fertilizer) was presented earlier. A fertilizer containing all three major fertilizer elements, nitrogen, phosphorus, and potassium, is a *complete fertilizer*.

For Example...

A 100 lb bag of 13-13-13 contains 13 lb N, 13 lb P_2O_5 and 13 lb of K_2O.

A 15 lb box of 8-4-2 contains 1.2 lb N, 0.6 lb P_2O_5 and 0.3 lb K_2O.

---

b. *Ratio* is the mathematical relationship of one fertilizer element to another within the analysis. A 20-10-5 has a 4:2:1 ratio; 12-12-12 is a 1:1:1 ratio fertilizer. Fertilizers are sometimes specified or recommended as ratios, especially for turfgrass management. Ratios higher in phosphorus or potassium are used to correct deficiencies while controlling nitrogen rates.

Table 10.6.

Foliar element ranges for woody plants

Data are based on recently matured leaves, midway on shoots of current season's growth for deciduous plants and on terminal cuttings from evergreens. These serve as guidelines for interpreting tissue analyses of landscape plants.

Macronutrient	Low (%)	Sufficient (%)	High (%)
Nitrogen			
evergreen	1.0-1.5	1.5-3.5	3.5-5.5
deciduous	1.5-2.0	2.0-4.5	4.5-7.0
Phosphorus	0.1-0.2	0.2-0.6	0.6-1.0
Potassium	1.0-1.5	1.5-3.5	3.5-6.0
Calcium	0.2-0.5	0.5-2.5	2.5-4.0
Magnesium			
evergreens	0.1-0.2	0.2-2.0	2.0-2.5
deciduous	0.2-0.3	0.3-1.0	1.0-2.5

Micronutrient	Low (ppm)	Sufficient (ppm)	High (ppm)
Boron	20-30	30-50	50-100
Copper	4.0-6.0	6.0-50	50-200
Iron	30-50	50-700	700-1,000
Manganese	20-30	30-800	800-1,000
Molybdenum	0.4-0.6	0.6-6.0	6.0-20
Zinc	25-30	30-75	75-100

Adapted From: *Fertilizing Landscape and Field Grown Nursery Crops.* Ohio State University Cooperative Extension Service Bulletin 650.

Table 10.7.

Nutrient content (%), reaction, solubility, and salt index of common inorganic fertilizers used in landscape management

	Percentage composition									
Fertilizer	N	P_2O_5	K_2O	MgO	CaO	S	Other	Salt Index[a]	Acidic or Basic[b]	Water Solubility
Nitrogen source materials										
Ammonium nitrate	34							105	A	High
Calcium nitrate	15				4			53	B	High
Potassium nitrate	14		47					74	B	High
Sodium nitrate	16							100	B	High
Ammonium sulfate	21					24		69	A	Medium
Monoammonium phosphate	11	52						26	A	Low
Diammonium phosphate	18	46						29	A	Very low
Urea	45							75	A	High
Phosphorus source materials										
Monoammonium phosphate	11	52						30	A	Low
Diammonium phosphate	18	46						34	A	Very low
Monopotassium phosphate		52	35					8	B	Medium
Superphosphate, single		20			23	9		8	N	Very low
Superphosphate, triple		45			20	2		10	N	Very low
Potassium source materials										
Potassium chloride			60					116	N	High
Potassium nitrate	13		44					74	N	High
Monopotassium phosphate		52	35					8	N	Medium
Potassium sulfate			50			18		46	N	Medium
Sulfate of potash-magnesia			22	18		22		43	N	Medium
Magnesium source materials										
Dolomite				22	31			1	B	Very low
Magnesium ammonium phosphate	6	29					16 Mg	8	A	Low
Magnesium sulfate				16		13	20 Mg	44	N	High
Sulfate of potash-magnesia			22	18		22		43	N	Medium
Calcium source materials										
Dolomite				22	31			1	N	Very low
Lime calcium					57			5	B	Very low
Superphosphate, single		20			23	9		8	N	Very low
Gypsum					30	16		8	N	Very low
Calcium Nitrate	15				3			53	B	High
Other[c]										
Boric Acid							13 B			Soluble
Copper sulfate						12	25 Cu			Soluble
Ferrous sulfate							20 Fe			Soluble
Iron chelate (EDDHA/DPTA)							6-10 Fe			Soluble
Manganese sulfate						13	25 Mn			Soluble
Zinc sulfate						12	23 Zn			Soluble

[a]Salt index. A measure of the effect of fertilizers on the concentration of the soil solution. The concentration of the soil solution is compared against an equal weight of sodium nitrate, which was assigned a value of 100.

[b]A = Acid reaction, B = Basic reaction, N = Neutral

[c]These nutrients are applied in such minute quantities that any effect on soil acidity is negligible except for iron sulfate which can be applied in quantities large enough to increase acidity.

Adapted from: Swanson, B., C. Rosen, R. Munter, and C. Lane. 1986. *Soil Testing and Fertilizer Applications for Nursery Management and Production*. University of Minnesota Agricultural Extension Service Bulletin AG-BU-2830.

c. The source of nutrients is important. The percent of fast- versus slow-release nitrogen will affect duration, result, and price of the material. *Acid-based* fertilizers are preferred for acid-loving plants and to lower soil pH.

For Example...

The fertilizer label summarizes a great deal of valuable information. The label indicates sources of nitrogen units, and whether they are from a controlled release source. The fertilizer in Illustration 10.1 has a guaranteed analysis of 28-3-8, with 5.1 percent from a coated slow-release nitrogen, and 3.6 percent from a water-insoluble source. The remainder of the nitrogen is in a readily available form.

d. Handling ease, method of application (dry or liquid), and *labor requirement* obviously affect purchase decisions. It is possible to purchase fertilizer and herbicide or insecticide combinations for use in turf. Combination products reduce application labor but these materials are more expensive. More importantly, determine if the combination product delivers the proper amount of nutrients *and* the necessary pesticide rate for the maintenance program. Separate applications of fertilizers and pesticides provide better options than combination materials.

Bulk fertilizer is much less expensive than bagged material. I remember one young manager who decided to save a great deal of money and ordered two tons of fertilizer in bulk. It made quite a nice pile in the middle of his garage. He had no place to properly store it and lost more in handling, labor, and waste than was saved.

e. Price varies with manufacturer, distributor, and brand. Price depends on source of nutrients, quantity purchased, transportation costs, incorporation of other materials (pesticides), and the distributor's markup. Calculate the cost of fertilizer elements by dividing the price per pound by the analysis percentage (as a decimal).

For Example...

If ammonium nitrate (33-0-0) costs $15.50 per 100 pounds; then $0.1550 per pound ÷ 0.33 (33% N) = $0.47 per pound nitrogen

If urea (45-0-0) costs $16.00 per 100 pounds, then $0.16 per pound ÷ 0.45 = $0.36 per pound of nitrogen.

Nitrogen is the least expensive fertilizer element. The cost of nitrogen increases in blended and slow-release materials. Phosphorus, especially in a completely soluble form, is the most expensive macronutrient. Micronutrients are very expensive on a per-pound basis, but are used in small quantities per acre.

Types of Fertilizers

The most familiar products are dry *inorganic* fertilizers. These are chemical salts that provide readily available plant nutrients. Inorganic fertilizers are often salts blended with low-cost filler. Inorganic fertilizers may provide specific elements, such as ammonium nitrate (33-0-0) or urea (45-0-0), or several elements when they are combined as blends, such as 27-3-3.

Liquid or *water-soluble* fertilizers are used in the greenhouse and turfgrass industries. Water-soluble formulations may be sprayed on plant fo-

Illustration 10.1.

Fertilizer labels list the guaranteed total nitrogen that the product contains by percent and typically list the actual nitrogen sources. Even though the product below is labeled as a slow-release material, more than half of the nitrogen is a quick release form (urea).

TURFGRASS FERTILIZER
Slow release fertilizer with
IBDU and SCU
28-3-8

Guaranteed analysis
Total nitrogen (N)* 28.0%

1.2% Ammoniacal N
3.6% Water-insoluble N
5.1% Coated slow-release urea N
18.1% Walter-soluble N

Available phosphoric acid (P_2O_5) . . . 3.0%
Soluble potash (K_2O) 8.0%
Sulfur (S) 7.0%

*Derived from ammoniated phosphates, urea, isobutylidene diurea, and sulfur coated urea.

liage or injected into the soil. In the soil, soluble nutrients act similar to those from dry formulations; there is no difference in the source of nutrients to the plant. Water-soluble forms of phosphorus and potassium are expensive but are valuable for providing nutrients when conventional application methods are unavailable.

Acidic fertilizers are available in dry and soluble formulations. These products use sulfur-based or other acidic sources of the nutrient, such as ammonium sulfate or ammonium phosphate. Acidic materials slightly lower soil pH over time. They are used for fertilizing Ericaceous species or where high soil or irrigation water pH is a problem. These materials are more expensive than other nutrient formulations but are worth the additional cost in specialized situations.

Slow-release formulations reduce nutrient loss due to leaching and provide controlled release of nutrients over time. Slow-release forms of potassium are used in turf management, especially sand based greens. In mineral soils, depletion of phosphorus and potassium is relatively slow; therefore, there is little need for slow-release formulations. Depletion and loss of nitrogen in most soils, however, is rapid. Controlled-release products are expensive but offer advantages, especially in turf management. Use of controlled-release materials may not be justified in ordinary tree and shrub care; however, they have advantages in low fertility and high rainfall areas, or where economics or inaccessibility dictates infrequent fertilizer applications.

Controlling release of nitrogen

Several mechanisms are used to control the release of nitrogen from landscape and turfgrass fertilizers.

Coatings. Coatings are described as any type of physical barrier (e.g. wax, sulfur, plastic) that surrounds a water-soluble fertilizer core. Included in this group are products such as Osmocote®, PolyOn®, Duration®, Nutricote®, and sulfur coated urea (SCU). The type and amount of coating generally regulates nitrogen release. A number of the new generation plastic coated fertilizers can have a significant effect on reducing the environmental impact of fertilizer. With most of these materials, release rate is tied closely to temperature.

Release rate is slower in the spring and fall than during the hot summer months.

Generally the amount of sulfur on a SCU fertilizer will have minimal effect on the soil pH. It should not be relied upon to reduce the pH of alkaline soils.

Synthetic organics. Synthetic organics consist of two sub-categories: materials whereby nitrogen release is dependent on microbial activity, and nitrogen release by a material with low water solubility.

Nitrogen release dependent on microbial activity. All of the urea formaldehyde reaction products (UF) are clear examples of nitrogen fertilizers that are dependent upon microbial activity for the release of nitrogen. These products range in total nitrogen from 38 to 40 percent, and have been used by the landscape industry for more than 40 years. This large class of products results from a reaction between water-soluble urea and formaldehyde under a controlled set of conditions. The mixture of short and long-chain nitrogen polymers can be varied depending on the amounts of specific reactants and the reactor conditions. The very short chain nitrogen products offer us an inexpensive, safe, nitrogen fertilizer that is immediately available. Methylene urea is one of these short-term products. The longest chain products provide long-term (six to 18 months) nitrogen fertilizers. These different reaction products can be classified as *cold water-soluble* (immediately available), *cold water-insoluble* (available over a moderate period), and *hot water-insoluble* nitrogen (release over a long period or unavailable).

Actual release rate of the nitrogen from urea formaldehyde products depends on soil microbial activity. Those conditions (i.e. temperature, moisture, oxygen) that favor strong microbial activity will increase the availability of nitrogen from these products. When soils are cold and wet, the release of nitrogen is slowed greatly with this type of slow-release fertilizer.

Urea formaldehyde and methylene urea nitrogen materials are very common in turf and ornamental fertilizer products. These products are available in micro-fine powders for soil injection in turf and ornamental applications. Urea formaldehyde is formulated with phosphorus and potassium into tablets for use at planting.

Low water solubility. Today, the only commercially available product in this category is isobutylidene diurea (IBDU), a 31% nitrogen material. The method to manufacture IBDU is similar to that of UF; however, the final product is more homogenous and does not contain the mixture of nitrogen polymers, as is the case with UF's. The nitrogen is released slowly by hydrolysis to urea and this process is controlled largely by the size of the fertilizer particle. Large chunks of IBDU last longer than small particle sizes. Release of nitrogen from IBDU is less affected by temperature when compared to the UF's; so, IBDU makes a good nitrogen source for late season fertilization of cool season turf.

Natural organic materials. Natural *organic* fertilizers (blood, bone and fish meal, sewage sludge, manures, and others) are low in nitrogen (usually less than six percent) and other elements. Nutrient availability depends on microbial release. Nitrogen is in an organic form and available slowly over a long period. Natural organics are low in the percentage of a given nutrient, expensive per pound of plant nutrient, difficult to handle, dependent upon the rate of organic decomposition to release nutrients, and may produce unpleasant odors. Research has proven conclusively that there is no difference in plant absorption and uptake of nutrients, regardless of whether they originate from chemical salts or from natural organic materials. All plant nutrient elements, whether from organic or inorganic sources are absorbed as inorganic ions, with the exception of urea, which may be absorbed as a compound. A plant cannot distinguish between ions originating from organic or inorganic sources.

Organic fertilizers, however, are making significant inroads in the landscape and turfgrass management markets. Composting and digestion are environmentally feasible methods to dispose of organic wastes that were once buried in landfills. Composting and digestion technology continue to improve. Waste handling operations have also increased in scale so that the material quan-

Table 10.8.
Approximate nutrient content (% analysis) of several organic fertilizers

Fertilizer	N	P_2O_5	K_2O	Comments
Blood, dried	12.0	1.5	0.5	Rapidly available source of nitrogen.
Bat Guano	6.0	9.0	3.0	Partially decomposed bat manure from caves in southwest US.
Bird Guano	13.0	11.0	2.0	Partially decomposed bird manure from islands near South America.
Kelp or Seaweed	1.0	0.5	9.0	Good source of potassium.
Manure				Manure is typically low in nutrients, but adds nutrients
Cattle	0.5	0.3	0.5	when used as a soil conditioner. Avoid fresh manure.
Chicken	1.0	0.5	0.8	Nutrient content varies, particularly with bedding
Horse	0.6	0.3	0.6	materials used. Uncomposted animal manure often
Sheep	0.9	0.6	0.8	contains weed seed.
Swine	0.6	0.5	1.0	
Raw bone meal	4.0	20.0	0.0	Phosphorus very slowly soluble.
Steamed bone meal	2.0	27.0	0.0	Phosphorus is more soluble, some nitrogen lost by steaming.
Cotton seed meal	6.0	2.5	2.0	Acid in reaction, good for ericaceous plants.
Hoof and horn meal	14.0	0.0	0.0	Good source of organic nitrogen.
Peanut hulls	1.0	0.0	1.0	Low in nutrients.
Sewage sludge	2.0	1.0	0.5	Varies with source; avoid those possibly contaminated with heavy metals.
Tobacco stems	1.5	1.0	6.0	Good source of potassium; alkaline reaction.
Wood ashes	0.0	2.0	6.0	Source of potassium; very alkaline.

Adapted from: *Soil Testing and Fertilizer Applications for Nursery Management and Production.* University of Minnesota Agricultural Extension Service Bulletin AGBU2830.

tities have increased and the price has decreased. Organic fertilizers are still expensive on a per pound nutrient basis.

The attitudes of contractors and clientele are also changing. New emphasis is being placed on non-chemical alternatives and ecologically sound management. Marketing of organic materials has become fierce; confusion and misconceptions have resulted.

Several claims have been made for organic fertilizers, with and without research support. Contrary to popular belief, plants will grow well using inorganic or organic nutrient sources.

Organic fertilizers have been shown to suppress some soil-borne pathogens. Research is continuing in this area. Some organic fertilizer marketers claim their products reduce thatch in turfgrass. Fertilizer source, however, has had no effect on the accumulation of thatch, according to published research. Natural organic fertilizers do add small amounts of organic matter to the soil. The effect may become significant over a period of time. Organic fertilizers reduce nitrate movement; however, that same benefit is accorded synthetic slow-release nitrogen sources.

One commercial source, Milorganite® (6-2-0-4% Fe), is comprised of dried and processed sewage sludge from Milwaukee, WI. It has long been, and is still used, as a non-burning, slow-release fertilizer in some segments of the turf and golf course industries. The nitrogen content of natural organic fertilizers is seldom greater than two to three percent. Natural organic fertilizers with a nitrogen analysis greater than this are supplemented or fortified with organic or inorganic chemical fertilizers.

Surface Application Methods

Surface application of dry fertilizer (ornamentals and turf). Application of dry fertilizer to the soil surface is the most economical and fastest delivery method. Surface application is appropriate for nutrients that move readily in the soil, notably nitrogen and most chelated micro-

---

Table 10.9.
Definitions for organic fertilizers

There are no universally accepted terms or legal definitions describing organic products used in the landscape. The Professional Lawn Care Association of America (PLCAA) has provided definitions to standardize marketing and to reduce misunderstandings. The following are not legal definitions, but guidelines for landscape professionals.

- *Natural:* Products derived from animal, biological, mineral, or plant source in a form substantially the same as it occurs in nature. The materials may be altered or manipulated to improve distribution.
- *Organic:* Any substance containing carbon is organic. Organic materials may be naturally occurring or manmade.
- *Natural based:* A mixture that includes natural materials, but the proportion is not generally defined. Some sources feel that the material should contain at least 50 percent natural material by weight or volume to deserve the term natural based.
- *Organic based:* A mixture that includes some portion of organic materials. Some sources feel that the material should contain 50 percent or more organic material by weight or volume to deserve the term organic based.
- *Natural fertilizer:* A substance composed only of natural organic and/or natural inorganic fertilizers and fillers.
- *Natural organic fertilizer:* Fertilizers derived from plant or animal products containing one or more essential elements for plant growth. These materials may be subjected to biological degradation.
- *Natural inorganic fertilizer:* A nutrient source produced by or existing in nature. These materials may be subjected to biological degradation. It may be altered in its original state for distribution.

225

nutrients. Research has shown no difference in plant response if nitrogen was surface applied, applied as a deep root application or liquid injected into the soil. Soil applied methods were superior to foliar application of nitrogen.

For an individual tree or groups of trees, surface apply fertilizer to the approximate crown area. This can be calculated as a circle or rectangle. The crown area is a convenient area to calculate and apply fertilizer. Tree roots extend beyond the drip line; however, there are more than sufficient roots beneath the crown to absorb the surface-applied material.

Fertilizer can be surface applied with drop or impeller (cyclone-type) spreaders. When using a drop spreader, divide the amount of material to be applied in half and apply the two halves separately. Make the second application perpendicular, or at a right angle, to the first. Irrigate the area to remove granules from the turf and begin moving it into the root zone.

Surface application to shrub beds is made over the entire bed. Be careful of the turf if applying high rates of nitrogen or at times other than scheduled turf fertilization. Most managers do not schedule separate applications for shrub beds. They make sure that the material applied to turf is also applied to shrub areas. DO NOT apply a broadleaf weed-and-feed product using an impeller type spreader near ornamental beds. Irrigate lightly after surface fertilizer applications to prevent damage to groundcovers in shrub beds.

Turf beneath trees in under- or non-fertilized turf may be stimulated resulting in an "oasis" effect. Extending the treatment area past the drip line compensates for this. Fertilized turf may be over-stimulated if high rates of nitrogen are surface applied. Split-surface, deep root applications, or soil injection, will reduce damage if additional nitrogen over and above that applied to the grass is required.

Surface application of soluble fertilizer through irrigation (ornamentals and turf). Soluble fertilizers can be applied through irrigation. This is referred to as *fertigation*, and is by no means a new technique. It has been applied with success for over 30 years in the agricultural and golf course industries. Fertigation can be effective for soil-mobile nutrients and newer technology is making affordable proportioner sys-

Photo 10.2. Surface application is the most cost effective method of applying nutrients that are relatively mobile in the soil.

tems for small commercial and residential proprieties. Soluble nutrient formulations are readily available but offer no other special advantages over dry formulations. However, the cost of labor and equipment to apply dry formulations is eliminated. Soil injection of water-soluble fertilizer is an excellent method to fertilize and water trees with restricted or limited surface area access.

Equipment costs vary with size and complexity of area to be covered. Golf courses and agricultural fields may require from $3,000 to $10,000 for equipment requiring electrical power, drainage for waste water, a concrete foundation, a building, and storage tanks. Smaller application equipment for residential and commercial sites may range from $100 to $3,000.

Fertigation is most frequently used for summer applications of nitrogen to warm season turf in the South. It has limitations for cool season turf and will not likely be adapted in the majority of the nation. Wholesale application of soluble nutrients is an environmentally questionable practice in light of concerns about water and groundwater pollution.

Subsurface Application Methods

Deep Root Application (mostly trees). *Punch or drill method* application of fertilizers into the root zone of the tree assures availability of non-mobile nutrients such as phosphorus or potassium. Historically, this has been the method for applying fertilizers to trees. Holes are punched on two-foot centers with a steel bar or drilled (by a manual or power soil auger) under the crown, starting two to three feet from the trunk. This requires 250 holes per 1,000 square feet. The holes should be eight to 12 inches deep. Fertilizer placement should be shallow enough so that the majority of the roots can intercept the soluble nutrients.

The fertilizer is divided into equal increments and placed into each hole. Dry fertilizer can be mixed with sand or other material for easier application. The holes may be filled with the original soil, sand, calcined clay, perlite, or other granular material.

This method is expensive and time consuming. Punching 12-inch deep holes every two feet with an iron bar makes for a *very* long day. Using a punch bar may also compact the sides of the holes, reducing air and fertilizer movement. Soil augers are preferred for deep root fertilizer applications as they avoid compacting the holes and are much more rapid.

Deep root application avoids the oasis of surface applied nitrogen. The operator can use higher rates of nitrogen in a single application with no damage to the turfgrass. It may, however, produce tufts of green grass in the spring. It is an effective method to move phosphorus and potassium into the root zone if they are required. This method is also used to successfully apply sulfur:iron sulfate mixtures to combat iron chlorosis. It is seldom used in shrub beds as it can damage the root systems of many species.

Drilling holes with an auger is also effective in relieving compaction beneath established trees. Filling the holes with sand, perlite, vermiculite, calcined clay, or other aggregate produces long-term air channels to the root system. Research in Ohio showed trees in poorly drained silt and clay-loam soils benefited as much from drilled holes with no fertilizer as they did from drilled holes with fertilizer.

Soil Injection (trees). *Dry material injection or the injection* of dry fertilizer, usually mixed with sand or other solid carrier, with high-pressure air requires specialized and expensive equipment and is not widely used in the industry. In-

Photo 10.3. Soil augers are used to add fertilizers to the root zone. Augers also relieve compaction and provide air channels. Photograph by James Robbins.

jection of dry fertilizer can use any source of nutrients, including slow-release formulations. The blast fractures soil and relieves compaction; the sand or other aggregate carriers or bulking agents may further alleviate compaction.

Liquid injection of fertilizers for trees and shrubs has become common. Shallow injections on mounds, berms, or slopes, and in compacted soil, reduces the amount of fertilizer run off due to rain or irrigation. Liquid injection is more rapid and economic than punch and drill methods. The high-pressure hydraulic sprayers used by lawn services and pesticide applicators can be easily adapted to soil injection. Fertilizer solutions are corrosive, but stainless steel or plastic lined tanks reduce equipment maintenance. Pumps, lines, and non-protected tanks must be cleaned thoroughly after fertilizer application.

Injection sites should be two to three feet apart, somewhat wider than recommended for punch or drill deep root applications, and eight to 12 inches deep. Limit pressure to 150 to 200 psi. The fertilizer is distributed equally among the holes. Delivery can be calibrated by meters, or more commonly, by timing each injection to determine the total amount of fertilizer solution, and therefore nitrogen, applied. Soil injection can also improve aeration and water penetration.

Numerous brands and types of soluble complete and specialized fertilizers are available. Many managers mix their own, adding expensive soluble phosphorus and potassium only if the situ-

Photo 10.4. A soil injection lance used for liquid injection fertilizers into the root zone of trees and shrubs. Photograph by James Robbins.

ation warrants. Urea is frequently used as an inexpensive soluble nitrogen source. A micro-fine ground urea formaldehyde product is available to provide slow-release nitrogen. This material can be used in soil injection systems without damage to equipment, according to the manufacturer. Soluble iron and other micronutrients, as well as acidifying agents, are also available.

Liquid soil injection is an efficient method of incorporating fertilizer into the soil and is becoming the most popular method of providing supplementary fertilization for landscape trees.

Tree spikes (**mainly trees**). Tree spikes, available from several manufacturers, are solid, bullet-shaped chunks of fertilizer that are implanted into soil. The spikes contain a complete fertilizer with a slow-release nitrogen source, with or without micronutrients. They are marketed as different formulations for trees, shrubs, fruit trees, and broadleaf evergreens. The number of spikes driven into the ground depends on the size of the tree to be treated.

As a fertilizer, they are probably the most expensive source of nitrogen available. The spikes are also probably the least effective method of fertilization. The salt content of the fertilizer material is very high; turf is often killed in areas surrounding soil-implanted spikes. It requires several months for the fertilizer salts from the spikes

to dissolve and disperse in the soil to a level low enough to allow effective absorption without potential damage to the roots. Palm fertilizer spikes containing magnesium, potassium, and manganese have been used for correcting deficiencies of these elements. Some landscape managers that I have spoken with have been pleased with the results of these products in palm nutrition programs.

Foliar Application Methods (Trees, Ornamentals, and Turf)

Application of nutrients to leaves is not as effective as soil treatment. Leaves absorb nutrients; however, the absorption may be limited. Foliar sprays can be used to apply macro- and micronutrients in situations where traditional soil application is difficult or impossible, such as trees in parking lots, above- or below-ground planters, or plants where the root zone is covered by a surface.

Fertilizers used in aerial sprays are soluble and dilute. Addition of a surfactant increases nutrient foliar absorption; however, excessive surfactant may cause the fertilizer to burn the leaves. Foliar fertilization must be repeated more frequently, up to six or more times per year in some situations. Thorough coverage is essential, and plant absorption and damage are influenced by temperature, moisture, and relative humidity. Leaf and over-spray residues may not be desirable. Foliar application on hot, sunny days may result in leaf damage or defoliation.

Trunk Implants and Injections (Trees)

Trunk implants and injections of nutrients are effective ways to supply micronutrients (iron, manganese, and possibly zinc) that would be tied up if soil applied. There are no reasons to apply nitrogen, phosphorus, or potassium as a trunk injection. The amount that can be supplied via injections or implants is negligible compared to the plant's requirements and the possibility of defoliating the tree is very high.

One implant system available from several companies uses dry water-soluble salts or chelates of micronutrients in gelatin capsules. These gelatin capsules are inserted into holes drilled into the tree trunk; they dissolve and the payload is delivered to the leaves via the transpiration stream. Some implants require the hole be sealed,

Photo 10.5. Foliar application of soluble nutrients is the only way to fertilize some trees where the root zone is inaccessible.

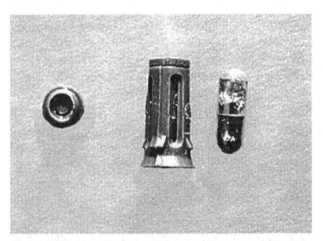

Photo 10.6. A solid implant of an iron compound for treatment of iron chlorosis in trees. Treatments last up to two to three years. Photograph by James Robbins.

but others do not. Insecticides and other materials are also available as implant capsules.

Pressure injection systems using bottled nitrogen, compressed air, or an adapted pressure sprayer, are used to inject micronutrients, growth regulators, insecticides, and fungicides into a tree.

Most species can be successfully treated in this manner; however, it appears butternut (*Juglans cinerea*), shagbark hickory (*Carya ovata*), white ash (*Fraxinus americana*), some maples, firs, and pines, and a few other species, do not readily accept injection solutions.

The Mauget® system uses a small volume of concentrated nutrient or other solutions injected into trees under slight pressure using plastic reservoirs. This system makes the smallest wound of any of the injection or implant systems discussed. Several variations of this method are available from other manufacturers.

A *gravity-fed system* is used to inject iron sulfate for iron chlorosis (Medi-ject®). Iron sulfate and water are placed in a reservoir elevated above and connected to several injection sites at the base of the tree trunk. The material enters the trunk and is carried via the transpiration stream. Time required for emptying the reservoir varies and is much more rapid under conditions where the tree is rapidly transpiring.

Objection to all injections and implants centers on the wounding of the tree. Trees are permanently damaged by injections and potential benefits must outweigh this damage. Injection wounds provide potential entry to decay and disease organisms, discoloring of the wood, and possible weakening of the trunks of small trees. Other potential problems include sap leakage from holes, damage to the cambium at insertion points, and leaf burn and defoliation when too much nutrient is applied at the wrong time to sensitive species.

To minimize potential injury to the tree:

1) use the smallest injection holes possible;

2) inject as low on the trunk or root flare as possible;

3) space sites in a spiral around the trunk; and

4) always follow label directions for recommended rates and materials.

Trunk injections and implants are effective and efficient methods of providing some micronutrients and other materials to a tree that could not be accommodated in other ways. Trunk treatment with micronutrients will last up to several years. Certain precautions should be taken, however, to reduce potential plant injury. I know of

Photo 10.7. Power injection of trees can result in bark spitting and trunk cracks to some species if the injection is improperly done.

Photo 10.8. The Mauget® system can be easily used to inject minor nutrients, fungicides, or insecticides under low pressure. Photograph by James Robbins.

no situations where injections or implants have been recommended for or applied to shrubs.

Soil Reaction (pH)

Soil reaction, or pH, refers to the *acidity* or *alkalinity* of the soil. It is a measure of the relative concentration of hydrogen (H+) ions. Soil pH is measured on a 14-point scale. The middle, pH 7.0, is neutral. Values greater than pH 7.0 are alkaline, and those below are acidic. The scale is logarithmic. A soil pH of 6.0 is, therefore, ten times more alkaline (less acid) than a pH of 5.0. A pH of 7.0 is 100 times more alkaline than pH 5.0; a pH of 8.0 is 1,000 times more alkaline, and so on.

Soil reaction information is necessary for determining soil fertilizer requirements and for developing fertilization programs. The pH of a soil affects the availability of nutrients to the plant and the activity of microorganisms. Soil pH is not the only factor governing nutrient availability, but it has a tremendous impact (Figure 10.2). All micronutrients, except molybdenum and chloride, become less available as soil alkalinity increases. Phosphorus also becomes less available in high pH soils. Iron and manganese become seriously deficient in alkaline soils. The pH at which iron and manganese deficiencies affect growth or elicit symptoms varies among plant species and individuals within a species. Conversely, manganese and aluminum can reach toxic levels under highly acid conditions.

Most plants will tolerate a range of pH, usually from 5.0 to 7.5. A pH of 8.3 is as high as calcium-based soils can go. Soils with higher pH values involve sodium or other salts, and growth is limited to tolerant species. Soil pH below 4.0 is toxic to all but a few tolerant species. The best or ideal soil pH for ornamental plant growth is between 5.5 and 6.5.

Adjusting Soil pH

Soil pH can be adjusted by addition of *lime* or *sulfur*. The amount of material necessary depends upon the level of change desired, soil texture, organic matter, and the material used. Fine-textured soils or those high in organic matter require more lime or sulfur to attain a given change in pH than coarser-textured soils.

Photo 10.9. The Medi-ject® system infuses iron sulfate for treatment of iron chlorosis in trees. Results last for up to five or more years. Photograph by James Robbins.

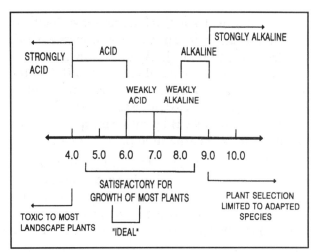

Figure 10.1. Soil pH.

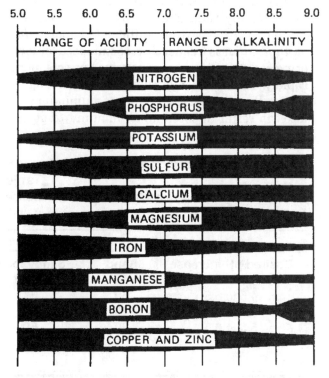

Figure 10.2. Availability of nutrients in a mineral soil.

Acid soil pH is moderated by addition of ground or *agricultural limestone* (calcium carbonate) or *dolomite* (calcium magnesium carbonate). *Quicklime* (calcium and magnesium oxides) and *slaked lime* (calcium and magnesium hydroxides) act more quickly than limestone, but they are more expensive and difficult to handle. The duration of the change in pH is shorter than from limestone. Particle size also influences reactivity. Finer particles affect soil pH more quickly than coarse materials.

Soil pH should never be adjusted except under the guidance of a soil test. The amount of amendment necessary is determined by a separate soil test using a buffer to measure the potential soil acidity or alkalinity. Table 10.10 indicates the approximate amounts of ground limestone or dolomitic lime necessary to achieve a change in pH. These amounts are based upon a water extract pH.

To be most effective, lime should be spread evenly over the soil surface and incorporated. Ideally, pH adjustment should occur before planting. Lime can be surface applied over existing turf and around ornamental plants with no damage. The change in pH by surface applied material will take longer to occur since the limestone must dissolve and leach into the soil.

Applying agricultural sulfur acidifies alkaline soils. The amount of sulfur required to lower pH is greatly influenced by the buffering capacity of the soil. Limestone-based soils are difficult to successfully acidify for long periods. The carbonate in the soil provides a constant source of neutralizing material. It is much easier to increase soil pH, than it is to lower it. Again, sulfur should be added on the basis of a soil test. Table 10.11 provides approximate rates of agricultural sulfur based upon water pH for three soil types. Like lime, modification of soil pH by sulfur is most effective when it can be incorporated prior to planting.

Sulfur can be applied to turf and existing ornamental plantings. Foliar burn can occur during periods of temperatures over 80°F and high humidity. Do not apply more than five pounds of sulfur per 1,000 square feet per application over turf.

Finely ground dusting and spray sulfur can also be used to lower soil reaction. These work more rapidly than agricultural sulfur but are much more expensive and difficult to handle. *Aluminum sulfate* is frequently recommended for lowering soil pH. It is more expensive but acts more rapidly. The duration of change is not as long as with sulfur. Excessive amounts of aluminum sulfate can result in potential aluminum toxicity at low soil pH. Additions of sulfur or lime do not prompt permanent changes in soil pH; periodic re-treatment will be necessary.

Environmental Issues

Concern about contamination of ground and surface water is increasing among the general public and professional grounds managers. Some states are seriously contemplating certification or licensing for fertilizer applicators. Agriculture is a major contributor to fertilizer and pesticide pollution. The landscape management industry is highly visible. A great deal of public concern has been directed toward it. Some of this criticism is warranted, but some is not. Regardless, concern over fertilizer and pesticides will continue in the future. The green industry must police itself, otherwise, someone else will.

Nitrate nitrogen moves through the soil with water and enters ground and surface water primarily through leaching. Phosphorus loss is almost entirely due to erosion of soil particles, although phosphorus can leach from sandy soils.

Table 10.10.

Amounts of agricultural limestone needed to increase soil pH to approximately 6.5 in several soils. Dolomitic limestone containing calcium and magnesium is preferred where magnesium deficiencies exist.

	Limestone (pounds/1,000 square feet.)				
Desired pH increase	Sand	Sandy loam	Loam	Silt loam	Clay loam
4.0 to 6.5	60	115	165	200	230
4.5 to 6.5	50	100	135	165	195
5.0 to 6.5	45	80	110	130	155
5.5 to 6.5	30	60	80	95	110
6.0 to 6.5	15	35	40	50	60

Table 10.11.

Amount of sulfur needed to reduce soil pH of several soils to approximately 6.5

	Sulfur (pounds/1,000 sq. ft)		
Desired change in pH	Sands	Loams	Clays
8.5 - 6.5	50	60	70
8.0 - 6.5	28	35	50
7.5 - 6.5	12	20	25
7.0 - 6.5	3	4	7

Table 10.12
Factors affecting nitrate runoff in turfgrass
- Amount and timing of first irrigation or precipitation event after fertilization.
- Soil texture.
- Soil structure and compaction.
- Type of turf.
- Nitrogen source, timing, and rate.

The following are some guidelines that can minimize the impact of nutrient pollution:

1. Do not regularly over-water. Excessive irrigation leaches nitrates.

2. Keep erosion to a minimum, especially near bodies of water.

3. Apply only the amount of nitrogen fertilizer needed. Apply it at the optimum time for plant utilization and apply it in a manner to minimize loss.

4. Use slow-release fertilizers where economically and ecologically practical.

5. Avoid using phosphate fertilizers on landscape plantings unless required. Be careful of phosphate applications to turfgrass and landscape beds in sandy soils or sites with surface run-off or erosion.

6. Avoid getting fertilizer on non-plant areas such as driveways and sidewalks.

Photo 10.10. Take special care when developing nutrient programs and making fertilizer application around water.

Bibliography

1. Anonymous. 1991. Tree fertilization. *Arbor Age* 11(2):32.

2. Anonymous. 1991. PLACCA offers guideline on advertising. *LESCO News* 23(5):16.

3. Barnard, B. 1990. Methods and materials. *Tree Care Industry* 1(3):8.

4. Broschat, T. 1998. Why aren't your palms green? *Horticulture Newsletter Ft Lauderdale RECr.* 10(1):1.

5. Broschat, T. and A. Meerow. 1992. *Palm Nutrition Guide.* Univ. of Florida Coop. Ext. Ser. Bul. SS-ORH-02.

6. Carpenter, P., and T. Walker. 1990. *Plants in the Landscape.* W.H. Freeman, New York, NY.

7. Carrow, R. 1982. Efficient use of nitrogen fertilizer. *Grounds Maintenance* 17(7):10.

8. Chapman, D. 1982. Timing and methods for landscape trees. *Weeds, Trees and Turf* 19(3):66.

9. Chase, A. and T. Broschat. 1991. *Diseases and Disorders of Ornamental Palms.* APS Press St. Paul, MN.

10. Doughty, S. 1988. The basics of tree fertilization. *Landscape Contractor* 29(9):11.

11. Ferrandiz, L. 1990. Tree fertilization techniques. *Grounds Maintenance* 25(6):10.

12. Feucht, J. and J. Butler. 1988. *Landscape Management*. Van Nostrand Reinhold Co., NY.

13. Fischbach, J. and B. Webster. 1982. New method of injecting iron into pin oaks. *Journal of Arboriculture* 8(9):240.

14. Funk, R. 1990. How trees take up nutrients. *Grounds Maintenance* 25(6):16.

15. Funk, R. 1990. Fertilizer basics. *American Nurseryman* 172(11):55.

16. Gerstenberger, P. 1990. Soil pH and nutrient availability. *Tree Care Industry* 1(3):12.

17. Gibson, H. 1990. Fertilizer spreaders. *Grounds Maintenance* 25(9):10.

18. Gitlin, B. 1993. Organic fertilizers. *Lawn & Landscape Maintenance* 13(5):52.

19. Good, G. 1989. Fertilizing shade trees. *Landscape Contractor* 30(5):20.

20. Guertal, E., 2000. Nitrogen: finding the form that fits. *Grounds Maintenance* 35(9):15.

21. Hall, R. 1991. Natural organic fertilizers. *Landscape Management* 30(12):8.

22. Harris, R. 1992. *Arboriculture. Integrated Management of Trees, Shrubs and Vines in the Landscape*. Prentice-Hall, Inc., Englewood Cliffs, NJ.

23. Harris, R., J. Clark and N. Matheny. 2004. *Arboriculture. Integrated Management of Trees, Shrubs and Vines 4th ed.* Prentice-Hall, Inc., Upper Saddle River, NJ

24. Harris, R., J. Paul and A. Leiser. 1977. *Fertilizing Woody Plants*. Univ. of California Ag. Sci. Lft. 2958.

25. Hensley, D. 1989. How to study for a soil test. *Nursery Manager* 5(7):104.

26. Hensley, D. 1995. Study for soil tests. *Hawaii Landscape* 9(3):6.

27. Hensley, D. 1996. Where to go for a soil test. *Hawaii Landscape* 10(4):11.

28. Hensley, D. 1999. Bougainvillea prefers slow-release nitrogen. *Hawaii Landscape* 3(2):14.

29. Hensley, D. and G. Aldridge. 1990. The effect of nitrogen fertilization on spring and fall Scotch pine. *Nursery Manager* 6(5):60.

30. Hensley, D., R. McNiel, and R. Sundheim. 1988. Management influences on growth of transplanted *Magnolia grandiflora*. *Journal of Arboriculture* 14(8):204.

31. Hensley, D., R. McNiel, and R. Sundheim. 1989. Magnolia grandiflora. *Nursery Manager* 5(2):62.

32. Hensley, D. and G. Meade. 1998. *Fertilizers for Trees and Shrubs*. Univ. of Hawaii Coop. Ext. Ser. Pub. L6.

33. Hodel, D. 1992. An update on the mineral nutrition of palms. *Pacific Coast Nurseryman* May:55.

34. Hoehn, C. 1993. Slow-release fertilizers: when is the price right? *Lawn & Landscape Maintenance* 14(8):24.

35. Kelsey, P. 1990. Salt in fertilizer. *Tree Care Industry* 1(3):18.

36. Kvaalen, V. and P. Carpenter. 1978. *Fertilizing Woody Plants*. Purdue Univ. Coop. Ext. Bul. HO-140.

37. Mathers, H. 1999. Uncommon deficiencies of woody ornamentals. *NMPro* 10(3):62.

38. Mathers, H. 1999. Common toxicities of woody ornamentals. *NMPro* 10(3):62.

39. McIver, T. 1990. Liquid vs. dry: the pendulum swings. *Landscape Management* 29(8):26.

40. Morris, R. and D. Devitt. 1999. Fertilization techniques more environmentally sensitive. *Southwest Trees & Turf* 5(4):5.

41. Morris, R. and B. Swanson. 1990. Iron chlorosis in trees. *Journal of Arboriculture* 16(10):279.

42. Mugaas, R., L. Agnew, and N. Christens. 1992. Fertilizing to protect surface water quality. *Landscape Management* 31:38.

43. Murphy, S. 2000. Fertilizer use. *Grounds Maintenance* 35(9):8.

44. Peck, T. 1981. What to expect from soil tests. *Journal of Arboriculture* 7(1):11.

45. Pirone, P., J. Hartman, M. Sall, and T. Pirone. 1988. *Tree Maintenance*. 6th edition. Oxford University Press, New York, NY.

46. Powell, M., T. Bilderback, and T. Disy. 1996. *Fertilizer Recommendations and Techniques to Maintain Landscapes and Protect Water Quality*. North Carolina State Univ. Coop. Ext. Pub. AG-508-5.

47. Rao, B. 1990. Iron chlorosis. *Grounds Maintenance* 25(6):44.

48. Robbins, J. 2001. Nice spread! *Grounds Maintenance* 36(6):33

49. Rogers, M. 1993. Slow-release nitrogen. *Grounds Maintenance* 28(7):12.

50. Schumaker, T. 2000. Fertigation facts. *Southwest Trees & Turf.* 12(5):13.

51. Schwartz, J. and R. Follett, 1979. *Liming Acid Soils*. USDA Fact Sheet AFS-4-5-4.

52. Smiley, E., S. Lilly, and P. Kelsey. 2002. *Best Management Practices: Tree and Shrub Fertilization*. International Society of Arboriculture, Champaign, IL.

53. Smiley, E. and A. Shirazi. 2003. Fall fertilization and cold hardiness in landscape trees. *Journal of Arboriculture* 29(6);342.

54. Smith, E. and C. Gilliam. 1980. Soil fertility practices are vital for growing healthy landscape plants. *American Nurseryman* 151(3):15.

55. Smith, E. 1978. Fertilizing trees and shrubs in the landscape. *Journal of Arboriculture* 4(7):157.

56. Smith, E. 1986. *Fertilizing Landscape and Field Grown Nursery Crops*. Ohio State Univ. Coop. Ext. Ser. Bul. 650.

57. Smith, E. 1988. Systemic fertilization of trees. *ALA* 9(9):32.

58. Smith, E. 1990. Tree fertilization. *Tree Care Industry* 1(3):4.

59. Snyder, C. *et al.* 1993. *Understanding the Numbers on Your Soil Test Report*. Univ. of Arkansas Coop. Ext. Bul. FSA2118.

60. Steele, B. 1991. Liquid vs. dry fertilizers: Perception and reality. *The Landscape Contractor* 32(3):16.

61. Stevens, R. 1993. Different fertilizers for different applications. *The Landscape Contractor* 34(7):12.

62. Stevens, R. 1993. Organic fertilizers: some comments. *The Landscape Contractor* 34(7):16.

63. Stevens, R. 1993. Soil testing for best results. *The Landscape Contractor* 34(7):18.

64. Struve, D. 2002. A review of shade tree nitrogen fertilization research in the United States. *Journal of Arboriculture* 28(6):252.

65. Swanson, B. and C. Rosen. 1984. *Tree Fertilization*. Univ. of Minnesota Coop. Ext. Bul. AG-FO-2421.

66. Swanson, B., *et. al.* 1986. *Soil testing and Fertilizer Applications for Nursery Management and Production*. Univ. of Minnesota Coop. Ext. Bul. AG-BU-2830.

67. Tatter, T. 1992. Recommendations for liquid soil fertilization of trees and shrubs. *Arbor Age* 12(2):28.

68. Trenholm, L., *et al.* 2002. *Fertilization and Irrigation Needs for Florida Lawns and Landscapes*. Univ. of Florida Coop. Ext. Bul. ENH860.

69. van de Werken, H. 1984. Why use obsolete fertilizer practices? *American Nurseryman* 159(7):65.

70. van de Werken, H. 1984. Fertilization practices as they influence growth rate of young trees. *Journal Environmental Horticulture* 2(2):64.

71. Vidic, T. 1993. Fertilizing woody landscape plants. *Landscape Management* 32(6):30.

72. Watson, G. 1992. Tree and shrub fertilization. *Grounds Maintenance* 27(1):42.

73. Watson, G. and P. Kelsey. 1993. Soils: The root of tree problems. *Arbor Age* 13(8):14.

74. Westrick, D. 1991. Perception vs. reality: How much fertilizer do trees need? *Lawn & Landscape Maintenance* 12(1):52.

75. Whitworth, D. 1989. Mediocre growing conditions accentuate need for fertilization. *Lawn and Landscape Maintenance* 10(10):50.

76. Williams, D. 1984. *Fertilizers for Landscape Plants*. Univ. of Illinois Coop. Ext. Ser. Bul. NC- 10.

77. Wisniewski, N. 2001. Simply soil. *Lawn and Landscape*. 22(3):66.

78. Wong, F. 2003. Palm tree disease update. *Southwest Trees & Turf* 9(1):7.

79. Yeager, T. and E. Gilman. 1990. *Fertilization of Trees and Shrubs in Home and Commercial Landscapes*. Univ. of Florida Coop. Ext. Ser. Special Series ORH-05.

Chapter 11
Commercial Color

David Hensley and Kimberly Krahl Hensley[1]

Color is the most striking component of any landscape and it has universal appeal. People prefer to live, work, and shop in pleasant environments and colorful plants contribute greatly to the outdoor environment. Home gardeners have long used annuals, perennials, bulbs, and other seasonal plants to produce continuous and changing colorful accents in their landscapes. Color is also paramount in successful commercial landscapes and landscape managers must be skilled in the use of color. Beds of annuals and perennials brighten and accent corporate headquarters, office buildings, hotels, shopping centers, apartment and condominium developments, parks, and metropolitan areas. A survey conducted in the late 1990s estimated that over 15 percent of the flowering bedding plants produced in the United States were used by commercial landscapers.

Color is the first element that draws attention to a landscape. Color has become an important selling tool in the competitive game of office and apartment leasing. Beds of flowering plants provide the competitive edge to persuade people to patronize a particular restaurant, hotel, mall, or apartment complex. Some commercial property managers consider the cost of annuals to be an advertising expense rather than a site maintenance cost. Many corporations and companies express their success and uniqueness by creating exceptional and distinctive landscapes around their business sites. Large residential complexes often use flowers and seasonal displays to make

Photo 11.1 Color from herbaceous and woody plants is an important part of commercial landscapes. Color adds interest, definition, and identity to the landscape. Photograph courtesy of James Robbins.

Photo 11.2 This floral display serves as the centerpiece for an urban courtyard. Photograph courtesy of Gerald Klingaman.

[1] Dr. Krahl is former Assistant Professor, Department of Landscape Architecture and Horticulture, Temple University Ambler Campus.

the residences seem more like individual homes. Color benefits entries, patios, views, and many other areas on any commercial or residential property.

A survey of employees at Kansas State University polled various aspects of campus life. The most frequently noted positive comment was about the beds of annual flowers on campus. This astounded the campus administration; they had never considered the impact of annual flowers beyond decoration and budget expenditure.

A seasonal color program is much more complex than planting a few geraniums and marigolds around a property and calling it good. Success with annual color requires selection of appropriate plants and sites, as well as adequate bed preparation and post-planting management.

Annuals

Annuals or *bedding plants* are general names applied to true botanical annuals and tender perennials that are unable to survive winter except in the mildest areas of the nation. Numerous species in endless colors and sizes are available. Annuals are one of the least expensive ways to brighten a dull landscape and to attract attention.

Perennials

In the past fifteen years or so the use of both hardy (able to survive winter and life spans of several to many years) and tender perennials has skyrocketed in residential, public, and commercial landscapes. Today, landscape managers have a much wider palette of perennial plants to choose from than ever before. With this increase in landscape possibilities is the requirement that managers become knowledgeable about a new and changing range of plant species and selections.

Design

Bedding plants and perennials are used in beds, borders, and containers to create focal points and liven up dull areas, and as subtle additions to passive landscapes. Select colors for annual displays carefully and do not use too many different colors. The design should not be a disconnected collection of color or species. Large massed beds of single-color annuals are attractive, sophisticated, and appropriate for many situations, especially commercial sites.

Commercial properties usually require relatively simple color schemes. People usually drive past commercial sites at faster speeds and the eye cannot easily process subtle gradations in color and texture. When dealing with masses of color, it is crucial to use only two or three main colors. Some designers for commercial proprieties use mostly primary colors (red, blue and yellow) and not many pastels. The intensity and dramatic effect of primary colors read easily across distance, whereas pastels wash out with distance and are best viewed at close range.

Residential properties benefit from more variety in color and texture. With residential proprieties, people are often sitting or walking or driving at a slower speed, so more color can be processed.

Some designers work with a range of colors, while others concentrate on colors within a hue, such as red using shades of red, rose, pink or lavender, with white used as an accent. The *color wheel* can help in choosing colors for the planting. Hues opposite each other on the color wheel

---

Table 11.1.

The most popular bedding plants, according to annual sales surveys. The specific placement for a bedding plant may vary slightly (geraniums were number two in 1993, but number three in 1999), but the top sellers remain:

- Impatiens
- Petunias
- Geraniums
- Begonias
- Pansies
- Vincas

Photo 11.3 Color plantings make large residential complexes seem more like home. Photograph courtesy of James Robbins.

Photo 11.4 A color planting along an Asheville, NC roadway. Photograph courtesy of James Robbins.

Photo 11.5 Use annuals and other color plantings in high visibility areas. Entry signs and areas where people congregate or view are prime locations. Photograph courtesy of James Robbins.

Photo 11.6 A color planting serves as a focal point for this outdoor restaurant area. Photograph courtesy of James Robbins.

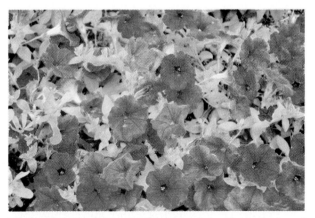

Photo 11.7 Residential properties can use greater diversity in color and texture.

Photo 11.8 Annuals or bedding plants are the mainstay of landscape color plantings. Petunia is one of the five species that make up the majority of bedding plants used in residential and commercial landscapes. Photograph courtesy of Gerald Klingaman.

are complementary, while those closer together on the color wheel clash in often appealing contrast.

If space, budget or the environment are limiting, concentrate on the critical areas. Key impact areas include entries, signs, outdoor eating areas, sitting or entertainment areas, and places where people congregate. Be imaginative! A relatively small number of different annual flowers are typically used in commercial color designs. Impatiens (*Impatiens walleriana*), begonias (*Begonia* spp.), marigolds (*Tagetes* spp.), petunias (*Petunia* x *hybrida*), and annual vinca (*Catharanthus roseus*) account for the vast majority of annuals planted in commercial landscapes. A growing number of commercial and most residential clients, however, ask for increasingly sophisticated displays of unusual or exotic plants to set them apart. These clients seek to differentiate themselves from the mundane, instead preferring (and paying for) unique designs, themes, plants, and colors.

Maintenance must always be kept in mind when designing annual beds. Although some bedding plants qualify as truly low-maintenance, many do not. Locate color beds away from street and parking lot curbs to reduce heat stress and salt pollution from snow/ice removal. Avoid small beds of less than 50 square feet. Color beds should be at least six feet from the base of shallow-rooted trees such as maples to reduce competition for nutrients and water. Be sure that there are water hookups near the bed. Even if there is an irrigation system, hand watering will be necessary during establishment and times of stress.

Commercial clients want extended landscape color, 12 months per year if possible. Beds are changed, replanted with new, fresh, seasonal plants, throughout the year. The number of *color changes* is driven by the client's budget and also depends on the environment. In milder climates, year-round color is relatively easy to achieve. In colder climates, however, the choices for late fall, winter, and early spring color are limited.

Pansies (*Viola* x *wittrockiana*) and spring-flowering bulbs are favorites for spring color and are usually followed by a summer display of flowering annuals. Fall displays of mums (*Chrysanthemum* x *morifolium*), flowering cabbage or kale (*Brassica oleracea*), pansies and violas (*Viola* spp.), hybrid pinks (*Dianthus chinesis x barbatus*), or snapdragons (*Antirrhinum majus*), can follow

summer annuals. Hellebores (*Helleborus* spp.) are planted for December and January bloom in much of the South.

Seasonal color must be *cost effective*. Some publications refer to a *cost:bloom* ratio. This is simply the cost per plant, including maintenance, divided by the days of effective floral display. The cost:bloom ratio allows an economic comparison of different design and color alternatives. Mums are a favorite fall flower in many areas; however, some landscape managers have found their limited bloom time difficult to justify in terms of cost. Transplants of some these plants may be difficult to find in the autumn.

Pansies are the top selling bedding plant in many milder areas providing a six-month bloom season from October to May. Planted in the fall, the humble pansy provides sporadic color throughout the late fall and winter, joins with bulbs in the spring, and is at its peak through spring, up to the time for planting summer annuals. Both cold hardiness and heat tolerance have been greatly improved in many newer varieties of pansies and violas.

Plant selection

There are many species of flowering annuals and perennials grown throughout the country. Within these, there are innumerable cultivars that vary in size, color, form, season of bloom, pest resistance, and environmental tolerance. Foremost, choose plants that tolerate the environment of the site. No amount of management can counteract the choice of the wrong plant for the site. Table 11.2 and 11.4 list some annuals and perennials tolerant of various environments. These lists are a guide and not all-inclusive.

Select and use only quality plants. Bedding plants should have healthy roots extending to all sides of the pot. The top should be deep green and well proportioned to the size of the container and character of the plant. Plants with excessive top growth use more water than their small root systems can supply upon planting. Plants should be free of insects and diseases and hardened-off (acclimated) to prevent scorching in full sun.

Plants grown in *cell packs* are the most important component of the retail bedding plant market. Commercial landscape managers generally prefer larger plants. Commercial sites typi-

Photo 11.9 Pansies are one of the most versatile fall/winter/spring color plants for milder areas of the country. Photograph courtesy of Gerald Klingaman.

Photo 11.10 Mums are a favorite fall display in the Midwest. Photograph courtesy of Gerald Klingaman.

Photo 11.11 Landscape firms producing their own bedding plant transplants assures quantities and delivery dates, and allows landscape managers flexibility in species and cultivar selection. Running a greenhouse, however, requires daily commitment and specialized knowledge.

cally use plants grown in large cell packs and four- and five-inch pots. Some managers prefer six-inch or even larger material. Plant prices increase in direct proportion to the pot size. Large plants, however, provide immediate effect and fewer plants are required to fill a bed. The client sees the results of his/her expenditure immediately. In actuality, the individual cost of the plant is small when compared to labor and equipment for preparing, planting, and maintaining the bed. Landscape firms can offer the client instant gratification with only a moderate increase in actual cost.

Most landscape management firms purchase bedding plants from local or regional wholesale greenhouses. Contact the greenhouse grower three to six months in advance to be sure that required quantities of specific plants will be available and ready on the desired date. Choice is limited to what the grower has or will produce; however, special-order crops are possible with adequate notice. Some growers have begun producing plants for summer and fall planting in addition to the traditional spring market.

Increasing numbers of landscape firms have found it advantageous and profitable to produce their own transplants. This assures quantities and delivery dates and allows more flexibility in species and cultivar choice. Consider the facility and material costs, as well as the special labor requirements, before plunging into the greenhouse business. Running a greenhouse requires daily commitment and specialized knowledge.

Bed Preparation

Success of annuals, perennials, and other color plants, depends on proper soil preparation. The area should be tilled to a depth of eight to 16 inches. Most floriculturists recommend incorporation of organic matter such as leaf mold, compost, peat moss, or sterilized manure. Organic matter improves moisture retention, drainage, aeration, and structure of the soil. Incorporate organic matter at a rate of approximately 20 to 25 percent of the volume of the root zone (*e.g.,* incorporate two inches of organic material if soil is tilled to an eight-inch depth).

Fertilizer is incorporated during bed preparation. Most summer annuals do not require a high level of fertilization. The fertilizer applied

Table 11.2.

The following are annuals or bedding plants recommended by various sources for specific environments or that may be adapted to special situations. This is by no means an exhaustive list. The list of available cultivars grows and changes each season.

Common name	Botanical name
Annuals that tolerate poor soil	
Love-lies-bleeding	*Amaranthus caudatus*
Cockscomb	*Celosia argentea* var. cristata
Spider flower	*Cleome hassleriana*
Coreopsis (Calliopsis)	*Coreopsis tinctoria*
California poppy	*Eschscholzia californica*
Gaillardia	*Gaillardia pulchella*
Sweet alyssum	*Lobularia maritima*
Four-o'clock	*Mirabilis jalapa*
Petunia	*Petunia* hybrids
Rose moss	*Portulaca grandiflora*
Mexican sunflower	*Tithonia rotundifolia*
Nasturtium	*Tropaeolum majus*
Annuals requiring or tolerating neutral or alkaline soil	
Pinks	*Dianthus* spp. and hybrids
Annual baby's breath	*Gypsophila* spp.
Candytuft	*Iberis* spp.
Impatiens	*Impatiens* spp.
Annual phlox	*Phlox drummondii*
Mignonette	*Reseda odorata*
Nasturtium	*Tropaeolum majus*
Zinnia	*Zinnia* spp. and hybrids
Annuals for full sun, hot, dry regions	
African daisy	*Arctotis* x hybrida
Prickly poppy	*Argemone* spp.
Ornamental pepper	*Capsicum annuum*
Vinca (Madagascar periwinkle)	*Catharanthus roseus*
Cockscomb	*Celosia argentia* var. cristata
Cornflower	*Centaurea cyanus*
Spider flower	*Cleome hassleriana*
Coreopsis (Calliopsis)	*Coreopsis tinctoria*
Cosmos	*Cosmos* spp.
Gaillardia	*Gaillardia pulchella*
Gazania	*Gazania rigens*
Globe amaranth	*Gomphrena globosa*
Sunflower	*Helianthus annuus*
Morning glory	*Ipomoea purpurea*
Summer cypress	*Kochia scoparia*
Lantana	*Lantana camara*
Medallion flower	*Melampodium paludosum*
Egyptian star cluster	*Pentas lanceolata*

Common name	Botanical name
Annuals for full sun, hot, dry regions (continued)	
Annual phlox	*Phlox drummondii*
Rose moss	*Portulaca grandiflora*
Salvia	*Salvia* spp.
Creeping zinnia	*Sanvitalia procumbens*
Fan flower	*Scaevola aemula*
Verbena	*Verbena* spp. and hybrids
Zinnia	*Zinnia* spp. and hybrids
Annuals for cooler, moist regions	
Blue woodruff	*Asperula orientalis*
Larkspur	*Consolida* spp.
Bedding lobelia	*Lobelia erinus*
Monkeyflower	*Mimulus* hybrids
Nemesia	*Nemesia strumosa*
South African daisy	*Osteospermum* hybrids
Painted tongue	*Salpiglossis sinuata*
Pansy and viola	*Viola* spp.
Annuals for partial shade	
Begonia	*Begonia semperflorens-cultorum*
Browallia	*Browallia speciosa*
Caladium	*Caladium bicolor*
Coleus	*Coleus* hybrids
Candytuft	*Iberis* spp.
Impatiens	*Impatiens walleriana*
Sweet alyssum	*Lobularia maritima*
Flowering tobacco	*Nicotiana* spp.
Wishbone flower	*Torenia fournieri*
Pansy and viola	*Viola* spp. and hybrids
Annuals for hanging baskets	
Flowering maple	*Abutilon* spp.
Browallia	*Browallia speciosa*
Trailing petunia	*Calibrachoa* x hybrida
Blue Daze	*Evolvulus pilosus*
Fuchsia	*Fuchsia* hybrids
Sweet potato vine	*Ipomoea batatas*
Lantana	*Lantana camara*
Ivy geranium	*Pelargonium peltatum*
Petunia	*Petunia* hybrids
Fan flower	*Scaevola aemula*
Bacopa	*Sutera grandiflora*
Black-eyed Susan vine	*Thunbergia alta*
Verbona	*Verbona* spp.

Table 11.3.

All-America Selections

Since 1933, All-America Selections has selected and promoted new, superior seed-grown cultivars that have been tested across North America. The winners for the past 10 years are:

Year	Common Name	Cultivar	Year	Common Name	Cultivar
2004	Hollyhock	Queeny Purple	2001	Eustoma	Forever Blue
2004	Cockscomb	Fresh Look Yellow	2001	Portulaca	Margarita Rosita
2004	Cockscomb	Fresh Look Red	2000	Tithonia	Fiesta Del Sol
2004	Petunia	Limbo Violet	2000	Sunflower	Soraya
2004	Gypsophila	Gypsy Deep Rose	2000	Dianthus	Melody Pink
2003	Agastache	Golden Jubilee	2000	Cosmos	Cosmic Orange
2003	Black-eyed Susan	Prairie Sun	2000	Vinca	Stardust Orchid
2003	Petunia	Merlin Blue Morn	1999	Zinnia	Profusion Orange
2003	Ornamental Millet	Purple Majesty	1999	Zinnia	Profusion Cherry
2003	Carnation	Can Can Scarlet	1999	Tritoma	Flamenco
2003	Petunia	Blue Wave	1999	Begonia	Pin Up Flame
2003	Vinca	Jaio Dark Red	1999	Verbena	Quartz Burgundy
2003	Gaillardia	Sundance Bicolor	1999	Portulaca	Sundial Peach
2003	Eustoma	Forever White	1999	Osteospermum	Passion Mix
2003	Dianthus	Corona Cherry Magic	1999	Marigold	Bonanza Bolero
2002	Black-eyed Susan	Cherokee Sunset	1998	Impatiens	Victorian Rose
2002	Petunia	Lavender Wave	1998	Petunia	Prism Sunshine
2002	Pansy	Ultima Morpho	1997	Cockscomb	Prestige Scarlet
2002	Cleome	Sparkler Blush	1997	Gypsophila	Gypsy
2002	Ornamental Pepper	Chilly Chili	1997	Zinnia	Crystal White
2002	Petunia	Tidal Wave Silver	1996	Salvia	Strata
2002	Geranium	Black Velvet Rose	1996	Petunia	Fantasy Pink Morn
2002	Vinca	Jaio Scarlet Eye	1995	Petunia	Purple Wave
2001	Sunflower	Ring of Fire	1995	Black-eyed Susan	Indian Summer
2001	Zinnia	Profusion White	1995	Petunia	Celebrity Chiffon Morn
2001	Nicotiana	Avalon Bright Pink	1994	Lavender	Lady

enhances establishment, vigorous initial growth, and subsequent flowering. Apply one to two pounds of nitrogen per 1,000 square feet of bed as a complete low-nitrogen fertilizer with a ratio of 1:2:1, 1:1:1, 1:2:2, or similar. Higher rates are sometimes used; however, excessive nitrogen promotes rank vegetative growth resulting in leggy plants with reduced flowering. Incorporate slow-release fertilizer products such as Osmocote® or sulfur coated urea as the nitrogen source at planting to reduce the need for supplemental additions of nitrogen later in the season. I have read no recommendations for use of high-nitrogen material such as ammonium nitrate or urea with annuals or perennials; all sources recommend a low-nitrogen complete fertilizer.

Research in Alabama indicated that a combination of granular, water-soluble, and slow-release fertilizers provided optimal growth of fall-planted seasonal color without significant leaching of nitrogen out of the plant root zones.

Most annuals and perennials tolerate a soil pH range from 5.0 to 7.0 or slightly higher. Do not apply lime, sulfur, or other pH adjusting materials except when based on a soil test. Use naturally tolerant species for more extreme alkaline or acidic sites.

Some landscape managers incorporate fungicides, wetting agents, root stimulators, and water-holding compounds into color beds. The cost and dubious benefits of some of these materials for bedding plants should be carefully evaluated and justified before increasing project costs. Except for soil application of certain fungicides where root diseases are problematic, there is little or no scientific literature supporting positive effects from the addition of these materials into landscape or annual beds.

After incorporating organic material and other amendments and thorough tilling, the beds should be raked smooth and slightly mounded. Remove sticks, roots, clods, and debris from the bed and the site.

Planting

Some bedding plants are relatively cold hardy (e.g. cornflower (*Centaurea cyanus*), foxglove (*Digitalis* spp.), larkspur (*Consolida* spp.), pansy, viola, sweet alyssum (*Lobularia maritima*), and many *Dianthus* hybrids) and are planted in the early spring or even the fall in some areas. Do not plant warm-season summer annuals (e.g. ageratum (*Ageratum* spp.), begonia (*Begonia* spp.), cockscomb (*Celosia* spp.), coleus (*Coleus* spp.), globe amaranth (*Gomphrena globosa*), impatiens, marigold, petunia, verbena, and zinnia until danger of frost is past and the soil has warmed up in the late spring. Store plants that cannot be planted immediately, due to scheduling or weather, in a lightly shaded area. Be sure they are watered as necessary (usually daily).

Keep plants moist during the planting operation. They may dry out quickly in the open. Carefully remove plants from the pot, including those growing in peat or paper pots. Peat and paper pots can act as wicks and deprive the root system of moisture. Gently crush the root mass with the fingers to stimulate root growth into the surrounding soil. Begin planting in the center of the bed and keep traffic in the worked soil to a minimum. Make the hole slightly larger than the root ball and set the plant at the same depth or slightly higher (if mulching) than it was growing in the container. Smooth out the soil around the plants after planting, including footprints. Planting aids and mechanical planters speed large-scale operations.

Mulching

Some landscape managers *mulch* annuals and perennials immediately after planting; others wait until the plants have set-up for a few days; others

(probably the majority) do not mulch at all. Mulch aids water conservation, weed control, and gives the bed a finished look. Apply organic mulches such as pine straw, bark, compost, fumigated or composted hay or straw two to three inches deep, but only about ½ inch deep around the base of the plants. Excessive amounts of mulch against the stem can increase disease problems. Incorporating the organic mulch from the previous year or planting adds organic matter to the bed. If fresh, non-composted organic mulch is used, broadcast a small amount of a low-nitrogen fertilizer to compensate for nitrogen loss during decomposition.

Watering-in

Water the newly planted bed *immediately* after planting or mulching. Use a water wand, breaker, or sprinkler to water the base of the plants. Water until the bed is wet to a depth of three inches for transplants from two-inch containers and deeper for those from larger pots. Keep the wand or breaker in motion to reduce washing of the soil or mulch.

Some managers water-in after transplanting with a starter solution containing a soluble, high-phosphate fertilizer such as 10-52-17.

Summer Fertilization

Summer annuals will require one or two additional applications of a 1:2:1, 1:1:1, or similar ratio fertilizer at the rate of one-half to one pound of nitrogen per 1,000 square feet of bed (*e.g.* one to two pounds of 5-10-5 per 100 square feet) during the growing season. An alternative is to water with a soluble fertilizer (20-20-20 or similar) every four to six weeks throughout the bedding plant season. The seasonal total application of nitrogen should not exceed four to six pounds of nitrogen per 1,000 square feet of bed area.

Irrigation

Color beds should not be in the same irrigation zone or on the same irrigation schedule as turfgrass or woody ornamentals. Color beds usually require less water than turf and more water than woody plants. Deep, less frequent irrigation encourages deeper rooting. Incorporation of organic matter during bed preparation increases water holding capacity and drainage and reduces

Photo 11.12 The cost of plants is small when compared to the cost of labor and equipment for preparing, planting, and maintaining an annual color bed. Photograph courtesy of James Robbins.

Photo 11.13 Annuals require diligent watering and care while awaiting installation.

irrigation requirements. Beds surrounded by turf should be slightly raised to prevent ponding of surface water from the lawn.

Annuals and perennials may be watered with drip irrigation, by hand, or with sprinklers. Minispray heads can easily be added to existing drip systems. Overhead impact sprinklers can result in damage to large or fragile blossoms and wet foliage predisposes some annuals and perennials to disease problems. Schedule overhead irrigation early in the day so the leaves will dry rapidly.

Physical Care

Petunias, snapdragons, and pansies frequently need to be pinched back after transplanting or following the first flush of bloom to control size and increase branching and subsequent flowering. Pinching requirements are less for some newer cultivars. Prune back alyssum (*Lobularia maritima*), phlox (*Phlox subulata*), and other creeping annuals or perennials if they encroach upon walks or other surfaces or if their foliage gets ratty looking.

Faded or dead flowers of calendula (*Calendula officinalis*), dahlia (*Dahlia* spp.), Coreopsis (*Coreopsis* spp.) geraniums (*Pelargonium* x *hortorum*), gloriosa daisy (*Rudbeckia* spp.), marigolds, some petunias, salvia (*Salvia* x *superba*), zinnia and a few other species should be periodically removed or *deadheaded*. Deadheading keeps the plants vigorous, reduces disease problems such as Botrytis,

Photo 11.14 Mulching annuals, perennials, and bulbs aids water conservation, weed control, and give beds a finished look. Photograph courtesy of James Robbins.

Photo 11.15 Proper irrigation of perennial and annual color plantings is essential for quality growth and reasonable maintenance.

and stimulates subsequent flowering. Blossoms can be pinched or removed by hand or with hand pruners. Check plants at least every week for needed deadheading. Remove dead leaves of annuals and perennials as prudent.

Weed Control

Weed control is often the most expensive maintenance item for seasonal color beds.

Much of the important weed management work is actually done *before* planting. Good site preparation includes scouting for perennial weeds and controlling them before bed preparation and planting. There are three options for controlling perennial weeds: cultivation, fumigation, or systemic postemergent herbicides. Cultivation before planting without use of postemergent herbicides allows some perennial weeds to escape and survive. Fumigation, while effective, is very expensive, requires special techniques, can be very dangerous, and is not usually practical for landscape situations. Prudent and timely application of systemic postemergent herbicides will effectively control many perennial weeds and reduce labor costs later in the season.

Mulching with organic mulch materials helps to physically control weeds until the plants grow together (canopy over) and shade-out sprouting weed seedlings. Mulching is the least expensive and one of the most effective methods for controlling weeds in color plantings. Organic mulches have positive effects on soil texture and tilth.

Black plastic is sometimes used as a physical barrier to weeds in lower maintenance situations. The plastic is spread over the prepared bed and the edges buried to secure them. Annuals are planted through holes made with a bulb planter or other device. Decrease the spacing between plants to ensure that plants will grow together and hide the plastic. Mulch the periphery of the beds to hide the edge of the plastic. Punch additional holes through the plastic between plants to increase water movement to the soil.

Preemergent herbicides (those that prevent weeds from germinating or growing) provide the most effective chemical control of weeds. Most landscape herbicides were developed for other crops and adapted for use with ornamentals. The number of different herbicides labeled for use with annual and perennial flowers has greatly increased as the market potential of color plantings has been realized. There are several preemergent herbicides that are safe and effective for a wide array of bedding species. Trifluralin, sold under several trade names, is labeled for use with an extensive number of color species.

Some *postemergent herbicides* selectively and safely remove annual grasses from seasonal color plantings. These materials, most notably fluazifop-butyl (Fusilade II®, Ornamec®) sethoxydim (Vantage®), clethodim (Envoy®), and fenoxaprop-ethyl (Acclaim®) can be applied over-the-top or as a directed spray to a variety of annuals and herbaceous perennials. However, these chemicals may damage or even kill certain herbaceous ornamental species. *Before applying any pesticide, always read and understand the label.*

A number of different bedding plant species planted in one site complicates chemical weed control. An herbicide tolerated by one species may be deadly to another. Many of our best bedding plants are close relatives of some of the targeted weeds. When developing the plant palette for a client, consider herbicide tolerance as well as aesthetic parameters. Beds using single or a few species simplify herbicide decisions.

The irregular shape and size of color beds can make calculation of the amount of herbicide needed difficult. Irregular bed shapes often make proper herbicide application troublesome if the material must be kept off the surrounding turf or ornamentals.

Pest Control

Pest problems (bacteria, fungi, insects, or mollusks) are minimal with most annuals and other color plants. Prevention is always the best control. Proper site selection, proper planting technique, proper spacing, and removal of dead leaves and flowers reduce insect and disease potential. In short, good management greatly reduces pest problems.

Some species and cultivars, however, such as calendula, grandiflora petunias, and many zinnias are prone to disease. Disease incidence and severity are compounded by poor air circulation, moderate shade, and overhead irrigation. Fungicides are effective for reducing or controlling fungal diseases and may be necessary. Avoid problematic species altogether or select resistant cultivars (if available) if disease problems persist or for less than ideal sites.

Aphids, white flies, thrips, and mites are the most common insect pests of ornamentals. Insect problems increase with the stress of summer and pesticide applications may be warranted. Use chemicals as infrequently as possible to ensure the greatest benefit.

Slugs and snails can be a serious problem for young annuals and other herbaceous plantings. They are especially fond of marigolds, petunias, annual salvias (*Salvia* x *superba*), and hostas (*Hosta* spp.). Poisonous baits placed in the planting are about the only effective means of control. Place baits where animals or children cannot consume them.

Containers and Hanging Baskets

Movable or stationary *containers* add color to areas where planting beds are not feasible. Con-
tainers of annuals can be moved into critical impact areas when they are at their peak and then moved out as they wane. Although management of color plantings in containers is more exacting than for ground beds, many landscape managers and designers have found them ideal to dress up entrances, pool areas, and amenity areas.

The type of pot used as a container depends on the landscape setting, amount of decoration desired, and budget. Regardless of construction material, *drainage* is essential. If drainage holes are not provided then they should be installed. Some grounds managers use a thick layer of gravel in the bottom of undrained containers. This should be done *only* if drilling drainage holes in the container is impossible.

Hanging baskets provide unique appeal when filled with trailing annuals or foliage plants. They brighten or soften entries, patios, pool areas, public areas, and private landscapes. Chains used to display hanging baskets must be sturdy and should not rust. Locate containers and hanging

Photo 11.16 Aphids can be a problem for annuals and many perennials. Photograph courtesy of Gerald Klingaman.

Photo 11.17 A container plant in an aquatic setting. Photograph courtesy of James Robbins.

Photos 11.18 and 11.19 Containers of various materials and design make mobile and interesting color displays and accents for residential, commercial, and public landscapes. Photographs courtesy of James Robbins.

Photo 11.20 / Photo 11.21 Hanging baskets filled with trailing annuals or foliage plants provide unique appeal for commercial and residential landscapes. They brighten or soften patios, entries, pool areas, public areas, and private landscapes. Photographs courtesy of James Robbins.

baskets with traffic and safety as well as display in mind. Consider the size of the hanging basket and its ultimate weight when filled with media and water. One gallon of water weighs eight pounds.

Hanging baskets are available in a variety of materials and come in every imaginable configuration. The most common materials are plastic and sphagnum moss. Reservoirs can be added to the bottom of solid sided hanging baskets to reduce drainage onto surfaces and store water.

Avoid soil as a growing medium in containers or hanging baskets. Purchase a pre-packaged soilless medium of bark or peat mixed with aggregate materials such as perlite, vermiculite, or rice hulls. Some landscape managers mix their own container medium, but pre-packaged materials are often more economical considering material, labor, storage, and handling costs. Most commercially available media contain adequate initial nutrients for annuals. Fill containers with media to within one-inch of the rim for easier watering. Leave additional space if mulch is added. Fill hanging baskets with media to within ½-inch of the rim. Transplant plants as usual. Water-in immediately after planting until water begins to run out of the drainage holes of the container.

Select plants for hanging baskets and containers suited for the environment in which they will be placed. Several popular container and hanging basket plants are listed in Table 11.2.

Completely remove the old medium when replanting previously used containers. Some site managers, however, only replace the upper six

inches of large containers with fresh medium during the second year. Re-using old container media increases the chance of soluble salt toxicity, nutrient deficiencies, and soil borne insects and diseases. In most situations, complete replacement of the planting medium provides economical insurance for the landscape.

Containers require more attention to watering than ground beds since the growing area and water reservoir are limited. Containers and hanging baskets often require daily irrigation. Large pots and containers may require less frequent irrigation. Containers or hanging baskets placed in an exposed environment (sun and/or wind) lose water even more rapidly. Keep this in mind when planning, locating, and bidding maintenance of containerized color. Drip irrigation can be adapted to containers and hanging baskets.

Due to the frequency of irrigation and thus nutrient leaching, containers require careful monitoring of plant nutrient levels. Fertilize containerized plants with a dilute water-soluble fertilizer during irrigation. Some landscape managers irrigate regularly with a dilute fertilizer solution; however, most mangers fertilize with a water-soluble material only once every week or two. Incorporating a slow-release nitrogen source into the planting media provides a nutrient reservoir and reduces the need for periodic additional fertilization. Considering the amount of irrigation that containers and hanging baskets require, there is a fine line between adequate nutrition and over-fertilization. Excess nitrogen fertilization results in rank vegetative growth and reduced flowering.

Containerized annuals require the same dead-heading and monitoring for pest problems as those in ground beds. Turn or rotate containers and hanging baskets occasionally to keep growth of the composition symmetrical. Hanging baskets may require occasional pruning to keep the cascading growth uniform. Some work on hanging baskets may require stepladders, a factor that should be considered when bidding, budgeting, and locating hanging baskets.

Herbaceous Perennials

Herbaceous perennials, including ornamental grasses, have enjoyed a tremendous surge of interest in both residential and commercial landscapes. *Perennials* or *herbaceous perennials* are broadly defined as plants that will survive for three or more years in the landscape (as opposed to annuals or biennials). The term *herbaceous* is frequently appended to perennials to distinguish the soft fleshy stems of these plants from those of woody shrubs and trees. These species enter dormancy each winter with the top growth of most dying down while the roots survive winter; new top growth appears the next spring. A growing number of landscape companies specialize in designing, planting, and maintaining perennial landscapes.

Perennials are especially useful in apartment, condominium, and corporate landscapes where color is desired throughout the season. A carefully chosen palette of perennials can provide a succession of bloom with moderate management.

Herbaceous perennials offer a wide and expanding range of color, form, texture, and flowering season. Some perennials such as the ornamental grasses offer winter interest. There are perennials suitable for every climate, soil type, moisture condition, and light situation. Perennials can be adapted to formal, informal or naturalistic landscapes.

Perennial gardens or beds are not without problems or maintenance. *Deadheading* is necessary to maintain plant vigor, to increase repeat flowering and to control re-seeding by certain species. Perennial beds require a large area relative to annual color beds because of the larger mature size and spread of many perennials. A variety of different perennial species are necessary to maintain flowering throughout the season. Some pe-

rennials must be divided and replanted on a three- or four-year cycle; some very vigorous species require annual division. A few perennials are extremely invasive and can become serious weeds.

Quality maintenance of perennial beds and gardens requires understanding and knowledge of perennial plant species. This text is too limited in scope to attempt to address the requirements and maintenance techniques of the vast number of perennial species used across the country. Before bidding or engaging in the perennial management business, collect and study some of the informative texts available in the field.

Educate yourself about perennials that do well in your area by observing established landscapes, by visiting local botanic gardens, nurseries, private gardens and universities. Talk to knowledgeable professionals (landscape managers, designers, and horticulturists) and home gardeners in your area. Join and attend meetings of state and local organizations dedicated to perennial plant culture and perennial garden design. As with everything in life, a great deal of knowledge comes from experience. Be prepared to make and to learn from mistakes.

Spring Bulbs

Spring flowering bulbs are favorite color plants in residential and commercial landscapes throughout many areas of the country. Post Properties in Atlanta, Georgia, a large multi-family residential company, plants more than 1,000,000 spring bulbs annually. Flowering bulbs lend themselves to many different landscape design styles. Daffodils, as an example, can be stately in formal beds or informal in naturalized settings.

Tulips (*Tulipa* spp.) are the most popular bulbs used commercially. Tulips should be thought of as an annual, rather than a perennial color planting. Tulip bulbs are usually destroyed during preparation for subsequent plantings of summer flowering annuals. Transplanting spent tulip bulbs is expensive and re-establishment success is limited. Bloom of undisturbed tulips among established landscape ornamentals declines in a few years.

Photo 11.22 Herbaceous perennial flowering and foliage plants are important elements in continuous color displays in residential, commercial, and public landscapes. Photograph courtesy of Gerald Klingaman.

Photo 11.23 Water gardens combining perennials and water plants are popular among many landscape clientele and designers.

Photo 11.24 Some perennials add interest to the winter landscape. Photograph by Gerald Klingaman.

Photo 11.25 *Oenothera speciosa* (pink ladies or pink evening primrose) is a popular perennial, but it can be invasive. Photograph by Gerald Klingaman.

Table 11.4.

Perennials recommended by various sources for specific environments or that may be adapted to special situations. This is by no means an exhaustive list and he list of available cultivars grows and changes each season.

Common name	Botanical name

Perennials for full sun

Yarrow	Achillea spp. & hybrids
Hollyhock	Alcea rosea
Amsonia	Amsonia spp.
Common thrift	Armeria maritima
Butterfly weed	Asclepias tuberosa
Aster	Aster spp. & hybrids
False indigo	Baptisia spp. & hybrids
Blackberry lily	Belamcanda chinensis
Bellflower	Campanula spp.
Coreopsis	Coreopsis spp.
Pinks	Dianthus spp. & hybrids
Shasta daisy	Leucanthemum x superbum & hybrids
Purple coneflower	Echinacea purpurea
Hardy geranium	Geranium spp. & hybrids
Heliopsis	Heliopsis helianthoides
Daylily	Hemerocallis hybrids
Gayfeather	Liatris spp.
Russian sage	Perovskia atriplicifolia
Garden phlox	Phlox paniculata
Balloon flower	Platycodon grandiflorus
Rudbeckia	Rudbeckia spp. & hybrids
Salvia	Salvia spp. & hybrids
Scabiosa	Scabiosa columbaria
Stokes' aster	Stokesia laevis
Speedwell	Veronica spp.

Perennials for partial shade

Columbine	Aquilegia spp. & hybrids
Goat's beard	Aruncus spp.
False spirea	Astilbe spp. & hybrids
Bugbane	Cimicifuga spp.
Bleeding heart	Dicentra spp. & hybrids
Foxglove	Digitalis spp. & hybrids
Coral bells	Heuchera spp. & hybrids
Evergreen candytuft	Iberis sempervirens
Hosta	Hosta spp. & hybrids
Lungwort	Pulmonaria spp. & hybrids
Primrose	Primula spp. & hybrids
Foamflower	Tiarella cordifolia

Perennials tolerating neutral or alkaline soil

Yarrow	Achillea spp. & hybrids
Japanese anemone	Anemone x hybrida
Milky bellflower	Campanula lactiflora
Cupid's dart	Catanache caerulea
Jupiter's beard	Centranthus ruber
Pinks	Dianthus spp. & hybrids
Helen's flower	Helenium autumnale
Coral bells	Heuchera spp. & hybrids
Hybrid sage	Salvia x sylvestris
Speedwell	Veronica spp.

Perennials that are long-blooming

Yarrow	Achillea spp. & hybrids
Anise hyssop	Agastache spp. & hybrids
Coreopsis (selected spp.)	Coreopsis verticillata, C. rosea, C. auriculata 'Nana'
Shasta daisy	Chrysanthemum x superbum
Fringed bleeding heart	Dicentra eximia hybrids
Purple coneflower	Echinacea purpurea
Hardy geranium	Geranium spp. & hybrids
Reblooming daylilly	Hemerocallis hybrids (e.g. 'Stella de Oro, 'Happy Returns', etc.)
Russian sage	Perovskia atriplicifolia
Garden phox	Phlox paniculata
Snakeweed	Polygonum bistorta
Rudbeckia	Rudbeckia spp. & hybrids
Scabiosa	Scabiosa columbaria'
Autumn Joy' sedum	Sedum 'Autumn Joy'

Perennials tolerating dry soil once established

Yarrow	Achillea spp. & hybrids
Butterfly weed	Asclepias tuberosa
Common thrift	Armeria maritima
False indigo	Baptisia spp. & hybrids
Boltonia	Boltonia asteroides
Coreopsis	Coreopsis spp.
Pinks	Dianthus spp. & hybrids
Purple coneflower	Echinacea purpurea
Blanket flower	Gaillardia x grandiflora
Gaura	Gaura lindheimeri
Russian sage	Perovskia atriplicifolia
Sage	Salvia spp. & hybrids
Goldenrod	Solidago hybrids
Stokes' aster	Stokesia laevis
Southern lupine	Thermopsis caroliniana

Lower maintenance perennials

Amsonia	Amsonia spp.
Butterfly weed	Asclepias tuberosa
False indigo	Baptisia spp. & hybrids
Boltonia	Boltonia asteroides
Coreopsis (selected spp.)	Coreopsis verticillata, C. rosea, C. auriculata 'Nana'
Gaura	Gaura lindheimeri
Hardy geranium	Geranium spp. & hybrids
Hellebore	Helleborus spp. & hybrids
Siberian iris	Iris siberica
Gayfeather	Liatris spp.
Russian sage	Perovskia atriplicifolia
Balloon flower	Platycodon grandiflorus
'Goldsturm' rudbeckia	Rudbeckia fulgida 'Goldsturm'
Hybrid sage	Salvia x sylvestris
Foamflower	Tiarella cordifolia

Table 11.5.

Some hardy ornamental grasses recommended for landscape use

The number of available cultivars grows and changes each season.

Common name	Botanical name	Height	Comments
Big bluestem	*Andropogon gerardii*	5 – 8'	Sun; easy culture; orange and copper-red fall color; ornamental through winter; native grass.
Feather reed grass	*Calamagrostis x acutiflora*	2 – 4'	Sun/partial shade; upright grass; plume-like seed heads; ornamental spring through winter.
Northern sea oats	*Chasmanthium latifolium*	4'	Sun/partial shade (tolerates even dry shade); pendant oat-like seed heads turn bronze in fall; no winter interest; native grass.
Pampas grass	*Cortaderia selloana*	10'	Sun; very easy culture; narrow foliage; huge one to two-foot long feathery seed heads; variegated cultivars available; evergreen; ornamental through winter.
Blue wheat grass	*Elymus magellanicus*	2'	Partial shade; requires excellent drainage; most intense blue foliage of all grasses; thrives in cool weather; suffers in hot, humid weather; no winter interest.
Blue fescue	*Festuca ovina*	6 – 10"	Sun; requires well-drained soil; fine textured blue foliage; thrives in cool weather; goes dormant or dies in hot weather; no winter interest.
Hakone grass	*Hakonechloa macra*	1'	Partial shade (excellent with hostas); moist soil; graceful lime green cascading foliage; variegated cultivars available; foliage turns reddish in fall, bronze in winter; hardy to zone 7 (zone 6 with protection); winter interest.
'Red Baron' Japanese blood grass	*Imperata cylindrica* 'Red Baron'	12 – 18"	Sun; drought tolerant once established; very slow growing; red-tipped leaves with solid red fall color; foliage less red the further south it's grown; no winter interest.
Miscanthus	*Miscanthus sinensis*	3 – 8'	Sun; easy culture; many cultivars differing in size, texture, foliage color, and fall color; ornamental through winter.
Muhly grass	*Muhlenbergia capillaries*	3'	Sun; drought tolerant; fine texture; dark green foliage and delicate, airy pink to rose seed heads; hardy to zone 7; little winter interest; native grass.
Switch grass	*Panicum virgatum*	4 – 8'	Sun; easy culture; large airy seed heads; several cultivars available differing in foliage color and fall color; ornamental through winter; native grass.
Fountain grass	*Pennisetum alopecuroides*	1 – 5'	Sun/partial shade; thrive in hot, humid summers; narrow foliage; foxtail-like seed heads; many cultivars differing in size, foliage color, seed head color and fall color; little winter interest.
Ribbon grass	*Phalaris arundinacea* 'Picta'	3'	Sun/partial shade; often goes dormant in midsummer in hot climates; dramatic green and white striped foliage; beware: invasive and can take over large areas; no winter interest.

Table 11.6.
Perennial Plants of the Year

Since 1990, the Perennial Plant Association has selected an outstanding perennial to be its plant of the year. The winners are:

- 1990 *Phlox stolonifera*: USDA zones 2 to 8. Creeping phlox is a shade tolerant, low-growing species with violet to lavender flowers; spreads by stolons. Numerous cultivars with variety of flower color.

- 1991 *Heuchera micrantha* 'Palace Purple': USDA zones 4 to 8. Reddish-bronze foliage and small, off-white summer flowers.

- 1992 *Coreopsis verticillata* 'Moonbeam': USDA zones 4 to 8. Fine-textured foliage and long blooming, pale-yellow flowers.

- 1993 *Veronica* 'Sunny Border Blue': USDA zones 3 to 8, featuring deep green foliage, a long bloom period, easy to grow and minimal maintenance.

- 1994 *Astilbe* 'Sprite': USDA zones 3 to 8. Finely dissected, crinkle-edged, rich-green foliage. Produces tiny, pink flowers in summer.

- 1995 *Perovskia atriplicifolia*: USDA zones 3 to 8. Light blue flowers.

- 1996 *Penstemon digitalis* 'Husker Red': USDA zones 3 to 8. Rich bronze-red foliage and masses of white flowers. Go Big Red.

- 1997 *Salvia* 'May Night': USDA zones 4 to 8. Dark blue-black rigid flower spikes in late spring and aromatic, blue-gray leaves.

- 1998 *Echinacea purpurea* 'Magnus': USDA zones 3 to 8. Two- to four-foot tall carmine non-drooping flowers midsummer.

- 1999 *Rudbeckia fulgida* var. *sullivanti* 'Goldsturm': USDA zones 3 to 9. Golden yellow blooms on 18- to 30-inch stems from June to October.

- 2000 *Scabiosa columbaria* 'Butterfly Blue': USDA zones 3 to 9. Lavender blue pincushion flowers mid-spring to early fall, with good insect and disease-resistance.

- 2001 *Chalamagrostis acutiflora* 'Karl Foerster': A feather reed grass cultivar suitable in USDA zones four to nine. Features narrow growth four-seven feet, wide environmental tolerance and inflorescences that emerge purple and fade to golden-yellow in summer.

- 2002 *Phlox paniculata* 'David': USDA zones 3 to 8. Tall garden phlox, to four to five feet with thick stems and dark green leaves. Typically quite resistant to mildew

- 2003 *Leucanthemum x superbum* 'Becky': USDA zones 3 to 9. Shasta daisy, with bright white flowers, sturdy stems, and long season of bloom.

- 2004 *Athyrium niponicum* 'Pictum': USDA zones 3 to 8. Japanese painted fern has impressive contrasting foliage in shade.

- 2005 *Helleborus x hybridus*: USDA zones 4 to 9. Glossy leaves, evergreen in most climates. Plants reach 15 inches tall by 24 inches wide, tolerate shade, and are deer-resistant. One-inch flowers late winter through spring ranging in color from white to red to deep lavender.

Hyacinths (*Hyacinthus* spp.) are also planted for color and provide a recognizable and subtle fragrance. Hyacinths are best used in areas that are enjoyed at close range. Hyacinth bulbs are more expensive than tulips and they too should be considered as a one-time plant in commercial landscape color designs.

Daffodils (*Narcissus* spp.) are hardy, prolific, and long-lived spring-flowering bulbs. They are valuable additions to landscape beds, wooded areas, or naturalized landscapes. Daffodils thrive and increase for many years with little maintenance.

Crocus (*Crocus* spp.) is actually a corm, rather than a bulb. Crocus make an attractive, low maintenance color plant for naturalizing or landscape beds. Crocus can be planted in turf areas as they bloom very early and have stored adequate carbohydrates by the beginning of the mowing season. Both daffodils and crocus are most effective used in mass plantings or drifts.

Planting Bulbs

In most areas of the country with a cold winter season, spring flowering bulbs are planted in the autumn, before the ground freezes. Spring flowering bulbs require a physiologically predetermined number of hours of cool temperature (below 40°F.) for good flowering. Previous color plants are removed and the bed tilled and prepared as discussed earlier.

In the South and Southwest (roughly South Carolina to southern California) cold-treated bulbs

Photo 11.26 Flowering bulbs signal the awakening of spring. Photograph courtesy of James Robbins.

Photo 11.27 Tulips are the most popular spring-flowering bulbs for professional and home gardeners.

Photo 11.28 Daffodils and narcissus (*Narcissus* spp.) are hardy, prolific, and long-lived spring-flowering bulbs. Photograph courtesy of Gerald Klingaman.

Photo 11.29 Daffodils thrive and increase for many years with little maintenance making them valuable additions to wooded areas or naturalized landscapes. Photograph by Gerald Klingaman.

Photo 11.30 Crocus are corms rather than bulbs. They provide long-term inexpensive color for naturalized areas and planted beds. Photograph by James Robbins.

Photo 11.31 Naturalized crocus flourish and multiply for many years.

Photo 11.32 Minor bulbs, such as *Muscari armenica* are gaining favor in many commercial landscapes. Photograph courtesy of Gerald Klingaman.

can be planted in mid-January. Store pre-cooled bulbs in reliable dry storage at 40° F until planting time. They should bloom eight to ten weeks after planting.

Label crates and boxes of bulbs carefully upon receipt. Lost tags lead to strange color combinations; a yellow tulip cannot be distinguished from a red one without a label. Store bulbs in a cool, dry area until planting.

Incorporate fertilizer into spring bulb beds at the same rate prescribed earlier for flowering annuals. Reduce the amount of fertilizer applied for fall planted bulbs if the summer annuals were adequately fertilized throughout the growing season. Eliminate fertilization for bulbs entirely if fall color plants were planted and fertilized. Some recommendations suggest that bonemeal be added at planting for all bulbs. Bonemeal is simply an expensive low nitrogen (4-12-0) slow-release fertilizer. It imparts no protection for the bulbs and possesses no special attributes.

Space most bulbs four to six inches apart (Table 11.7). Lay out the entire bed before planting, especially if pansies or another cold-tolerant annual will be added as a companion planting later. Bulbs may be planted with a bulb planter, trowel, or in a pre-dug trench. The depth of planting depends on the type of bulb. Plant bulbs with the flat side (basal root plate) down and the pointed side up. On higher budget sites, beds are raked to level the area and one to two inches of organic mulch (such as pine straw or bark) are spread for appearance, to reduce erosion and fluctuation of soil temperature during the winter. Nature will usually supply the watering-in moisture necessary for fall-planted bulbs, although post-planting irrigation should be supplied if the site or season is dry.

Maintenance

Bulbs sometimes sprout or show foliage during early or mid-winter warm periods. This is not usually a problem; spring bulbs are very cold tolerant. Extreme temperatures occasionally may yellow the foliage and flowers can be damaged under severe conditions. Mulching beds reduces fluctuations in soil temperatures and premature sprouting.

For bulbs used as a one-time color display, no maintenance procedures are necessary. If quality

Table 11.7
Planting depth and spacing for some common landscape bulbs and corms

Flowering time	Planting Depth (inches)	Spacing (inches)	Flowering Height (inches)
Very early			
Galanthus (Snowdrops)	4	1	VL
Eranthis (Winter aconite)	4	1	VL
Iris reticulata (Dwarf Iris)	4	4	VL
Scilla sibirica (Siberian squill)	4	4	VL
Crocus	4	2	VL
Chionodoxa (Glory of the snow)	4	2	VL
Puschkinia scilloides (Striped squill)	4	2	VL
Fritillaria meleagris	4	2	VL
	4	4	L
Early			
Kaufmanniana tulip	6	6	VL
Fosteriana tulip	6	6	VL
Single and double early tulips	6	6	L
Muscari armeniacum (Grape hyacinth)	4	2	VL
Daffodil	6-8	4-6	L/M/T
Hyacinth	6-8	6	L
Mid-season			
Greigii tulip	6	6	L/M
Mendel and Triumph tulip	6	6	M/T
Darwin hybrid tulip	6	6	M/T
Fritillaria imperialis (Crown imperial)	6-8	12	VT
Daffodil	6-8	4-6	M/T
Late			
Hyacinthoides hispanica (Spanish	4	3	L
squill)	6-8	6	M/T
Parrot tulip	6-8	6	M/T
Double late tulip	6-8	6	T
Lily-flowered tulip	6-8	6	T/VT
Darwin and cottage tulips			
Very late			
Dutch iris	6-8	4	M/T
Lily	4-8	12	M/T/VT

VL = Very low, up to 6 inches
L = Low, 6 to 12 inches
M = Medium, 12-20 inches
T = Tall, 20 to 28 inches
VT = Very tall, over 28 inches.

bulbs and planting procedures have been used, nature will do the rest. The plants can be deadheaded after the blossoms fade for a neater appearance. Allow foliage to remain for appearance if there will be a delay before bed preparation for annuals. Remove the bulbs when preparing the beds for annuals.

Remove the faded flowers of tulips, narcissus, or daffodils that will remain in place more than one season to prevent seed formation. Seed production uses carbohydrates that would otherwise be stored in the bulb. Keep the leaves intact as long as possible. Ideally, the leaves should be allowed to turn yellow before they are removed. Delay mowing of the turf in areas containing naturalized crocus, narcissus, and other small bulbs as long as possible.

Bulbs planted in permanent beds with other ornamentals receive adequate nutrition from fertilizer applications to the beds. No additional or special applications are necessary. Insects and diseases seldom trouble bulbs.

Roses

Roses, the "Queen of Flowers," are popular in home gardens and are sometimes used in commercial and public landscapes. Roses are most frequently found in apartment, condominium and residential communities, plus parks and public gardens, rather than in corporate landscapes. Roses are best enjoyed where people have time to relax, enjoy, and to stop and smell the roses.

Roses provide incredible diversity in color, form, and texture. Climbing roses can be trained on fences to add another dimension to the landscape. Shrub and miniature roses can be used as groundcovers. Some shrub cultivars make striking and effective bank covers, especially in the milder regions of the nation. Roses, however, can also be one of the most demanding and exacting plants in the landscape. Some roses, such as the hybrid teas, require an enormous expenditure of time, capital, and dedication to keep them presentable in many areas. Roses ranked number one among all shrubs in the amount of hours required per 100 square feet of bed in a survey conducted by the University of California. Limit roses to landscapes that can afford the high labor cost required.

Site Selection and Planting. Select a well-drained site with a minimum five to six hours of full sun. Soil pH should be adjusted to 6.0 to 7.2. Roses are sometimes susceptible to iron chlorosis in alkaline soils. A soil test provides a true picture of the nutrients that should be incorporated before planting. In the absence of a soil test, incorporate one pound of nitrogen as a 1:2:1, 1:1:1 or similar complete fertilizer per 1,000 square feet. Organic matter, approximately 25 percent of the root zone volume, may be incorporated prior to planting to improve the water and nutrient reserve, drainage, and soil structure. Most rose beds are constructed to be higher than the surrounding soil surface to improve drainage.

Planting holes for roses are the same as those for any other ornamental. Position the bud union (the knob-like area where the scion is grafted to the rootstock) two inches below the soil surface. This provides additional protection against cold temperatures. Organic mulches improve rose bed appearance, aid water conservation, control weeds, and moderate soil temperatures.

Management. Roses should receive one to two inches of rainfall or supplemental irrigation per week. Irrigate to moisten the soil to a depth of six to 10 inches. Drip irrigation or soaker hoses are preferred since wetting the foliage promotes disease. If overhead watering is necessary, irrigate in the early morning so the foliage will dry rapidly.

Fertilize established roses when they begin to leaf out in the spring. Fertilizers incorporating systemic insecticides help reduce some of the inevitable pesticide applications that will be necessary. Follow label directions for rates and timing of insecticide-fertilizer combinations or specialized rose fertilizers. A complete fertilizer (3:1:1, 2:1:1, or similar) applied once every four weeks is sufficient for proper growth and flowering. Spread a small amount (four to eight ounces) of fertilizer around individual plants or broadcast fertilize at a rate of ½- to one-pound nitrogen per 1,000 square feet over the entire bed.

Insect and Disease Control. Some shrub, groundcover, and hybrid tea selections have resistance to some diseases; however, most roses are plagued by a variety of diseases and insects. They require a weekly or bi-monthly spray program beginning with emergence of the first five-leaflet leaf.

Disease pressure can be reduced by proper site selection (full sun and good air circulation) and by avoiding wetting the leaves during irrigation. Remove dead and fallen leaves that host blackspot and other fungal diseases. For the best control, alternate different fungicides in the spray program.

Commercial and home gardeners use insecticide-fertilizer combinations to reduce insect feeding. Regardless, monitor the plants carefully and be especially watchful for aphids, mites, and thrips.

Pruning. Prune hybrid tea and grandiflora roses in spring as buds begin to swell or just after new growth has begun. Remove all dead, diseased, or damaged canes. Cut back canes showing winter damage to healthy wood. Remove any suckers from below the graft union. Remove all but three to five healthy canes and cut these back to a lateral branch or bud within 12 to 18 inches of ground level. Prune remaining canes at an angle sloping away from the bud about ¼-inch above an outfacing bud.

Floribunda roses should not be pruned as heavily as hybrid tea and grandiflora types. Select six to eight healthy, vigorous canes and cut them back to within 18 to 24 inches of ground level.

Hybrid tea, floribunda, and grandiflora roses must be pruned frequently during the growing season, often once per week. When pruning, first remove all dead, diseased, and weak (thin and spindly) growth. Remove all branches with stem disease or cankers at least one inch below the diseased portion and disinfect the pruner with a 70 percent (or greater) alcohol or a 10 percent bleach solution before making another cut to prevent disease spread. Pruning cuts should be made ¼-inch above an out-facing active bud or branch at a 30 to 45 degree angle in the direction of the bud. This keeps the center of the shrub open, increasing sun exposure and air circulation and reducing disease pressure.

Remove faded flowers to prevent setting of seed and reduction in future flowering. Remove flowers by cutting the stem back to above a five-leaflet leaf. For vigorous-growing cultivars or to control the size of the plant, count down to the third to fifth five-leaflet leaf before removing the faded flower. New shoots will form quickly below this cut and produce the next flower in the shortest possible time. Do not deadhead after September in areas where winter damage to new growth can occur.

Miniature roses require only a light pruning to shape them in the early spring. Remove dead, diseased, and damaged wood as necessary during the growing season. Miniatures also require periodic deadheading during the summer. Groundcover roses seldom need pruning.

Climbing roses. Most climbing roses bloom only on one-year-old or older canes. Climbing roses are not usually pruned during the first two or three years after planting except to remove dead, diseased, or damaged canes, and to train them. Climbing roses that bloom periodically throughout the summer should be pruned in the spring. Those that flower only in the spring are pruned immediately after flowering.

During annual pruning of climbing roses remove older canes to ground level and leave five or six of the healthiest, most vigorous canes. Thin excessive growth on the remaining canes to a side branch or bud.

Winter Protection. Hybrid tea roses require some form of winter protection in most regions of the country. Most climbing, shrub, and miniature roses are reasonably cold hardy except in extreme northern regions. Winter protection usually consists of mounding eight to 10 inches of soil or bark mulch over the center of the plant in late fall, following the first hard freeze. Rose canes can be pruned back to 10 to 14 inches to facilitate covering. Some rose growers cover this soil or bark mound with an additional layer of straw, hay, or bark mulch. The greater the danger of winter injury, the greater the protection required. Straw and hay, however, serve as an excellent winter abode for rodents. Styrofoam or plastic rose cones are also used to cover roses. These, however, provide minimal protection and are not adequate in northern regions where winter injury is likely.

The soil or mulch should not be removed until just before growth resumes in the spring and danger of extreme cold is past. Bark mulch has an advantage in that it can be spread over the bed as the current season's mulch.

Photo 11.33 The rose is one of the best loved landscape plants. Unfortunately, roses usually require much more care than other landscape ornamentals. Photograph provided courtesy of the Rainbird Corporation.

Photo 11.34 Roses put to bed for the winter under a blanket of hardwood mulch. The mulch is spread over the bed when the plants are uncovered after danger of frost in the spring.

In areas with mild winters where mounding or additional protection is not needed, hybrid tea roses are pruned to three to four feet in the late fall. Plants are again pruned in early spring to remove dead and winter-damaged canes. Four to six healthy canes are selected as the main branches of the plant for that season and pruned back to 18 to 20 inches.

Bibliography

1. Altland, J., C. Gilliam, *et al.* 2003. Fertilization methods affect growth, color and nitrogen leaching of winter annuals in landscape beds. *Journal of Environmental Horticulture* 21(2):99.

2. Anonymous. 1981. *Labor Requirement Analysis for Landscape Maintenance.* Univ. of California Coop. Ext. Ser. Leaflet 21232.

3. Anonymous. 1986. Perennials mean easier-not forgotten maintenance. *Landscape Contractor* 27(9):16.

4. Anonymous. 1989. *The Professional Guide to Flowering Annuals.* Professional Plant Growers Association, Lansing, MI.

5. Anonymous. 1994. Best of the bunch. *American Nurseryman* 179(10):15.

6. Anonymous. 1998. *Selecting Annuals for Special Uses.* Michigan State Univ. Coop. Ext. Ser. Bul. 399.

7. Anonymous. 1999. *Turf & Ornamental Reference for Plant Protection Products.* C&P Press, New York.

8. Anonymous. 2000. Pansies reign paramount for fall. *Lawn & Landscape* 21(11):10.

9. Anonymous. 2001. Daffodil days. *Lawn & Landscape* 22(3):10.

10. Anonymous. 2003. Perennials. *American Nurseryman* 198 (12):46.

11. Armitage, A. 2000. *Armitage's Garden Perennials: A Color Encyclopedia.* Timber Press, Portland, OR.

12. Armitage, A. 2001. *Armitage's Manual of Annuals, Biennials, and Half Hardy Perennials.* Timber Press, Portland, OR.

13. Armitage, A. 1997. *Herbaceous Perennial Plants,* 2nd ed. Stipes Publishing, Champaign, IL.

14. Atchison, J. 2003. The color of success. *American Nurseryman* 198(10):16.

15. Baily, D. 1999. *Selection and Use of Stress-tolerant Bedding Plants for the Landscape*. North Carolina State Univ. Coop. Ext. Ser. Leaflet 552.

16. Baily, D. 1999. *Under-utilized Bedding Plants for the North Carolina Landscape*. North Carolina State Univ. Coop. Ext. Ser. Leaflet 556.

17. Baily, D. and M. Powell. 1999. *Installation and Maintenance of Landscape Bedding Plants*. North Carolina State Univ. Coop. Ext. Ser. Leaflet 555.

18. Baily, D. and S. Warren, and W. Fonteno. 1999. *Bed Preparation and Fertilization Recommendations for Bedding Plants in the Landscape*. North Carolina State Univ. Coop. Ext. Ser. Leaflet 551.

19. Braun, G. 1997. Post renaissance apartment homes. *Grounds Maintenance* 32(8):c2.

20. Bryant, D. 1993. Spring color. *Western Turf Management* 4(3):6.

21. Cathy, H. 1977. *Spring Flowering Bulbs*. USDA-ARS Home and Garden Bull. No. 136.

22. Cybulski, A. 2001. Flowering cabbage and kale. *Lawn & Landscape* 22(11):32.

23. Cybulski, A. 2003. 10 steps to fuss-free color. *Lawn & Landscape* 23(4):30.

24. Darke, R. 1999. *The Color Encyclopedia of Ornamental Grasses*. Timber Press, Portland, OR.

25. de Vroomen, R. 1984. Bulbs in the landscape design. *Landscape Contractor* 25(10):12.

26. DiSabato-Aust, T. 1998. *The Well-Tended Perennial Garden: Planting and Pruning Techniques*. Timber Press, Portland, OR.

27. Fech, J. 2003. Standing out. *Grounds Maintenance* 38(10):15.

28. Ferguson, S. 1992. Bulbs offer many choices for spring color. *Landscape and Irrigation* 16(10):22.

29. Graber, D. and D. Hensley. 1987. Evaluation of postemergent grass herbicides for use in annual flower and groundcover plantings. *HortScience* 22(6):1281.

30. Hampshire, K. 2001. Flower power. *Lawn & Landscape* 22(2):67.

31. Hampshire, K. 2001. Get with the program. *Lawn & Landscape* 22(5):94.

32. Hensley, D. 1991. Color your world with bulbs. *Nursery Manager* 7(10):73.

33. Hensley, D. 1996. Preparation is the key to planting annuals. *T&O Service Tech* 1(2):8.

34. Hensley, D. 1996. Caring for bedding plants. *T&O Service Tech* 1(3):11.

35. Hensley, D. 1996. Commercial color provides a competitive edge. *T&O Service Tech* 1(3):11.

36. Hensley, D. and F. Gibbons. 1985. Tolerance of some garden flowers to selected preemergence herbicides. *Transactions Kansas Academy of Science* 88(3-4):1.

37. Hensley, D. and L. McGillivary. 1991. Let ornamental grasses spice up the landscape. *Nursery Manager* 7(5):70.

38. Hensley, D., M. Witte, J. Hartman, and R. Scheibner. 1980. *Roses and Their Care*. Univ. of Kentucky Coop. Ext. Ser. Fact Sheet HO-53.

39. Kerkhoff. K. 2000. Fall into action. *Grounds Maintenance* 35(11)35.

40. Leuthold, L. 1989. *Flowering Perennials*. Kansas State Univ. Coop. Ext. Ser. Circular MF-707 Revised.

41. Leuthold, L. 1989. *Flowering Annuals*. Kansas State Univ. Coop. Ext. Ser. Circular MF-706 Revised.

42. Lewis, A. 1988. Commercial color. *American Nurseryman* 168(12):24.

43. Lindgren, D. 1996. *Annual Flowers for Specific Uses in Nebraska*. Univ. Nebraska Coop. Ext. Ser. Circular G77-344-A.

44. Manzel, K. 1997. A parade of perennials. *American Nurseryman* 186(9):32.

45. Martin, J. 1988. *Bedding Plants in Ohio and the United States*. Ohio State Univ. Coop. Ext. Ser. Pub. HYG-1235-88.

46. Martin, J. 2002. Picking the right perennial. *Lawn & Landscape* 23(11):34.

47. McGarigle, C. 1990. Ravishing roses have a past, present and great future in landscape plans. *Landscape Contractor* 31(2):24.

48. Mills, L. 2002. Coming up roses. *Southwest Trees & Turf* 7(5):8.

49. Neal, J. and S. Warren. 1998. *Weed Management in Annual Color Beds*. North Carolina State Univ. Coop. Ext. Ser. Leaflet 644.

50. Norcini, J. 1999. *Postemergent Herbicides for Use in Ornamentals*. Univ. of Florida Coop. Ext. Ser. Pub. ENH-95.

51. Peppler, K. 1990. Colorful landscape uses of popular plant materials. *Lawn & Landscape Management* 11(4):54.

52. Phillips, E. and C. Burrell. 2004. *Rodale's Illustrated Encyclopedia of Perennials*. Rodale Press, Emmaus, PA.

53. Price, S. 2000. Annuals light up shady areas. *Grounds Maintenance* 35(11):c12.

54. Professional Plant Growers Assn. 1989. Keeping the landscape colorful with flowering annuals. *ALA/Maintenance* 10(6):52.

55. Reilly, A. 1988. Here today...here tomorrow. *Landscape Management* 27(3):42.

56. Russ, K. and B. Polomski. 1999. *Growing Annuals*. Clemson Univ. Coop. Ext. Ser. Bul. HGIC 1152.

57. Schilling, N. 2000. Soil preparation for color. 5(9):1.

58. Schmidt, J. and G. Stack. 1998. In living color. *American Nurseryman* 189(5):76.

59. Simmons, D. 1999. Sudden impact. *American Nurseryman* 190(10) 30.

60. Sinnes, A. 1981. *All About Annuals*. Ortho Books. San Francisco, CA

61. Smith, S. 1989 Flower power. *American Nurseryman* 170(8):69.

62. Stack, L. 1990. Flower power on the golf course. *Landscape Management* 29(3):72.

63. Stack, L. 1997. Creating flower beds in the landscape. *Landscape & Irrigation* 21(1):26.

64. Still, S. 1994. *Manual of Herbaceous Ornamental Plants*, 4th ed. Stipes Publishing, Champaign, IL.

65. Sutton, C. 1998. Combine bulbs and perennials to extend bloom. *Grounds Maintenance* 33(3):50.

66. Sutton, C. 1999. Landscaping with bulbs. *Lawn & Landscape* 20(11):66.

67. Thomas, P. 1995. *Flowering Annuals for Georgia Gardens*. Univ. of Georgia Coop. Ext. Serv. Bul. 954.

68. Thomas, P. 1999. *Flowering Perennials for Georgia Gardens*. Univ. of Georgia Coop. Ext. Serv. Bul. 944.

69. Thompson, E. 1992. *Ornamental Grasses*. Ohio State Univ. Coop. Ext. Ser. Bul. HYG-1238-92.

70. van der Hoeven, G. 1990. Learn to design perennial flower gardens. *Grounds Maintenance* 25(4):102.

71. Williams, D. 1981. Fertilizers for nonwoody ornamentals. *Grounds Maintenance* 16(1):14.

72. Wisniewski, D. 2000. Plan ahead for color at its best. *Southwest Trees & Turf* 5(1):1.

Chapter 12
Turfgrass Management

by Roch Gaussoin[1] and David Hensley

Turfgrass is the nation's most popular groundcover. Turfgrass management represents a significant portion of the labor expended for landscape management and profit margin of many firms. Full service landscape management companies report that turfgrass maintenance represents 70 percent or more of their effort and gross sales. Any successful landscape management firm must offer some facet of turfgrass management. Programs range from chemical applications to full-service site management, including cultural and physical management. Every landscape manager must understand the fundamentals of turfgrass management. The intent of this chapter is to provide a rudimentary understanding of turfgrass management techniques. Refer to the references at the end of this chapter for further information.

Introduction

Turfgrass is the surface layer of vegetation used to stabilize the soil, provide a recreational surface, and to enhance the aesthetics of a landscape. Grasses are categorized as *cool* or *warm* season. As this classification implies, *cool season grasses* are best adapted to the cooler regions of the US; *warm season grasses* are better adapted to warmer environments. The *Transition Zone*

Photo 12.1. Turfgrass is the nation's most popular groundcover. Photograph courtesy of Jerome M. Renick.

Photo 12.2. Golf courses require intensive and specialized management to maintain the high quality expected by their clientele.

[1]Professor and Extension Turfgrass Specialist, Department of Agronomy and Horticulture, University of Nebraska, Lincoln, NE.

(Illustration 12.1) is the area where both warm and cool season grasses may be grown; but conditions are ideal for neither. The Transition Zone presents the greatest challenge to turfgrass managers. Cool season grasses are susceptible to summer stresses and warm season grasses are prone to winterkill.

Establishment and Renovation

Turfgrasses can be established from seed or vegetatively propagated using sod, sprigs, or plugs. Establishment methods depend on species, availability, and economics. The basics of establishment for cool and warm season grasses are identical, except for timing. Cool season grasses are generally best established in the late summer or early fall, whereas warm season grasses are best installed in the late spring or early summer. Proper site preparation is critical for long-term success of the lawn and its perpetual management. Greater numbers of customer complaints are received about poor or spotty lawns than any other facet of landscape installation or management.

New Turf Installation. The steps for successful turfgrass establishment are:

Illustration 12.1.

Table 12.1.
Characteristics of commonly used turfgrasses

Cool season turfgrass		Environmental Tolerance*					
		Heat	Cold	Shade	Drought	Wear	Recuperative Potential
Creeping Bentgrass	*Agrostis palustris*	VG	VG	G	P	P	VG
Kentucky Bluegrass	*Poa pratensis*	G	G	F	G	F	G
Rough Bluegrass	*Poa trivialis*	P	G	VG	P	F	F
Chewings Fescue	*Festuca rubra* spp. *Commutate*	F	F	VG	VG	F	F
Hard Fescue	*Festuca longifolia*	F	F	VG	VG	F	F
Creeping Red Fescue	*Festuca rubra*	F	F	VG	VG	F	F
Tall Fescue	*Festuca arundinacea*	VG	P	G	VG	VG	F
Perennial Ryegrass	*Lolium perenne*	F	P	F	P	G	F
Annual Ryegrass	*Lolium multiflorum*	P	P	F	VP	G	P
Warm season turfgrass							
Bahiagrass	*Paspalum notatum*	VG	P	F	F	G	G
Bermudagrass	*Cynodon dactylon*	VG	F	VP	VG	G	VG
Improved Bermudagrass	*Cynodon* spp.	VG	F	P	G	VG	VG
Buffalograss	*Buchloe dactyloides*	VG	VG	P	VG	F	VG
Carpetgrass	*Axonopus* spp.	VG	P	F	VP	P	G
Centipedegrass	*Eremochloa ophiuroides*	G	P	F	VP	P	P
St. Augustinegrass	*Stenotaphrum secundatum*	VG	P	VG	P	F	VG
Seashore paspalum	*Paspalum vaginatum*	VG	VP	F	P	G	VG
Zoysiagrass	*Zoysia* spp.	VG	G	G	G	VG	P

*VG = Very Good; G = Good; F = Fair; P = Poor; VP = Very Poor

All characteristics are relative to tolerance within each grouping (i.e. cool vs. warm season). Considerable variation exists within species and cultivars. Check with local seed companies or the county extension office concerning specific cultivar recommendations.

1. **Soil Test.** At a minimum, test for phosphorous, potassium and pH. This information serves as the basis for pre-plant and post-plant nutrient applications.

2. **Weed Control.** Weed populations can be significantly reduced if proper steps are taken during establishment.

   Before seeding, irrigation, followed by a light, mechanical cultivation, will alleviate weed pressure prevalent in a new site. This approach is more successful for annual than for perennial weeds. Perennial weeds require application of a systemic, non-selective herbicide such as glyphosate at a suitable interval before cultivation.

   A more aggressive, but expensive, approach to weed control is sterilization of the area before seeding. Sterilization, when done properly, eliminates soil-borne plant pathogens and insects, as well as weeds. Sterilization is, however, expensive and requires the services of a certified and experienced applicator. It is not an operation for the novice.

3. **Rough Grading.** Fill low spots and level high areas. Contour grade, according to landscape installation plan and specifications. Install supplementary drainage if required. If rough grading is extensive, remove and stockpile topsoil for use in establishing the final grade. Avoid adding or removing more than two inches of soil around existing trees. Extensive excavation around prized trees requires use of tree wells and other specialized techniques to insure survival.

4. **Addition of soil amendments.** After establishing the rough grade, add any required or desired soil amendments. The soil pH (obtained from the soil test) may indicate the need for lime or sulfur. Consider lime if the soil pH is below 5.5. *Starter fertilizers* are added or incorporated before seeding. Starter fertilizers usually have a ratio of 1:1:1 and are important in the early growth and establishment of new turfgrass plantings.

5. **Final Grade.** Final grading should be done immediately before seeding, sodding, or sprigging. Remove rocks and other debris. Rake or drag to smooth the area for seeding. Ideally, no soil particles should be present that are larger than a garden pea.

6. **Apply seed, sprigs, plugs, or sod.** The choice between seed and vegetative propagation material depends on several management factors. Establishment by seed is the least expensive method, but it is also the slowest and most labor intensive post-planting. See Table 12.2 for seeding rates.

Table 12.2.
Recommended seeding rates (pounds of seed per 1,000 square feet) for major turfgrass species

Species	High*	Medium**	Low***
Cool season turfgrass			
Kentucky Bluegrass	2 – 3	2 – 3	1 – 2
Perennial Ryegrass	6 – 8	6 – 8	4 – 6
Tall Fescue	8 – 10	8 – 10	8 – 10
Creeping Bentgrass	1 – 2	1	not recommended
Fine Fescues	not recommended	4 – 6	3 – 4
Warm season turfgrass			
Bahiagrass	not recommended	6 – 8	4 – 6
Bermudagrass (hulled)	1 – 2	1 – 2	1
Buffalograss (burs)	2 – 3	1 – 2	1
Centipedegrass	not recommended	1	1
Zoysiagrass	not recommended	2 – 3	2 – 3

*Relatively high management inputs, such as golf course greens and fairways and sports turfs.
**Golf course fairways, home lawns, or showcase grounds.
***Utility turfs, parks, or general grounds.

Sodding is the most expensive initially, but establishment time is greatly diminished, compared to seeding. Subsequent management following sodding is less costly than for seeding. The time to establishment and the cost for sprigging or plugging fall between that for seeding and sodding, depending on species.

Use only certified seed. Sod is certified in some states. *Certification* assures that the grass is true to name and relatively free of weeds and pathogens.

7. *Rake and/or roll.* Seed and vegetative materials must be in intimate contact with the soil for successful establishment. Raking facilitates good soil contact after broadcast seeding. Rolling sod with a light roller firms the soil and eliminates air pockets.

8. *Irrigation.* Moisture is critical for new turfgrass installations. Frequent, light irrigation is necessary until the new root system develops from seed or sprigs. Sod and plug installations must be thoroughly soaked so that the underlying soil is wet. Roots will not grow into dry soil.

10. *Mowing.* During initial establishment, the turf should be mowed frequently. Mowing promotes lateral growth and spread, and can significantly speed establishment. The first mowing after planting should occur as soon as the grass is high enough to mow at optimal height. See the mowing section of this chapter for height recommendations for various turf species.

Photo 12.3. Moisture is the most critical factor for new turfgrass installations. Photograph courtesy of Roch Gaussoin.

Renovation. Turfgrass declines with neglect and over time. Clients or managers may also be interested in changing the existing turf to an improved or less management-intensive species or cultivar. The overseeding or conversion of an existing turf is referred to as *renovation*. Many of the steps described for establishment plantings are used in renovation, with minor exceptions.

When converting from one cultivar to another within a single species stand, it is not necessary to eradicate the existing planting. However, when changing from one species to another and retaining a solid stand, it is essential to eradicate the existing turf with a non-selective herbicide. Vegetation control is also not necessary for overseeding bare or thin spots in an existing turf. Renovation with sod or sprigs requires more aggressive site preparation, similar to that required for establishment of a new turf. The existing cover is killed and the site tilled and ordered.

Winter Overseeding. Overseeding of dormant warm season turfs, usually bermudagrass, with a cool season species is common in the southern United States. Annual or perennial ryegrass is the most commonly used for winter overseeding, but fine fescues have become an acceptable overseeding choice in some areas. All of the perennial grasses offer improved quality, stress tolerance, pest resistance, and greater manageability than annual ryegrass. Winter overseeding success depends on the cool season grass selected, seedbed preparation, timing, and post planting maintenance.

Overseeding of warm season turfgrasses is done in the fall, approximately one month before the grass goes off-color. The warm season turf is scalped (mown as low as possible) and the seed is broadcast at five to 10 pounds per 1,000 square feet. Slit-seeding provides a more even stand and is preferred, if the equipment is available.

Developing a Turfgrass Nitrogen Fertility Program

Turfgrass fertility programs determine the pace and requirements for other management practices. Differences in geographic location, soil, climate, turfgrass species, and maintenance level strongly influence nutrient application timing. The general recommendations for timing and rates presented here should be viewed as a guideline. Make adjustments for individual sites and programs as necessary.

Timing. Application timing is determined by turfgrass species. Warm season turfs, like bermudagrass, buffalograss, or zoysiagrass, are fertilized at a different time of year than cool season turfs, like tall fescue and Kentucky bluegrass. Differences in timing fertilizer applications are related to the period when the turfs are actively growing. Warm season turfgrasses go off color in early fall and, depending upon location, will not green-up until late spring, as late as April or May, in some regions. The most active growth period for warm season grasses is summer. Cool season turfs, on the other hand, grow actively in the spring and fall, but minimally during late summer. Fertilizer is applied to an actively growing turf. There are, however, exceptions to this guideline.

Cool season turfgrass. Cool season turfgrasses should receive the majority of their annual application in the fall. University research and practical experience have shown that turf that is fertilized in the late fall has better root growth, fewer weeds, disease and thatch, green color later in fall, and earlier spring green-up than cool season turf that is heavily fertilized in the spring. A demonstrated disadvantage of heavy spring fertilization is the promotion of a flush of top-growth, at the expense of root growth, prior to the summer stress period. In general, cool season turfs should receive two-thirds of their total annual nitrogen (N) application in the fall and one-third in the spring. For example: if the desired annual nitrogen application is three pounds of nitrogen per 1,000 sq. ft., one pound should be applied in the spring and two pounds in the fall. How these applications are applied (i.e., as single or split applications) depends on the fertilizer carrier (slow or quick release) and length of growing season.

Warm season turfgrass. Warm season grass fertility programs should begin in the early spring, as the turf becomes active, and continue through the active growing season. Avoid over stimulating warm season grasses in late fall with heavy applications of nitrogen. Succulent growth is more susceptible to frost damage or winterkill.

Rates. Application rates of nitrogen fertilizers depend on species, as well as the level of main-

Photo 12.4. Small cyclone-type or impeller spreaders can be calibrated to deliver the correct amount of fertilizer to residential sites. Photograph courtesy of James Robbins.

Photo 12.5. Larger spreaders efficiently apply fertilizer to large turf areas.

tenance desired. Turf that is abundantly fertilized requires more frequent mowing and irrigation, but the turf is of higher quality. Other management practices also influence fertility rate. For example, if clippings are removed, higher rates of fertilizer need to be applied to compensate for the nutrients lost in the removed clippings. Additionally, if the turf is irrigated frequently, grown on sandy soils, or in a high rainfall region, higher nitrogen levels should be used. See Table 12.3 for monthly nitrogen requirements for most turfgrass species.

To use Table 12.3, locate the turfgrass species in *Column 1* and the level of management appropriate for the site in *Column 2, 3,* or *4.* The rate represents a range of the *monthly* nitrogen requirement during the growing season. For ex-

Table 12.3.

Monthly nitrogen requirements for different turfgrasses at three management levels

Higher ends of nitrogen fertilization ranges are suggested for sites that are irrigated frequently, in high rainfall areas, those with sandy soil, or if clippings are regularly removed after mowing. Low maintenance levels are used for sites with low management inputs, such as parks or other general turfs. Medium to high maintenance levels are used for general and home landscape turf with regular management inputs (water, mowing, and other care). Very high maintenance fertilization levels should be used only for highly maintained recreational turf sites, such as golf courses or athletic fields.

	Pounds of nitrogen per 1,000 sq. ft. per growing month		
	Level of management		
	Low	**Medium to High**	**Very High**
Cool season turfgrass			
Chewing Fescue	0.2 – 0.3	0.4 – 0.6	not adapted
Red Fescue	0.2 – 0.3	0.4 – 0.6	not adapted
Kentucky Bluegrass (common)	0.3 – 0.4	0.5 – 0.6	0.7 – 0.8
Kentucky Bluegrass (improved cultivars)	0.4 – 0.5	0.6 – 0.7	0.8 – 1.5
Perennial Ryegrass	0.3 – 0.4	0.5 – 0.6	0.7 – 0.8
Tall Fescue	0.3 – 0.4	0.5 – 0.6	0.7 – 1.0
Colonial Bentgrass	0.3 – 0.4	0.5 – 0.6	0.7 – 0.8
Annual Bluegrass	0.3 – 0.4	0.5 – 0.6	0.7 – 1.0
Creeping Bentgrass	0.3 – 0.4	0.5 – 0.6	0.7 – 1.5
Warm season turfgrass			
Bahiagrass	0.0 – 0.1	0.2 – 0.4	not adapted
Bermudagrass	0.3 – 0.4	0.5 – 0.7	0.8 – 1.5
Buffalograss	0.0 – 0.1	0.2 – 0.4	0.2 – 0.4
Centipedegrass	0.0 – 0.1	0.2 – 0.4	not adapted
Carpetgrass	0.2 – 0.3	0.4 – 0.6	not adapted
St. Augustinegrass	0.3 – 0.4	0.5 – 0.7	0.8 – 1.0
Zoysiagrass	0.3 – 0.4	0.5 – 0.7	0.8 – 1.0

ample, if you were maintaining *bermudagrass* at a *very high level of management*, the monthly nitrogen requirement would be *0.8 to 1.5 pounds of nitrogen* per 1,000 square feet *per growing month*. If the growing season in this example were 11 months, then the total annual nitrogen requirement would be 8.8 to 16.5 pounds per 1,000 square feet. Obviously this amount would not be applied in a single application or necessarily in 11 monthly applications. The number of applications and application timing depends on fertilizer carrier, scheduling, fertility program, budget, and other restrictions within the operation.

As another example, suppose a managed residential property has a lawn of *Kentucky bluegrass*. Home lawns are managed at a *medium to high*

Photo 12.6. Improper application of nitrogen fertilizer can result in striping of the turf. Photograph courtesy of James Robbins.

Table 12.4.

Determine your needs before buying a mower

Mowers, like all equipment, are expensive. The large number of options and differences among the brands available can be confusing. Before committing to a purchase, consider the following:

- What are the present and anticipated acreage requirements?
- Who are your primary mowing clients: small sites, large commercial, utility turf, manicured turf, or other?
- How many different types of mowing units are required?
- What types of topography (slopes, ditches, berms) are most prevalent on the site?
- How often will mowing of wet or soggy turf be required?
- Will the equipment be required or useful in other operations, such as snow removal, parking lot cleaning, etc.?
- What brands are presently used and how do you like them?
- Are service and parts readily available?

maintenance level. The corresponding monthly nitrogen fertility requirement would therefore be *0.6 to 0.7 pounds* of nitrogen per 1,000 sq. ft. As with the bermudagrass example, the number and timing of applications depends on site-specific circumstances and the fertility program.

Mowing

Mowing is the most frequent maintenance event occurring on a landscaped site. Mowing strongly influences the development of the turfgrass plant. It results in a temporary decline in root growth, reduces carbohydrate production, creates entry ports for disease-causing organisms, and upsets plant water relations. Mowing also has a tremendous impact on management budgets and profits. Since this most basic, and often mundane, maintenance procedure is conducted frequently and expansively, small changes can significantly influence mowing time and costs. Mowing is also one of the most frequent topics of client complaints. Mowing should never be taken for granted, but viewed with a serious eye toward efficiency and profit.

Equipment selection. Landscape managers have a seemingly infinite choice of mowing products, sizes, brands, and accessories. Choosing the wrong mower can be an expensive mistake. Every type of mower has its optimum performance areas and limitations. Before buying, carefully consider your needs. No two operations or sites are identical.

The type, size, and number of mowers required for economical and efficient operation depends upon:

A. The *area* to be mown;

B. The turf *species*;

C. The *management intensity* and *type of use* for the site;

D. The numbers and type of *obstacles*;

E. The *topography*; and

F. The available *labor force*.

Regardless, the mowing unit selected must be maneuverable, adequately powered, easily adjusted, readily serviced, and efficient in fuel, dollars, and labor.

Mower types

Rotary mowers are the most versatile and popular type available to the landscape manager. The 36-inch walk-behind rotary mower is probably the mainstay of most landscape maintenance companies. Rotary mowers can be used for quality turf, for rough areas, to remove seed heads, and to pulverize fallen leaves. They are best suited for cutting turf to heights between one to five inches.

Blades of a rotary mower travel at high speeds on a horizontal plane and cut the leaf blade upon impact, like a scythe. This results in some tearing

Photo 12.7. Rotary mowers are the most versatile and popular type available to the landscape manager. Cutting width varies from 18-inch trim mowers to multiple blade units that mow up to 27 feet or more.

Photo 12.8. The quality of cut for reel mowers depends on the number and hone of the blades. Photograph courtesy of James Robbins.

Photo 12.9. Reel mowers are used for high quality turf cut at one-inch in height or less. Photograph courtesy of James Robbins.

of the blade. The quality of the cut depends upon the sharpness and balance of the blade and the type and condition of the turf. Scalping of the turf can be a problem, especially on uneven terrain.

Cutting width for rotary equipment varies from 18-inch trim mowers to multiple blade units that mow up to 27 feet or more. Rotary mowers have a high power requirement. Pay special attention to safety features when selecting rotary mowers. Ejection of stones and debris offers potential injury to operators and bystanders.

Reel mowers are the preferred machine for quality turf situations, especially for turfs mowed at one-inch or less. They are the standard mowers for greens, tees, and for high-quality residential or commercial turf. Reel mowers are preferred

for dense turf such as zoysiagrass and bermudagrass. The power input is very low, only about one to one and one-half horsepower per foot of cut. Ground-driven reel gangs are the most economical method of mowing large acreage.

Reel mowers cut by a scissors action of the reel against a bedknife. Reel mowers cut, not rip, the turf blade. Reel mowers provide a quality cut from two inches down to 3/32 inches, but have problems dealing with tall grass. The quality of cut depends on the number, speed, and hone of the blades, and the type and height of the turf. A quality sharpening machine or service must be available. Reel mowers require a relatively level surface for effective and efficient operation. Reels, rocks, and other hard debris do not mix well. Self-powered or pulled units offer from as little as a few feet in cut width, to over 26-feet wide swaths at a single pass.

Flail or *vertical mowers* cut by the impact of a fixed or free-swinging blade in a vertical plane. In the US, flail mowers are not frequently used for high quality turf situations, but are commonly used for large-scale mowing and vegetation control situations such as roadsides, parks, and utility turf. Flail mowers are used extensively on quality turfs in Europe. Flail mowers may actually cut more acres than any of the other mower types, despite their rough reputation. The quality of the cut varies with the sharpness, number, and spacing of the blades. Wider blades provide fast and efficient cutting of vegetation where appearance is not a prime concern. Smaller blades result in a higher quality cut for more visible areas.

Throwing rocks and debris is not a great problem with flail mowers, so they work well along roadsides. Flail mowers are available as self-powered units or can be tractor-mounted and powered by the Power Take-Off (PTO). Cutting width varies from five feet to 20 feet with multiple unit machines.

Sickle bar mowers are used for cutting hay and mowing tall grass and weeds such as along roadsides. Sickle bars cut by the action of a reciprocating knife across a plate. They require less power than flail mowers but most must be attached to a tractor. They are relatively inexpensive and maneuverable, but require frequent adjustment for efficient operation. Sickle bar mowers are slower than other types. They are primarily adapted to coarse bunch-type grasses and may clog frequently in fine-textured, dense grasses. They also produce an undesirable swath of cut grass that may smother remaining cover.

Mulching mowers have become an industry standard for rotary mowers. Restrictions on dumping clippings and other lawn wastes in public landfills became a reality in the early 1990s. Thirty-three percent of the respondents to a 1990 trade publication survey used mulching mowers in their commercial mowing operations. Of these, 38 percent began using them less than three years ago. Recent surveys indicate that two-thirds of the mowers used commercially are mulching mowers.

Photo 12.10. Flail mowers cut with a swinging blade on a vertical axis. They are widely used for mowing rough areas.

Photo 12.11. Mulching mowers cut and re-cut grass clippings forcing the small pieces into the turf. Mulching mowers use multiple or special blades and a different body to assure clippings are finely cut. Mulching mowers make clippings smaller and help hide them; however, they do not eliminate clippings.

Mulching mowers are designed to direct the clippings around the deck and back into the blade(s) to cut and re-cut them into small pieces before dropping them onto the turf. The technology varies from providing additional blades and adjusting the pitch of the blades, to re-designed and re-engineered decks. Kits are available to retrofit present rotary mowers for use as mulching units. Mulching mowers vary from 21-inch trim mowers to 70-inch riders.

Mulching mowers avoid collecting clippings and contributing to landfill overuse. They can reduce mowing time. Mulching clippings is also valuable in returning nutrients to the turf. When turf is mowed at the proper frequency, the clippings do not contribute to thatch build-up or to disease or insect problems.

Use of mulching mowers may require mowing the site more frequently or on a regular cutting schedule. The concept and practicality of the units allow less leeway for letting the turf go one or two days past the normal schedule. Mulching mowers have higher power and energy requirements. Lastly, mulching mowers cut the clippings more finely, but they do not make them disappear completely.

Zero-turning radius mowers or ZTR's can literally turn on a dime and give you a nickel in change. Such machines provide incredible maneuverability with an experienced operator and can increase productivity in open turf. These units also feature a hydrostatic drive that eliminates belts and chains in the drive system. ZTR's present superior traction and drive in wet situations, the capability of running the mower in reverse, and increased speed. They also require larger power units and are much more sophisticated machines than standard mowers. Repairs are more costly and usually cannot be made in the field. Mowers featuring hydrostatic drives and zero-turning radius have made steady increases in market share to a point where they may be the most common type of riding mower used by commercial operations. Because of their short turning radius, severe injury can result if operators are not properly trained or careful.

Slopes. Mowing excessive slopes productively and safely presents a challenge. Solutions have included having employees mow steep slopes with cleats instead of boots to lowering rotary mowers down steep grades with ropes. There are several specialty mowers on the market designed to make frequent slope mowing profitable and safer. These may utilize: self-leveling features to keep the engine and operator level; dual-hydrostatic or all-wheel drives; tilting decks; roll-over protection systems providing operator safety in case of accident; and/or automatic seat leveling to keep the operator upright reducing fatigue and accidents. These features do not come free, but can be justified if sufficient areas of steep grades (over 25 percent) require servicing. Due to OSHA regula-

Photo 12.12. Zero-turning radius mowers provide incredible maneuverability with an experienced operator and can increase productivity in open turf. Photograph courtesy of Hustler Turf Equipment, Hesston, KS.

Photo 12.13. Heavy-duty rotary and flail mowers are used for utility turf and rough terrain. This unit has all drive/all wheel steering, a 65 horsepower engine, and safety equipment to protect the operator. Photograph courtesy of Hustler Turf Equipment, Hesston, KS.

tions roll-over protection has become mandatory and increased the safety of mowers, especially when used in sloped conditions.

Simple modifications can aid in adapting conventional mowers for occasional slope use. A low center of gravity and wide tires improve stability. Machine weights or weighting the tires increases traction, but also increases compaction and fuel consumption. Power steering and hydrostatic drive increase the machine's maneuverability. Slopes are ideal locations to consider establishing slow-growing turf species or groundcovers, and use growth regulators to reduce the number of required mowings.

Hovering Mowers. Hovering, floating, or Fly mowers are actually line trimmers floating on a cushion of air. The operator guides the mower over the top of the turf. They are used, but not in large measure, because of their ability to glide over rocks, wet areas, and slopes. Floating mowers are more than a novelty and are used commercially by golf courses to mow bunkers and slopes and by commercial managers for problem sites. Disadvantages include their small, 15- to 21-inch cutting width, potential cost, and the difficulty in finding one to purchase.

Mowing Height

Mowing height depends upon the kind of grass, the intensity of culture, climate, stress, and the time of year. Each grass has a lower and upper tolerance limit for mowing. Close mowing reduces tolerance to environmental stresses, dis-

Photo 12.14. A floating mower that rides on a cushion of air is useful for maintaining turf on slopes or near water.

eases, weeds, and requires more careful management of other factors. Cool season grasses are mowed taller than warm season grasses because of their erect growth habit. Bermudagrass and zoysiagrass build up excessive thatch if mowed too tall. Table 12.5 lists recommended mowing heights for common landscape turfgrasses.

Most managers of cool season turfgrasses cut the lawn higher in the summer than in the spring

---

Table 12.5.
Recommended mowing heights

The mowing height depends upon the type of turf, use, and management of the area. The following are general guidelines for common landscape turfs. The mowing height for cool season turf is sometimes raised during the summer to compensate for heat and drought stress. Alternatively, some managers mow at the summer height all season. Warm season turfs are typically mown at the same height year round. Some managers will raise the height of warm season turf slightly in early and late season to compensate for cooler temperatures.

	Mowing height (inches)		
Cool season turfgrass	**Spring**	**Summer**	**Fall**
Chewing and Red Fescue	2.0 - 2.5	2.5 – 3.5	2.0 - 2.5
Kentucky Bluegrass	2.0 - 2.5	2.5 – 3.5	2.0 - 2.5
Perennial Ryegrass	1.5 – 2.0	2.5 – 3.5	2.0 - 2.5
Tall Fescue	2.5 – 3.0	3.0 – 4.0	2.5 – 3.0
Warm season turfgrass	**All year**		
Bahiagrass	2.5 – 3.0		
Bermudagrass	0.5 – 1.5		
Buffalograss	1.0 – unmown		
Carpetgrass	1.0 – 2.0		
Centipedegrass	0.75 – 1.5		
St. Augustinegrass	1.5 – 3.5		
Seashore Paspalum	0.5 – 1.0		
Zoysiagrass	0.75 – 2.0		

Table 12.6.

Adaptation to mowing height of some common turfgrass species
Turfgrasses vary in their adaptation to close mowing. The highest quality turf and most efficient management result from cutting the grass at the proper height. The following indicates the relative tolerance of difference turfgrasses for high or low mowing heights.

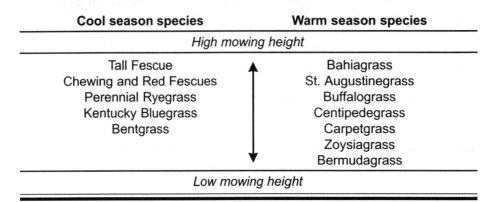

Cool season species	Warm season species
High mowing height	
Tall Fescue	Bahiagrass
Chewing and Red Fescues	St. Augustinegrass
Perennial Ryegrass	Buffalograss
Kentucky Bluegrass	Centipedegrass
Bentgrass	Carpetgrass
	Zoysiagrass
	Bermudagrass
Low mowing height	

Table 12.7.

Mower safety

Mowers injure thousands of people every year. These common machines should never be taken for granted. The following can help you and your employees mow safely:

- All safety features should be in place and in working order.
- Make sure all bystanders, especially children and pets, are removed from the mowing area.
  Debris thrown from a power mower can travel at lethal speed, sometimes over 200 miles per hour.
- Dress properly.
  - Avoid loose fitting clothing that can become tangled in moving parts.
  - Avoid shorts, sandals, or other open shoes.
  - Keep exposed skin covered if possible.
  - Shoes and boots should provide solid footing.
  - Several firms require or supply steel-toed boots for their mowing employees.
- Gasoline is extremely explosive; treat it with respect. Never refuel with the engine running.
- Never leave unattended mowers running.
- Do not disable automatic kill or cut-off switches.
- Take special precautions on slopes.
  - Mowers are designed to be pushed, rather than pulled.
  - Mow across the slope.
  - Start at the top of the grade and work down the slope.
  - When changing directions, turn so that the mower is always downhill to the operator.
- Check the area before mowing, especially when the grass is tall, for rocks and other potential missiles.
- Watch where you are mowing. There should be a clear field of vision for three to four feet in front of the machine.
- Stop the engine and disconnect the spark plug wire before working on the engine or blade.

274

and fall. The additional foliage improves the grass's environmental tolerance by increasing carbohydrate-producing area, maintains deeper roots, improves turf competition with weeds, and increases shading of the soil. Similarly, managers of warm season turfgrasses will sometimes raise the mowing height in the early and late portions of the growing season as a compensation measure for cold stress and reduced photosynthetic activity.

Regardless of the mowing height, sharp blades are essential to a quality operation. Dull blades bludgeon the leaf, leaving frayed tips that give the lawn a whitish cast. Sharp blades also improve efficiency and save fuel. Most operations keep extra sets of sharpened, balanced blades and make one or more exchanges for dull blades per week, depending on the quantity and type of turf mown. Sharp blades are especially important for quality mowing of zoysiagrass, ryegrasses, and tall fescue.

Mowing Frequency

Turfgrass may be mown from once a day on golf greens, to once or twice per season along roadsides. High quality landscapes are usually associated with frequent, consistent mowing. For most landscape turfs, a generally accepted guide is not to remove more than one-third of the total leaf surface at any one mowing. Waiting too long between mowing results in an imbalance between the shoot and roots and retards growth. In addition, mowing grass that is too tall requires more time and fuel, produces a great deal of clippings that must be removed, and can result in sunscald during the summer.

Seed head formation also influences mowing frequency. Bahiagrass, bluegrass, buffalograss, carpetgrass, St. Augustinegrass, centipedegrass, and some bermudagrasses, produce excessive numbers of seed heads that disrupt an otherwise uniform lawn. Mowing operations may be primarily to remove these and flowering structures of weeds during certain times of the year.

Ideally, mowing schedules, specifications, and contracts should be based upon the growth rate of the grass, rather than a set time schedule. This is difficult to schedule and bid. Mowing may be required twice a week in the spring, every two weeks in the summer, and once a week in the fall.

Weather conditions, irrigation schedules, and fertility practices all affect the amount of mowing that must be accomplished. Unfortunately, most clients and contracts are attuned to a set number of mowings per season. Fortunately, turfgrass is less vulnerable to damage from removing more than one-third to one-half of the foliage during non-stress periods. Violations of the one-third rule to cool season turfgrasses are of less consequence to the plant during the spring and fall than during the heat of the summer.

If mowing frequencies in specifications and contracts cannot be established on the growth rate of the turfgrass, then some compensation should be added. Many managers establish five-day or twice-a-week mowing schedules during the fastest growing part of the growing season. This helps meet the needs of the turfgrass, as well as those of the client and manager to have a set number of mowings to budget and schedule.

Mowing Pattern

Mowing patterns affect efficiency and the end result. Perimeters should always be mowed first so that trimming and blowing work can commence. The property can be "squared-off" with bagging mowers to keep walks, drives, and pools free of clippings. Another method used to reduce clipping clean-up without bagging is to discharge clippings away from critical areas and into the uncut turf. Mowers will rarely blow clipping further than a distance equal to four times the width of the mower deck. If the first four passes are dis-

Photo 12.15. Schedule mowing before irrigation or delay mowing after a heavy rain to prevent tracking and complaints.

charged away from walks, then few, if any, clippings will be blown onto them when the mower changes directions for the fifth pass. If all clippings are to be collected, then the discharge direction is of little consequence.

When grass is mown in the same direction repeatedly, it tends to lean and grow horizontally in that direction. This is referred to as *grain* and is especially a problem on golf greens. Mowing landscape turf constantly in the same direction has similar consequences. This phenomenon is common in home lawns. In addition, turf wear and compaction from the mower wheels is accentuated by mowing repeated in the same pattern and direction.

The direction and pattern for mowing landscape turf should be alternated to minimize formation of a grain. Further, many managers mow landscape turf diagonally to the street or longest property line. They, and many clients, feel that this provides a baseball field striping and increases curb appeal. The direction of the diagonal is alternated each mowing.

Turf can be mowed more efficiently, according to some sources, by mowing constantly around the site and inward. This is sometimes called a *hockey rink* mowing pattern. This eliminates sharp turnarounds and backtracking. However, the same, continuous pattern results in grain, even if the mowing direction is alternated. The wheels also run in the same area each mowing and establish compacted tracks.

Some managers *double-cut*, mowing the property a second time in the opposite direction, so that the turf stands tall. This obviously increases the cost, but if the client requests and is willing to pay for this quality look, then why not? It will not damage the grass. Other firms alternate the size of equipment used on a site to keep from establishing tracks. They may use 36-inch walk-behinds one week and 52-inch riders the next.

Brushes or combs are sometimes attached to the front of mowers to assist in straightening or lifting turf for more effective mowing if grain is a particular problem. Brushing turf with a power broom will also lift the turf and dispel clumps of grass. This may be especially useful if the turf must be mowed when it is wet.

Photo 12.16. Graining in turf is reduced by changing mowing direction, alternating mowing equipment, use of brushes, and by double-cutting.

Chemical mowing refers to the use of plant growth regulators (PGR's) to limit seedheads, reduce plant height, decrease clippings, or increase the interval between mowings. Refer to the PGR section near the end of this chapter for more information.

Clipping Removal

Collecting and removing clippings adds 15 to 25 percent to mowing time. Grass clippings also account for 20 to 50 percent of the residential solid waste added to municipal landfills each week of the growing season. Yard waste bans are common throughout the US. Unfortunately, some clients demand that clippings be bagged and removed.

Clipping removal is largely dependent upon mowing frequency. Short clippings from frequent mowings filter down into the turf and need not be removed for any organic reason. The reasons for removing clippings are purely aesthetic and contractual. The contribution of clippings to thatch is minimal, if any, since the leaf blades decompose rapidly. There is also no increase in the incidence of disease as a result of not collecting normal clippings. On the positive side, clippings are a source of plant nutrients, especially nitrogen.

Excess or long clippings that remain on the top of the grass should be removed. These will be unsightly and elicit a call from the client. They also exclude sunlight and favor disease development. They are not the mark of high quality mowing or management.

If clippings are to be collected, then it should be done efficiently. Baggers and catchers should hold a significant amount to reduce emptying required. The catchers should not be so large that they become too heavy to handle or affect mower operation. Keep the receptacle or truck for holding clippings as close to the mowing operation as possible.

Some firms do not catch the clippings, but rake them into piles and onto canvas for loading. The raking works many of the small clippings into the turf and reduces the bulk that must be removed. These managers feel that the time and cost of raking are no greater than that required for catching the clippings and emptying the catchers. Raking may actually be more efficient in the case of wet or very tall turf.

Trimming and Edging

Edging and trimming provide crisp edges that improve the appearance and curb appeal of the landscape. Both operations put the finishing touch on maintenance operations. *Edging* is the cutting of turfgrass along a sidewalk, curb, or planted bed to create a delineating edge. It may be done by hand, or more typically with a power edger using a vertical blade. Edging should not expose a wide strip of soil that can be invaded by weeds. *Trimming* is the horizontal cutting of grass around buildings, signs, trees, and other obstacles in the lawn area. Trimming is typically conducted with a power line trimmer or reciprocating blade trimmer.

The frequency of edging and trimming depends on the maintenance level of the site, turf species and growth rate, and budget. Both operations may be conducted every mowing, sometimes needlessly. Trimming around objects in the landscape will require attention to keep the tufts of turf from being noticed. Sidewalks, on the other hand do not generally require edging every week. Bermudagrass, bluegrass, and other creeping-type grasses require more frequent edging, possibly every second or third mowing. Tall fescue and other bunch-type grasses do not rapidly encroach upon walks and may only require edging two or three times per season. Reducing weekly edgings on the site is one way to reduce or negotiate a budget without dramatically affecting visible quality.

Photo 12.17. Removal of clippings from the site should be efficient. This mower has a large capacity catcher and dumps into a truck for removal. Photograph courtesy of Hustler Turf Equipment, Hesston, KS.

Photo 12.18. Edging cuts the grass along a sidewalk, curb, or planted bed to create a crisp edge. Edging may be done by hand, or more typically with a power edger using a vertical blade. Photograph courtesy of Little Wonder Division, Schiller-Pfeiffer, Inc., Southampton, PA.

Mowing aids reduce trimming around trees and objects in the landscape. Mowing aids range from brick or other permanent mowing strips along buildings and curbs, to weed-free bands around trees and signposts. Many landscape management firms spray narrow bands of non-selective postemergence herbicides, sometimes tank-mixed with a preemergent, around obstacles that require trimming. These narrow bands prevent the grass from growing up to the object. All necessary trimming can be done with the mower; string trimming is eliminated entirely. I have

Photo 12.19. Line trimmers are standard equipment for trimming grass around signs and objects in turf. Photograph courtesy of Mr. Mark Yahn, Ground Control™ Landscaping and Maintenance, Orlando, FL.

Photo 12.20. Line trimmers easily damage the trunks of trees growing in turf without some type of barrier. Girdling by line trimmers operated by inexperienced or careless employees is a major cause of loss of landscape trees. Photograph courtesy of James Robbins.

known of companies that offer banding around trees and other obstacles at little or no charge to the client in order to reduce trimming operations.

In some landscapes the turf is removed around trees, signs, buildings, or other obstacles and replaced with mulch. This limits grass from growing up to the object and eliminates hand trimming. Small, mulched beds around trees also add a quality appearance to the landscape. The use of steel, plastic, or wooden edging around mulched landscape beds prevents encroachment of bunch-type grasses, but does not prevent growth of rhizomatous or stoloniferous species into the beds.

Blowing

Typically, the final task in the landscape mowing-edging operation is the use of a power blower to remove unwanted clippings from walks and parking lots. Power blowers have become indispensable utensils in management operations, replacing the push broom. They serve many functions and add to the professional appearance of managed landscapes.

Use professional manners with power blowers. Several municipalities and neighborhood associations, and condominiums have limited or banned their use because of noise.

Turf Irrigation

Irrigation is essential for growing high-quality turf in most areas of the country. Seasonal distribution of precipitation is inadequate to main-

Photo 12.21. A trimmer with a reciprocating blade cuts grass and protects trees.

Photo 12.22. Clean up with a power blower is the final step for mowing operations. Clippings are blown back into the cut grass or collected and removed from the site. Photograph courtesy of Little Wonder Division, Schiller-Pfeiffer, Inc., Southampton, PA.

tain uniformly green, vigorous grass throughout the growing season. Irrigation is costly in terms of the capital investment, as well as labor, if the system is not automated. The cost of water is a significant portion of many landscape budgets, especially in arid and semi-arid regions. The cost, availability and quality of irrigation water are an increasing concern for landscape and turf managers. Landscape managers must contend with the many problems associated with too little and too much water. Chapter 9 details water management and irrigation for landscape sites. A few particulars of turfgrass irrigation should be addressed separately.

Performance of turfgrass, and plants in general, is influenced by soil, weather, and plant growth characteristics. The water requirements must be considered during planting design and planning for irrigation. Many grasses perform well under extended drought or with reduced irrigation (Table 12.8). These turfgrasses may be installed initially or as a renovation in water-critical situations.

Irrigation Scheduling

A single, all encompassing irrigation schedule cannot be specified because of variances in sites, soils, turf species, management practices, growing season, climate, and requirements of the client. Careful irrigation scheduling, however, is critical for quality turfgrass.

Table 12.8.
Relative tolerance and performance of common turfgrasses under extended drought or reduced irrigation stress

Performance rating	Cool season	Warm season
Excellent		Bermudagrass Buffalograss Zoysiagrass
Good	Tall Fescue Canada Bluegrass	Bahiagrass Seashore Paspalum
Fair	Red Fescue Kentucky Bluegrass	St. Augustinegrass
Poor	Annual Bluegrass Bentgrasses Perennial Ryegrass	Centipedegrass

Frequent, shallow irrigation of established turf causes the grass plants to be shallow rooted. The turf is thereby more susceptible to the effects of drought and less able to exploit water reserves in the soil. Shallow irrigation also encourages disease, weed infestation, thatch accumulation, and soil compaction. Shallow-rooted turf is more sensitive to injury from high and low temperatures, as well as winter desiccation. A similar situation can be found in heavy soils that are continuously over-watered. The turfgrass rooting depth is reduced by inadequate oxygen deeper in the soil and problems synonymous with shallow rooting are found.

Generally, watering once a week is adequate except during periods of severe stress. More frequent watering is needed on sandy soils, on south-facing slopes, berms or mounds, where competition for water from trees and shrubs is severe, in areas bordering pavement, and under more intense management. Compaction and thatch complicate irrigation scheduling and rates.

Irrigation scheduling can be facilitated by soil water measuring devices such as tensiometers. Typically, the more sophisticated the site, the more sophisticated soil and/or plant water measurements required to assure quality. Managers of golf courses and other heavily managed, intensive use sites, make greater use of evapotranspiration calculations for irrigation scheduling than do managers of more typical landscapes.

Apply adequate water to thoroughly wet the upper six to eight inches of the turfgrass root zone. It is preferable to apply sufficient water to penetrate to the subsoil moisture avoiding a dry layer in between that would restrict rooting. The rate of application should allow maximum infiltration without run-off, depending on soil texture, structure, compaction, and degree of slope.

Newly seeded areas. A newly seeded lawn is the exception to these ideas for watering frequency and quantity. Frequent, shallow irrigation is required for seed germination and to promote growth of newly emerged seedlings. As the seedlings grow and mature, the watering interval should become less frequent, but the soil should be soaked to a greater depth, until normal irrigation management is achieved. Spring-seeded, cool season or late-planted warm season turf, require

careful and continued water management during the initial season.

Other management influences on irrigation. Landscape management and non-management factors affect irrigation scheduling. Aerating the turf reduces water loss from run-off. Aeration holes catch and hold water as well as increase infiltration. Removal or breaking of the thatch layer by aeration or verticutting speeds water movement into the soil.

Where disease is a factor, the best time to irrigate turf is in the pre-dawn morning. Golf courses, athletic fields, and high traffic public and corporate areas are frequently irrigated at night, so as not to impede play or daytime traffic. Nocturnal watering is also common in arid and semi-arid regions to reduce loss to evaporation on sunny, windy days, and to improve irrigation efficiency.

Shady areas require less water than those in sun or partial shade. Irrigation of shaded sections on the same schedule as sunny areas increases disease and weed problems. If possible, turf in shade should be irrigated and managed separately than that in full sun.

Irrigation of turf in winter is not often practiced in northern areas because of the time and cost of charging and re-draining the irrigation system. However, cool season turf in northern areas may require irrigation during dry, open winters, especially when associated with extended warm periods. Winter watering may be necessary for grasses with low levels of drought tolerance on exposed dry areas, compacted sites, extreme slopes, or on southern and western exposures of highly reflective buildings. It may be possible to install ample automatic drain values and design zones to accommodate winter irrigations of critical areas, if necessary. Typically only one or two irrigations are required; these can be done anytime the soil is not frozen. Irrigation of frozen soil is not beneficial and may have harmful effects.

Mowing and fertilization practices greatly affect irrigation practices and vice versa. While the transpiration rate of low-cut turf is less than that of taller-cut turf, taller grass has deeper roots. A more extensive root system allows for greater water harvesting from the soil. It is common to raise the cutting height of cool season turf during the peak water use periods of the summer. It is easier to manage water use and irrigation of taller turf during dry periods.

The fertilization program should reflect the potential and realistic irrigation expectations of the site and the manager. High levels of nutrients, especially nitrogen, used for heavily managed and high quality sites are wasted if the grass does not have the water resources to utilize these fertilizer additions for growth.

Aeration

Mechanical aeration or *cultivation* is a common management practice for golf courses, sports fields, and other intensive use sites. It has become a standard and annual management procedure for commercial and residential sites suffering from heavy soils, significant thatch, compaction, or traffic problems. Several companies specialize in me-

Table 12.9.

A comparison of different turf aeration methods

Method	Penetration depth (inches)	Tine spacing (inches)	Soil loosening (1 - 10[1])	Amount of soil brought to surface (1 - 5[2])	Best soil moisture for operation	Comments
Forking	6	2 to 4	3 to 4	2	FC[3]	First (historically) aeration method.
Hollow Tine Coring						
Spoons or hollow tines - tractor drawn or self-powered	3 to 6	6	4	2 to 4	FC	Several types and brands; some with changeable spoons. Spoons enter soil at an angle.
Drum type (hollow tine)	2 to 3	2 to 3	2	2 to 4	FC	Several types and brands available.
Vertically operated tines	3 to 5	2 to 6	4	3 to 5	FC	Most common form of aeration.
Verti-Drain®	10 to 12	1 to 8	8 to 10	2 to 4	FC or drier	Hollow tine.
Solid Tine Coring						
Vertically operated shatter-core	3 to 5	2 to 6	4 to 8	1	Less than FC	
Rotary pattern solid core units	3	4	4 to 10 (variable)	2	FC or drier	
Verti-Drain®	12 to 16	1 to 8	9 to 10	1	Drier than FC	
Slicing – Solid tines or blades						
Straight-line tines	3 to 7	6 to 12	2	1	FC	Many types and brands.
Straight-line blades	2 to 4	4	2	1	FC	
Off-set tines	6 to 8	7	4 to 8	1	Drier than FC	Aerway®
Spiking Pulled or motorized	½ to 2	1 to 2	2	1	FC	Several brands.
Hydroject®	4 to 20	3 to 6	4 to 6	1	FC	Uses high pressure water jets.

[1]Degree of soil loosening: 1 = none; 10 = most effective
[2]Amount of soil brought to surface by operation: 1 = none; 5 = large amount
[3]FC = Field capacity

chanical aeration as a major portion of their business. Mechanical aeration is one of the few maintenance practices that can actually improve soils under perennial turfgrass.

Coring. *Core aeration* or *coring* uses hollow tines or spoons to extract cores from the turf. The depth of the core depends upon the capabilities of the machine and the physical constraints (bulk density and moisture content) of the soil. Core depths of three inches or more are common and possible with modern equipment and reasonable soils. To maximize effectiveness, core as deeply as possible.

Coring is preferred to spiking or slicing for aerifying turf. Coring provides a physical channel through surface layers due to topdressing, surface compaction, and thatch. Water and air infiltration are vastly improved. While the aeration of the soil between and below the actual core holes may not be improved, significant benefits in the soil air content do occur. Root growth within the holes is stimulated and shoot growth on top of the holes is increased. The holes serve as major root development areas for many years. Drying of incessantly wet soils is also increased as a result of coring.

Coring increases turfgrass response to fertilizers, particularly those nutrients that are rela-

tively immobile in the soil such as calcium, phosphorous, and potassium sources. Coring prior to fertilization provides a means of inserting these materials into the root zone.

Cool season grasses are best core aerated during the spring or fall. Aeration in the fall is preferred. Areas with intensive problems or traffic may be core aerated in the spring and fall if necessary. Warm season turfs are commonly aerated in early summer. Spring coring may open the turf to increased pressure from annual grassy weeds if a preemergence herbicide is not used. Aerating after application of a preemergence herbicide does not reduce the chemical's effectiveness. Avoid coring during periods of stress as the holes allow the soil to dry more rapidly.

In taller-cut turf the cores are normally left on the surface of the ground. Irrigation, rain, or mowing breaks up the soil cores. The soil from the cores will work its way into the thatch layer, aiding in thatch control. A power rake or verticut mower can be used to break up the cores quickly if necessary. Set the height of the blades so that they hit the cores without damaging the turf. Dragging can also break up the cores. If the soil is of poor quality, it may be best to collect and discard the cores. Topdressing with a good quality soil or sand mixture is standard practice in golf course management, but is not often feasible, economical, or necessary for large or common landscape sites.

Slicing and Spiking. *Slicing* and *spiking* are less intensive aeration or cultivation practices. Slicing uses V-shaped knives mounted on disks to penetrate the turf and soil. Spiking makes shallow perforations in the turf with small knives and is primarily practiced on golf greens and tees. Both procedures do not remove cores; therefore, there is little disruption of the turf or its use. Slicing and spiking improve infiltration, relieve surface compaction, and help control thatch. Many grounds managers core aerate severely compacted or problem areas in spring and fall, and also slice the turf periodically during the summer. Slicing athletic fields during the playing season is preferred since there is less disruption of play. Slicing also makes the field more impact absorbing and increases play safety.

Photo 12.23. Small core aerators are useful to aerate and manage residential properties. Photograph courtesy of Roch Gaussoin.

Photo 12.24. A spike aerator pokes holes in compacted soil and thatch layers. Weights are added over the drum of this pull-behind unit to increase penetration. Photograph courtesy of Roch Gaussoin.

Photo 12.25. Innovations in aeration equipment have resulted in equipment capable of depths up to 12 inches. Photograph courtesy of Roch Gaussoin.

Thatch

Thatch is a common problem of many landscape sites. *Thatch* is an intermingled layer of living and dead roots and stems between the green vegetation and the soil surface. Thatch contains material that is largely undecomposed and some in an advanced stage of decomposition. What causes the thatch layer to develop is not completely understood. A typical explanation is that thatch accumulates because the production of stems, crowns, and roots exceeds the rate of decomposition. Factors that suppress the rate of organic matter decomposition or promote excessive plant growth are thought to trigger the event.

Certain turf species and cultivars are more prone to thatch problems. Species with high lignin content, a component of plants that resists decomposition, are more prone to thatch accumulation (Table 12.10). Turfgrass species that produce rhizomes or stolons such as zoysiagrass and creeping bentgrass build up thatch faster than bunch-type grasses, such as perennial ryegrass or tall fescue. Pesticides that adversely affect earthworms and other decomposing organisms also promote thatch.

Despite the common belief of some clients, grass clippings do not contribute to thatch. Clippings are 75 to 85 percent water and decompose quickly. They also contain little lignin.

The extent of a thatch problem is determined by removing a pie-shaped wedge of grass and soil

Table 12.10.	
Relative tendency of several turfgrasses to produce thatch	
Cool season species	**Warm season species**
High Tendency	
Bentgrasses	Zoysiagrass
Kentucky Bluegrass	Bermudagrass
Fine Fescues	St. Augustinegrass
Perennial Ryegrasses	Centipedegrass
Tall Fescue	Carpetgrass
	Bahiagrass
	Buffalograss
Low Tendency	

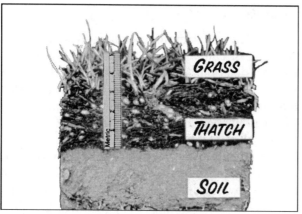

Photo 12.26. Thatch is the intermingled layer of living and dead roots, stolons, rhizomes, and stems between the green vegetation and the soil surface. Photograph courtesy of "Thatch in Turfgrass"- Crop Sci. Soc. of Am. 1982.

Photo 12.27. Dethatching or power-raking brings large amounts of organic material to the surface. This operation, however, only removes a portion of the true amount of thatch present on a site. Photograph courtesy of Roch Gaussoin.

and measuring the amount of organic matter accumulated. Sample several areas across the site, especially if the management programs differ. A small layer of thatch, less than one-half inch, is actually beneficial. It increases the grasses' resiliency, improves its tolerance to traffic, and insulates against abrupt changes in soil temperature. If the thatch layer exceeds one-half inch in cool season turf, steps should be taken to reduce it.

The turf's susceptibility to heat, cold, and drought damage increases with increasing amounts of thatch. Scalping during mowing, and insect and disease problems also increase because of thatch. Thatch is difficult to rewet after it has dried, so irrigation efficiency decreases and localized dry spots increase. A thatch layer impedes movement of fertilizer, herbicides, and other chemicals.

Removing thatch. Excessive thatch, over one-half inch, should be physically removed. This process can moderately to severely injure the turf. It should be accomplished during active growth and when there is a long period available for recovery. Cool season turfgrasses may be dethatched in the fall or spring. Fall is preferred since the area can be efficiently fertilized to hasten recovery. The area can also be over-seeded if necessary.

If thatch is removed from cool season grass in the spring, applications of preemergence herbicides and a light fertilization should be planned to reduce weed infestations and to enhance recovery. As a rule, schedule thatch removal from

cool season species when at least 30 days of favorable growing conditions are anticipated afterward.

Remove thatch from warm season turf after it has obtained 100 percent green-up in the spring. Make a regular application of fertilizer after mechanical removal. Avoid removal of thatch during summer or when the grass is under stress. High temperatures and water stress reduce growth and recuperation and encourage weed infestation.

Even though mechanical dethatching produces a tremendous volume of material on the surface, it only removes a portion of the thatch in the turf. Some sources claim that power raking removes as little as 25 percent of the organic material where there has been substantial build-up. The cause of the thatch accumulation must be determined and solved or the problem will return.

Mow the site closely before dethatching. Bag or rake clippings and remove the debris resulting from hand or power raking immediately. Soil moisture should be at or slightly less than field capacity for best results. Dethatching wet soil severely damages the turf and greatly reduces efficiency.

Equipment. Thatch is removed by hand or *power-raking*. Hand raking is laborious and only practical in very small areas. Power rakes or vertical mowers use wire tines or steel blades to lift the thatch and usually a small amount of soil to the surface.

Photo 12.28. A power rake removes thatch by combing up the material with wire tines. Photograph courtesy of James Robbins.

Core aeration. Core aeration or cultivation can be used to reduce thatch accumulation. Soil cores removed during core cultivation create a channel through the thatch layer to improve water and chemical penetration. Cores should be allowed to remain on the surface if acceptable to the client. The cores will breakdown and redistribute soil throughout the thatch, thus inoculating it with microorganisms that aid decomposition.

Biological control of thatch. Several biological dethatching materials are available. These materials usually contain specific microorganisms that supposedly increase the rate of thatch decomposition. Research trials on the efficacy of these materials have not been extensive; preliminary results have shown that irrigation and environment have a significant effect on thatch decomposition.

Management solutions and prevention. Good turf management minimizes thatch problems. Proper cultural practices are the most efficient and least expensive method to control thatch. Proper mowing frequency and height reduce the amount of grass stem cut and deposited upon the soil surface. Fertilizer should be applied at times and in amounts to meet, but not to exceed, the nutritional needs of the grass. Avoid light, frequent irrigations that encourage shallow rooting.

Apply pesticides only as needed. Pesticides can affect microorganism and earthworm populations. Earthworms, in addition to feeding on decaying grass tissue, provide channels that mix soil into the thatch and improve aeration and drainage.

Pest Management

The key to successful control of turfgrass pests, whether they are weeds, insects, or diseases, begins with cultural programs that promote healthy, vigorous growth. A properly managed turf outgrows many diseases or insect infestations, and competes against weeds.

Correct identification of the pest is also critical to successful pest management. Pest identification guides are available from state or county extension offices. Many universities offer diagnostic services for turf and landscape problems. This service is offered for free or for a nominal charge.

Disease Control. Over watering, improper fertilization, heavy thatch, susceptible species or cultivars, improper mowing practices, and environmental extremes contribute to disease incidence and severity. Chemical disease control is more expensive than chemical weed and insect control. Except for very high maintenance turf such as golf courses or sports fields, disease incidence is often tolerated or managed by subtle alterations in cultural practices.

Fungi cause the majority of turfgrass diseases. Fungicides used to control these pathogens are classified as *preventive* or *curative*. *Preventive* treatments are applied when conditions are favorable for development but disease symptoms are not evident. *Curative* treatments are applied after disease symptoms are evident. Disease symptomology is variable among pathogens and regions of the country. Consult local experts or regional publications for up-to-date disease descriptions and management strategies.

Insect Control. Identification of insect damage and the specific pest is less complex than for disease management. Insects damaging turfgrass may feed on the leaves (*surface feeders*) or roots (*sub-surface feeders*). The larval stage of most turfgrass insects is the most damaging.

Surface Feeders. Armyworms, cutworms, and sod webworms are larvae of moths or butterflies feeding on grass leaves. Sod webworms and cutworms are nocturnal feeders. An unusual amount of bird activity often indicates severe infestations of these insects. Chinch bugs damage grass plants by sucking plant sap. The damage is drought-like in appearance.

Table 12.11.

Feeding characteristics of common turfgrass insects

Insect		Feeding location	Life cycle state damaging turf
Billbug	*Spenophorous* spp.	above ground	larvae
Chinch Bug	*Blissus* spp.	above ground	all
Cutworm	*Noctuidae* family	above ground	larvae
White Grub	Numerous genera	below ground	larvae
Mites	Order Acarina	above ground	all
Mole Cricket	*Gryllotalpidae* family	below ground	all
Sod Webworm	*Crambus* spp.	above ground	larvae
Wireworm	*Elateridae* family	below ground	larvae
Ataenius Beetle	*Ataenius* spp.	below ground	larvae
Greenbug Aphid	*Aphididae* family	above ground	all

Effective control with insecticides requires correct identification and timing. Managers should thoroughly understand the target pest's life cycle and feeding habits before attempting chemical control.

Sub-surface Feeders. The larval stages of May/June beetles, Japanese beetles, and chafers are usually white or grayish with brown to dark brown heads and six true legs. The larvae appear like a plump "C." Injury appears similar to turf that needs irrigation. In some cases, where roots are severely damaged, the sod can be rolled back like a carpet. Mole crickets, a potentially serious pest in the southern US, and the larvae of several billbug species, also feed on grass roots. Wireworms, the larvae of click beetles, bore into the buried portion of a stem to feed on the roots.

Weed Control

Of the major pests in management of quality turfgrass, weed control offers the most rapid gratification. In most cases, once the weed is eradicated the turf is capable of rapidly filling-in the void. In some cases, however, weeds are indicative of a more serious site or cultural problem. Effective control requires altering the management or site to alleviate the original problem. For example, many weeds persist in conditions where soils are poorly drained. Solving the weed problem requires correction of the drainage problem. Herbicides may temporarily relieve the symptoms, but the turf will be weak and the weeds will return.

Weed control is a service expected by all clients. While some lawn care companies offer disease and insect control as an option to clients, all landscape and turfgrass maintenance firms offer weed control.

Two pieces of information are critical to successfully control turfgrass weeds; weed type (whether the weed is a *grass, broadleaf,* or *sedge*) and its life cycle. The correct choice of herbicide depends on the type of plant represented by the weed.

Grassy weeds (monocots) are easily distinguished from *broadleaf weeds* (dicots) by the orientation of the leaf veins. In grassy weeds the veins are parallel to each other along the entire length of the leaf. The veins of broadleaf weeds are netted or web-like.

A third group of weeds is the *annual* and *perennial sedges.* Sedges are often incorrectly referred to as grassy weeds because of their grass-like appearance and parallel veination. Sedges can be easily distinguished from the grasses by their triangular or three-sided stems.

Weeds in turfgrass can be classified by two life cycle types. *Perennials* live from year to year. Many perennial weeds have vigorous taproots or other below-ground storage organs (tubers, corms, or rhizomes). Perennial weeds can propagate by these underground storage organs or by seed.

Annuals are plants that complete their life cycle (seed to plant to seed) in one year. Annual weeds can be further classified as either *winter* or

Table 12.12.
Common turfgrass weeds, life cycle examples,
and optimal herbicide type and application timing

Weed		Optimal application timing
Perennial Grasses		
Quackgrass	*Agropyron repens*	Postemergence, late summer to late fall
Nimblewill	*Muhlenbergia schrebi*	Postemergence, late summer to late fall
Smooth Brome	*Bromus enermis*	Postemergence, late summer to late fall
Perennial Broadleafs		
Dandelion	*Taraxacum officinale*	Postemergence, late summer to late fall
Yellow Wood Sorrel	*Oxalis stricta*	Postemergence, late summer to late fall
Plantain	*Plantago* spp.	Postemergence, late summer to late fall
Ground Ivy	*Glechoma hederacea*	Postemergence, late summer to late fall
Wild Violet	*Viola* spp.	Postemergence, late summer to late fall
Mouseear Chickweed	*Cerastium vulgatum*	Postemergence, late summer to late fall
Mallow	*Malva* spp.	Postemergence, late summer to late fall
White Clover	*Trifolium repens*	Postemergence, late summer to late fall
Yarrow	*Achillea millefolium*	Postemergence, late summer to late fall
Summer Annual Grasses		
Crabgrass	*Digitaria* spp.	Preemergence, Jan/Feb in southern US; March/April in Transition Zone; U.S. April/May in northern US
Goosegrass	*Eleusine indica*	Preemergence, Jan/Feb in southern US; March/April in Transition Zone; April/May in northern US
Foxtail	*Setaria* spp.	Preemergence, Jan/Feb in southern US; March/April in Transition Zone; April/May in northern US
Barnyardgrass	*Echinochola crusgalli*	Preemergence, Jan/Feb in southern US; March/April in Transition Zone; April/May in northern US
Sandbur	*Cenchrus* spp.	Preemergence, Jan/Feb in southern US; March/April in Transition Zone; May/June in northern US
Summer Annual Broadleafs		
Spurge	*Euphorbia* spp.	Postemergence, when weed are young and actively growing (May/June) or preemergence with similar timing as summer annual grasses.
Purslane	*Portulaca oleracea*	Postemergence, when weed are young and actively growing (May/June) or preemergence with similar timing as summer annual grasses.
Carpetweed	*Mollugo verticillata*	Postemergence, when weed are young and actively growing (May/June) or preemergence with similar timing as summer annual grasses.
Black Medic	*Medicago lupulina*	Postemergence, when weed are young and actively growing (May/June) or preemergence with similar timing as summer annual grasses.
Prostrate Knotweed	*Polygonum aviculare*	Postemergence, when weed are young and actively growing (Feb/March) or preemergence with timing in late winter/early spring.
Winter Annual Broadleafs		
Henbit	*Lamium amplexlcaule*	Postemergence, when weeds are young and actively growing (Sept/Dec) or preemergence in early fall.
Common Chickweed	*Stellaria media*	Postemergence, when weeds are young and actively growing (Sept/Dec) or preemergence in early fall.
Speedwell	*Veronica* spp.	Postemergence, when weeds are young and actively growing (Sept/Dec) or preemergence in early fall.

summer annuals. *Winter annuals* germinate in the fall, over winter as a seedling, and set seed and die in late spring or early summer. *Summer annuals* germinate in the spring, set seed in late summer and are normally killed by the first frost.

Application timing. Herbicides are classified as *preemergence* (applied before weed germinates) or *postemergence* (applied after the weed emerges from the soil) materials. Some, but not many, herbicides act as both pre- and postemergence chemicals. Timing of applications depends on the type of herbicide used and the target weed. Obviously, preemergence herbicides must be applied before germination of the weed seed to be effective. Table 12.12 lists examples of life cycles and optimal application timing for several common lawn weeds.

Turfgrass Plant Growth Regulators

Synthetic *plant growth regulators (PGRs)* have been available for use in turfgrass management for several years. PGRs are used with varying success on golf courses, public parks and grounds, cemeteries, highway roadsides, and more recently, home lawns.

Managers must consider the cost effectiveness, longevity, and possible problems before including these materials in their programs. Turfgrass plant growth regulators are not fool proof and do not eliminate mowing. Environmental and management factors influence efficacy of the materials. PGRs, if used properly, may reduce mowing and suppress seed head formation.

Plant growth regulators are classified as either Type I or Type II regulators. *Type I regulators* control growth and suppress development (such as seedhead formation) of turfgrass plants. *Type II regulators* control only the growth of plants. If seedhead suppression is one of the management goals, only Type I regulators are recommended.

A factor to consider in PGR selection is *phytotoxicity*, or potential discoloration of the turf resulting from application. Many PGRs exhibit some degree of phytotoxicity; however, this is highly spe-

cies dependent. There has been some success in masking discoloration with nitrogen or iron fertilizers.

Application timing and absorption site are critical to PGR success. *Root absorbed compounds* must be watered in to be effective. The activity of *foliar absorbed compounds* is reduced by rainfall or irrigation following application.

PGRs applied during dormancy or prior to green-up delay initial green-up and reduce the size of emerging leaves. Root absorbed regulators can be effectively applied at this time, however, foliar absorbed materials are ineffective. They require green leaves for absorption.

Type I regulators applied during spring green-up reduce the number of seedheads by about 80 percent. Root absorbed Type I regulators applied at this time will suppress plants but delay green-up. Foliar active regulators only suppress those plants that have greened-up.

The greatest benefits from PGRs occur when applied during the rapid vertical growth period. Mowing requirements can be reduced by as much as 50 percent. Seedhead control at this application time is usually 90 percent. This application timing, however, often results in a slight loss of grass quality from the second to fourth week after application. The turf's green color, however, is enhanced during the seventh to tenth week.

The most detrimental time to apply PGRs to cool season grasses is when seedheads begin to appear and elongate. The plant is internally producing its own growth inhibitor. The combination of the natural and applied plant growth regulators can severely retard growth and thin the stand.

Additional Information

Most Land Grant Universities and Cooperative Extension Services or Divisions offer publications free, or for minimal cost, over the Internet on managing turfgrass and dealing with turf problems. Table 12.13 lists the Internet addresses of Cooperative Extension publication distribution offices throughout the US and Canada.

Table 12.13.

Internet addresses of Cooperative Extension publication distribution offices throughout the US and Canada.

Compiled by Dr. Roch Gaussoin, Extension Turfgrass Specialist, University of Nebraska, Lincoln, NE.

- ALABAMA: http://www.aces.edu/pubs/
- ALASKA: http://www.uaf.edu/coop-ext/publications/index.html
- ARIZONA: http://cals.arizona.edu/pubs/
- ARKANSAS: http://www.uaex.edu/Other_Areas/publications/default.asp
- CALIFORNIA:http://ucanr.org/pubs.shtml
- COLORADO: http://www.cerc.colostate.edu/
- CONNECTICUT: http://www.canr.uconn.edu/ces/forest/pub.htm
- DELAWARE: http://ag.udel.edu/extension/Information/publications_from_the_university.htm
- FLORIDA: http://ifas.ufl.edu/extension/ces.htm
- GEORGIA: http://pubs.caes.uga.edu/caespubs/pubs.html
- HAWAII: http://www2.ctahr.hawaii.edu/extout/extout.asp
- IDAHO: http://info.ag.uidaho.edu/Catalog/catalog.html
- ILLINOIS: http://www.extension.uiuc.edu/pubs.html
- INDIANA: http://www.ces.purdue.edu/extmedia/menu.htm
- IOWA: http://www.extension.iastate.edu/pubs/
- KANSAS: http://www.oznet.ksu.edu/library/
- KENTUCKY: http://www.oznet.ksu.edu/library/
- LOUISIANA: http://www.lsuagcenter.com/nav/publications/pubs.asp
- MAINE: http://www.umext.maine.edu/publications/pubs.htm
- MARYLAND: http://www.agnr.umd.edu/MCE/Publications/index.cfm
- MASSACHUSETTS: http://www.umassextension.org/Merchant2/merchant.mv
- MICHIGAN: http://web2.msue.msu.edu/bulletins/latestnews.cfm
- MINNESOTA: http://www.extension.umn.edu/units/dc/
- MISSISSIPPI: http://msucares.com/pubs/index.html
- MISSOURI: http://extension.missouri.edu/main/publications.shtml
- MONTANA: http://www.montana.edu/wwwpub/expubs.html
- NEBRASKA: http://ianrpubs.unl.edu/
- NEVADA: http://www.unce.unr.edu/pubs.html
- NEW HAMPSHIRE: http://ceinfo.unh.edu/Pubs/Pubs.htm
- NEW JERSEY: http://www.rce.rutgers.edu/pubs/default.asp
- NEW MEXICO: http://www.cahe.nmsu.edu/pubs/
- NEW YORK: http://www.cce.cornell.edu/store/customer/home.php
- NORTH CAROLINA: http://www.ces.ncsu.edu/resources/
- NORTH DAKOTA: http://www.ext.nodak.edu/extpubs/
- OHIO: http://ohioline.osu.edu/catalog/index.html
- OKLAHOMA: http://pearl.agcomm.okstate.edu/hort/
- OREGON: http://eesc.oregonstate.edu/
- PENNSYLVANIA: http://pubs.cas.psu.edu/
- RHODE ISLAND: http://www.uri.edu/ce/factsheets/index.htm
- SOUTH CAROLINA: http://www.clemson.edu/psapublishing/
- SOUTH DAKOTA: http://agbiopubs.sdstate.edu/
- TENNESSEE: http://www.utextension.utk.edu/publications/default.htm
- TEXAS: http://tcebookstore.org/about.cfm
- UTAH: http://extension.usu.edu/cooperative/publications/
- VERMONT: http://www.uvm.edu/extension/?Page=http://www.uvm.edu/~uvmext/publications/
- VIRGINIA: http://www.ext.vt.edu/resources/
- WASHINGTON: http://pubs.wsu.edu/pubs/pubindex.html
- WEST VIRGINIA: http://www.wvu.edu/~exten/infores/pubs.htm
- WISCONSIN: http://www.uwex.edu/topics/Publications_and_news.cfm
- WYOMING: http://www.uwyo.edu/ces/pubs2.htm
- CANADA: http://sis.agr.gc.ca/pls/meta/reports_distribution.display
- WESTERN CANADA: GOVERNMENT OF BRITISH COLOMBIA http://www.gov.bc.ca/bvprd/bc/channel.do?action=ministry&channelID=-8377&navId=NAV_ID_province
- UNIVERSITY OF ALBERTA: http://www.extension.ualberta.ca/faculty/publications.htm
- UNIVERSITY OF SASKATCHEWAN EXTENSION DIVISION: http://www.extension.usask.ca/ExtensionDivision/publications/index.html
- EASTERN CANADA: ONTARIO MINISTRY OF AGRICULTURE AND FOOD http://www.gov.on.ca/OMAFRA/english/products/soils.html

Bibliography

1. Abrahamson, S. 1990. Guidelines for establishing turf. *Grounds Maintenance* 25(8):10.

2. Abrahamson, S. 1991. Bidding lawn renovations. *Grounds Maintenance* 26(8):42.

3. Aldous, D. and I. Chivers. 2002. *Sports Turf & Amenity Grasses*. LandLinks Press, Victoria, AU.

4. Baxendale, F. and R. Gaussoin (ed.). 1997. *Integrated Turfgrass Management for the Northern Great Plains*. Univ. of Nebraska Coop. Ext. Pub. EC931557.

5. Beard, J. 1986. Thatch. *Grounds Maintenance* 21(11):36.

6. Boyd, J., R. Gaussoin and R. Duble. 1999. Pre-emergence herbicides: An early-season weed cure. *Landscape & Irrigation* 23(2) 22.

7. Brede, D. 2000. *Turf Maintenance Reduction Handbook*. Ann Arbor Press. Chelsea, MI

8. Buckingham, F. 1982. Controlling thatch and soil compaction. *Grounds Maintenance* 17(8):10.

9. Buckingham, F. 1987. One solution: aeration. *Grounds Maintenance* 22(6):7.

10. Carrow, R. 1987. The problem: compaction. *Grounds Maintenance* 22(6):6.

11. Carrow, R. 1990. Developing turfgrass cultivation programs. *Golf Course Management* 58(8):14.

12. Christians, N. 1998. *Fundamentals of Turfgrass Management*. Ann Arbor Press. Chelsea, MI

13. Cook, T. 1989. Good judgment, proper timing needed for renovation. *ALA/Maintenance* 10(4):56.

14. Daniel, W. and R. Freeborg. 1987. *Turf Managers Handbook*. Harvest Publishing Co. Cleveland, OH.

15. de Shazer, S., T. Riordan, F. Baxendale and R. Gaussoin. 1992. *Buffalograss: A Warm Season Native Grass for Turf*. Univ. of Nebraska Coop. Ext. Pub. EC92-1234-C.

16. Decker, H. and J. Decker. 1988. *Lawn Care: A Handbook for Professionals*. Prentice Hall, Englewood Cliffs, NJ.

17. Fech, J. and R. Gaussoin. 2001. Postemergence treatments: The war on weeds: Understanding postemergence products and application methods can help contractors destroy weeds. *Lawn and Landscape* 22(7):78.

18. Feucht, J. and J. Butler. 1988. *Landscape Management*. Van Nostrand Reinhold Co., New York.

19. Gaussoin, R. 1990. Early season fertilization. *Landscape Management* 29(3):69.

20. Gaussoin, R.1992. Selecting traffic-tolerant turfgrass varieties. *Landscape and Irrigation* 16(8):9.

21. Gaussoin, R. 1992. Understanding preemergence herbicides. *Golf Course Management* 60(12).

22. Gaussoin, R. 1998. Hydraulic oil spills: Reducing the damage. *Golf Course Management* 66(2):56.

23. Gaussoin, R. 2000. Overseed northern sports fields with bermudagrass. *Grounds Maintenance* 35(3) C1.

24. Gaussoin, R. 2000. A nonselective herbicide primer. *Golf Course Management* 68(2)56.

25. Gaussoin, R. and A. Martin. 1994. *Lawn Weed Prevention and Management*. Univ. of Nebraska Coop. Ext. Pub. G91-1045 (revised).

26. Gaussoin, R. and A. Martin. 1997. *Lawn Weeds and Their Control*. North Central Regional Ext. Pub. 26 (Revised).

27. Gaussoin, R. and T. Riordan. 1996. *Thatch Prevention and Control*. Univ. of Nebraska Coop. Ext. Pub. G85-751-A (Revised).

28. Gaussoin, R., R. Shearman, J. Watkins, and F Baxendale. 2003. *Kentucky Bluegrass Lawn Calendar*. Univ. Neb. Coop. Ext. Pub. G80-517 (revised).

29. Gibeault, V., J. Meyer, M. A. Harivandi, M. Henry, and S. Cockerham. 1991. *Managing Turfgrasses During Drought*. Univ. of California Coop. Ext. Leaflet 21499.

30. Halterman, D. 1988. Selecting core cultivation equipment. *ALA* 9(9):28.

31. Harivandi, A. 1993. Thatch: The hidden enemy. *Landscape and Irrigation* 17(6):8.

32. Kronenberg, J. 1989. The choice is yours: Improve the old or start anew *ALA/Maintenance* 10(4):26.

33. Landry, G. 1993. Success with overseeding warm-season grasses. *Landscape and Irrigation* 17(9):8.

34. Landry, G. and T. Murphy. 1990. Overseeded turfgrass in transition. *Grounds M a i n t e nance* 25(1):80.

35. McCarty L. and G. Miller. 2002. *Managing Bermudagrass Turf*. Ann Arbor Press. Chelsea, MI

36. Mace, A. (ed.). 1985. *All About Lawns*. Ortho Books, San Francisco, CA.

37. Mello, J. 1987. Bringing back the grass. *Landscape Management* 26(8):22.

38. Murdoch, C. 1985. Adaptation of turfgrasses in Hawaii. *Fertility and Ornamentals Short Course*. Univ. of Hawaii, Honolulu, HI.

39. Murphy, J. and P. Rieke. 1990. Comparing aerification techniques. *Grounds Maintenance* 25(7):10.

40. Murphy, J. and P. Rieke. 1991. Update on aerification. *Golf Course Management* 59(7):6.

41. Riordan, T., R. Gaussoin, F. Baxendale and J. Watkins. 1996. *Buffalograss: An Alternative Native Grass for Turf*. Univ. of Nebraska Coop. Ext. Pub. G96-1297-A.

42. Riordan, T., R. Gaussoin and G. Horst. 2004. *Tall Fescue Lawn Calendar*. Univ. of Nebraska Coop. Ext. Pub. G81-558-A (revised).

43. Rodie, S., J. Fech, R. Gaussoin and A. Streich. 1999. *Watering Nebraska Landscapes: When and How Much?* Univ. of Nebraska Coop. Ext. Pub. No G99-1400.

44. Roche, J. 1993. Minimizing compaction on athletic fields, golf courses. *Landscape Management* 32(8):22.

45. Shane, W. 1989. Rain, stress result in varied turfgrass problems. *Lawn and Landscape Maintenance* 10(9):44.

46. Shearman, R. and R. Gaussoin. 1999. *Zoysiagrass Lawn Calendar*. Univ. of Nebraska Coop. Ext. Pub. No G-88-877-A (revised).

547. Smiley, R., P. Dernoedon, and B. Clarke. 1992. *Compendium of Turfgrass Diseases* (2nd edition). APS Press, St. Paul, MN.

48. Steenbock, A. and D. Hensley. 1991. Disposal options reshape lawn care. *Northern Turf Management* 2(7):22.

49. Steinegger, D, R. Gaussoin and G. Horst. 1993. *Evaluating Your Irrigation system*. Univ. of Nebraska Coop. Ext. Pub. No G93-1181.

50. Steinegger, D., R. Gaussoin and D. Hay. 1994. *Checking the Performance of your Landscape Irrigation System*. Univ. of Nebraska Coop. Ext. Pub. No G94-1221-A.

51. Street, J. 1988. Properties of thatch. *ALA* 9(5):18.

52. Streich, A., S. Rodie and R. Gaussoin. 2001. *Turf in the Landscape*. Univ. of Nebraska Coop. Ext. Pub. G01-1418.

53. Tashiro, H. 1987. *Turfgrass Insects of the United States and Canada*. Cornell Univ. Press. Ithaca, NY.

54. Turgeon, A. 1988. Thatch. *Landscape Management* 27(3):58.

55. Turgeon, A. 1999. *Turfgrass Management* (5th edition). Prentice Hall, Englewood Cliffs, NJ.

56. Vargas, J. 1994. *Management of Turfgrass Diseases*. Lewis Publishing, Ann Arbor, MI.

57. Vengris, J. and W. Torello. 1982. *Lawns* (3rd edition). Thomson Publications, Fresno, CA.

58. Watkins, J. and R. Gaussoin. 1992. *Rust Diseases of Turfgrass*. Univ. of Nebraska Coop. Ext. Pub. G92-1119.

60. Watkins, J. and R. Gaussoin. 1993. *Stripe Smut Disease of Turfgrass*. Univ. of Nebraska Coop. Ext. Pub. G93-1149.

61. Watschke, T., P. Dernoeden and D. Shetlar. 1995. *Managing Turfgrass Pests*. Lewis Publishers. Ann Arbor, MI.

62. White, R. 1991. Turfgrasses: They're more than blades and roots. *Lawn and Landscape Maintenance* 12(6):32.

Chapter 13
Pesticide Management

by Roch Gaussoin[1]

Pest management is an extensive and essential part of landscape management. Pest management requires careful and judicious use of chemical pesticides or alternative means to reduce damage to the environment. Application of pesticides is a financially lucrative facet of most landscape management operations. Pesticide application also represents the landscape manager's greatest risk and liability. Safe and prudent pesticide use requires knowledge of pesticide regulations, the chemicals, environmental and human toxicology, and application technology. It is not within the scope of this chapter to comprehensively cover every aspect of pesticide use and application. References listed at the end of this chapter are recommended for a more thorough dialogue on specific topics.

Pesticide Regulations

Certification. The *Federal Insecticide, Fungicide, and Rodenticide Act (FIFRA)* was amended in 1972 to initiate a program to certify individuals who apply pesticides. These amendments to FIFRA include the following:

1. All pesticides must be classified as either *General* or *Restricted* use. *General Use* products present little or no hazard to the applicator and have minimal adverse effect on the environment when used according to label directions. Toxicity of *Restricted Use* materials presents a potential hazard to the applicator or other persons. Use of these products without additional regulatory restriction may cause adverse effects to the environment.

2. Persons applying *Restricted Use Pesticides* (RUP) as well as application of pesticides on sites not owned by the applicator or applied for profit (*i.e.* for a contract) are required to be *certified* in their safe and appropriate use. Provisions for civil and criminal penalties (up to $5,000.00 and one year in prison) were established for people violating FIFRA.

3. The Federal Government granted regulatory *primacy* to the states. This means that individual states have jurisdiction over all pesticide matters as long as the state's regulations meet the minimum Federal standards. Because pesticide certification became the responsibility of each state, certification requirements and pesticide regulations differ from state to state. In most states, however, pesticide regulations and certification requirements are more stringent than the

[1]Professor and Extension Turfgrass Specialist, Department of Agronomy and Horticulture, University of Nebraska, Lincoln, NE.

Photo 13.1. Regulations in many areas require posting of lawns treated with pesticides. Photograph by James Robbins.

minimum Federal requirements. Check with the pesticide regulatory board in each state in which the firm will be applying pesticides for specific information (see: http://npic.orst.edu/state1.htm#map for listing of all State pesticide agencies). Landscape and turfgrass management companies applying pesticides in more than one state must meet the requirements in each. Some states have reciprocal pesticide certification agreements with other states.

1988 Amendments to FIFRA. In the fall of 1988 Congress passed amendments to FIFRA that, in a failed attempt at humor, were referred to as *FIFRA LITE*. The impact on the landscape industry was anything but humorous. These amendments focused primarily on re-registration of existing pesticides and increased fees for registration. This legislation has resulted in a loss of a significant number of pesticides from the market, not necessarily because they were harmful to the environment. Manufacturers were reluctant to re-register a compound with minimal economic value when the re-registration fees were accounted for in cost-benefit analysis.

A positive result of these 1988 amendments was a decrease in the time required to bring a new pesticide product to market. Compounds shown to be *relatively non-toxic* and safe were accelerated in the registration process. This resulted in new, more efficacious products with lower use rates and lower animal and human toxicity being made available quicker to landscape professionals.

Worker Pesticide Protection Standard. In 1992, the *Worker Pesticide Protection Standard* became an EPA regulation resulting in significant changes in worker protection for individuals applying pesticides. The previous reentry into treated areas standard of *when spray has dried or dust has settled* was replaced with more rigid requirements based on type and form of pesticides applied. The new *restricted entry interval* (REI) is contained on each pesticide label and must be followed, when applicable, in landscape maintenance operations.

Right to Know Legislation. In 1986, the *Superfund Amendments and Reauthorization Act* (SARA) was signed into law. Title III of this legislation or the *Emergency Planning and Community Right to Know Act* directly affects landscape managers. Employers are required to inform and train employees about potential hazards associated with products and chemicals they may use or come in contact with. Companies are also required to obtain *Material Safety Data Sheets* (MSDS) for all chemicals, not just pesticides, used in the operation.

The MSDS provides information on physical and chemical characteristics, physical and health hazards, routes of entry, exposure limits, carcinogenicity, safe handling, first aid, and medical procedures for the chemical. The MSDS, at the very minimum, must be stored in a conspicuous location in the workplace. If chemicals are carried in a vehicle and applied elsewhere, then the vehicle must carry the appropriate MSDS. MSDSs are available from chemical distributors or manufacturers as well as on the Internet.

Additionally, the legislation requires firms to maintain an *inventory* of chemicals based on their hazard rating. If the inventory exceeds a certain level then the quantity must be reported. Further information concerning SARA may be obtained from regional Environmental Protection Agency (EPA) offices.

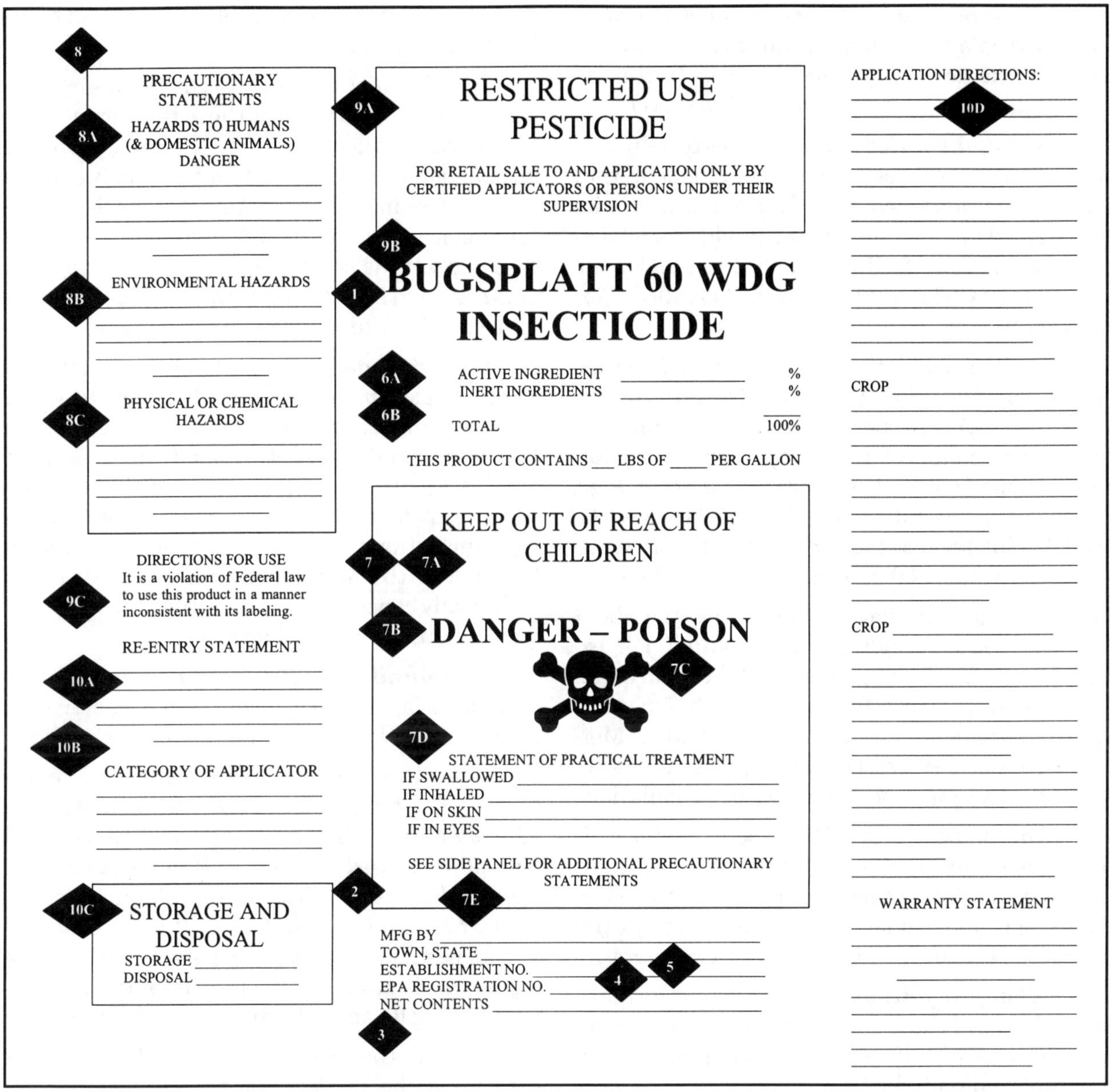

Illustration 13.1 Example of a pesticide label.

Within the illustration, the following text appears:

- 8 — PRECAUTIONARY STATEMENTS
- 8A — HAZARDS TO HUMANS (& DOMESTIC ANIMALS) DANGER
- 8B — ENVIRONMENTAL HAZARDS
- 8C — PHYSICAL OR CHEMICAL HAZARDS
- 9A — RESTRICTED USE PESTICIDE — FOR RETAIL SALE TO AND APPLICATION ONLY BY CERTIFIED APPLICATORS OR PERSONS UNDER THEIR SUPERVISION
- 9B, 1 — BUGSPLATT 60 WDG INSECTICIDE
- 6A — ACTIVE INGREDIENT _____ % / INERT INGREDIENTS _____ %
- 6B — TOTAL _____ 100%
- THIS PRODUCT CONTAINS ___ LBS OF ____ PER GALLON
- 7, 7A — KEEP OUT OF REACH OF CHILDREN
- 7B — DANGER – POISON
- 7C
- 7D — STATEMENT OF PRACTICAL TREATMENT — IF SWALLOWED _____ / IF INHALED _____ / IF ON SKIN _____ / IF IN EYES _____
- 7E — SEE SIDE PANEL FOR ADDITIONAL PRECAUTIONARY STATEMENTS
- 2 — MFG BY _____ / TOWN, STATE _____ / ESTABLISHMENT NO. _____ / EPA REGISTRATION NO. _____ / NET CONTENTS _____
- 4, 5, 3
- 9C — DIRECTIONS FOR USE — It is a violation of Federal law to use this product in a manner inconsistent with its labeling.
- RE-ENTRY STATEMENT
- 10A
- 10B — CATEGORY OF APPLICATOR
- 10C — STORAGE AND DISPOSAL — STORAGE _____ / DISPOSAL _____
- APPLICATION DIRECTIONS: — 10D
- CROP _____
- CROP _____
- WARRANTY STATEMENT

The Pesticide Label

The *pesticide label* is the written, printed, or graphic matter on, or attached to the pesticide or any of its containers or wrappers. The pesticide label constitutes a *legal and binding contract* between the applicator and the chemical company prohibiting the use of the pesticide in any application or procedure not consistent with the label. A thorough understanding of the components of the pesticide label is critical for proper pesticide use and application, as well as circumvention of potential liability for pesticide misuse. A generic pesticide label is shown in Illustration 13.1.

By Federal law, each pesticide label must contain certain specific information. The numbered sequence on Illustration 13.1 allows for explanation, if necessary, of each label component. Many of the components are self-explanatory.

1. *Product name.* This is the *trade name* chosen by the manufacturer or distributor for marketing purposes. The trade name is prominently displayed in large print and may not be used in the *active ingredient* section. In this generic example the trade name is **BUGSPLATT**.

Type of formulation. Pesticides usually contain from one to 70 percent active ingredient, they are seldom marketed as a 100 percent active ingredient. The remainder of the product is solvent and materials to facilitate application and/or increase safety. The resulting product is called a *formulation*.

Not all pesticides are available in all formulations. When faced with a choice, the information in Table 13.1 will aid the decision making process. The amount of active ingredient in dry formulations is normally expressed as a *percentage*. Bugsplatt (Illustration 13.1) is formulated as a *60 WDG*. This means it is a *water dispersible granule* and contains 60 percent active ingredient.

In liquid formulations the active ingredient is expressed as *weight per unit volume*. For example, a pesticide designated as a *7 EC* is an emulsifiable concentrate formulated with 7 pounds active ingredient per gallon of formulation. Metric formulations are usually expressed in kilograms active ingredient per liter of formulation.

Type of pesticide. The type of material is based on target species. In this example Bugsplatt is an *insecticide*. Other common types used in landscape management include *herbicides, fungicides, bactericides*, and *plant growth regulators*.

2. *Company name and address*. The name and address of the manufacturer and phone number to contact for questions or emergencies must be displayed on the label.

3. *Net contents.* This is the total amount of material in the package, including inert ingredients.

4, 5. *EPA pesticide registration number, EPA formulator manufacturer establishment number.* These are the numbers under which the product is registered and recorded with the EPA.

6A. *Ingredients statement.* The *official common name* is a name suggested by the manufacturer and approved by the Pesticide Regulation Division of the EPA. Regulations require that officially approved common names appear in the active ingredient section unless no common name has been approved.

The *chemical name* is the name designating the contents or formula of the actual toxin in the formulation. When an accepted common name is not available, the chemical name normally appears in the active ingredient section. If a pesticide contains more than one active ingredient, as is the case in pesticide combinations, all active ingredients are listed by both common and chemical name in decreasing order based on percentage.

The remainder of the pesticide formulation is classified as *inert ingredients*. This may be water or an organic solvent in liquid formulations, or talc or clay in dry formulations. If *surfactants* or *wetting agents* are added as part of the formulation, then their content is not expressed explicitly. Surfactants or wetting agents are lumped together with the inert ingredients. Although technically considered inert, many of these ingredients exhibit biological activity.

6B. *Pounds per gallon statement.* If the pesticide is a liquid, then the pounds of active ingredient (AI) will be listed in pounds per gallon.

7A — C. *Child Hazard Warning, "Keep Out of Reach of Children," Signal Word – "Danger, Warning or Caution," Skull and Crossbones and the word Poison (in red if applicable).* All pesticide labels contain the statement, *Keep Out of Reach of Children*. Additionally, all pesticides will contain *signal words*. These signal words group pesticides based on their toxicity to people, animals, and the environment.

Toxicity is based on scientific evaluations that determine the relative hazard of various compounds. The results of these investigations determine the LD_{50} (Lethal Dose, 50 percent) or LC_{50} (Lethal Concentration, 50 percent). Routes of exposure for toxic substances are *oral* (the toxin is ingested), *dermal* (the toxin comes in contact with the skin), or *inhalation* (the toxin is breathed in through the mouth or nose). The LD_{50} represents the amount of toxic substance relative to the weight of an organism that will cause death in 50 percent or more of the test organisms exposed to that amount.

The LD_{50} is expressed in milligrams of toxic substance per kilogram of body weight (mg/kg). To convert LD_{50} values to units easier to compre-

Table 13.1.

Comparison of pesticide formulations commonly used in landscape management

Formulation	Label abbreviation	Mixing/ loading hazards	Phytotoxicity	Effect on application equipment	Agitation required	Visible Residues[a]	Compatible with other formulations	AI[b] expressed as
Dry Formulation applied as sprays								
Wettable powers	WP	Dust inhalation	Safe	Abrasive	Yes	Yes	Very good	Percent
Dry flowable/water dispersible granules	DF WDG	Safe	Safe	Abrasive	Yes	Yes	Good	Percent
Liquid Formulations								
Emulsifiable concentrates	EC	Spills and splashes	Maybe	May affect rubber pump parts	Yes	No	Fair	Pounds per gallon
Flowables	F	Spills and splahes	Maybe	May affect rubber pump parts	Yes	Yes	Fair	Pounds per gallon
Dry Formulations, applied dry								
Dust	D	Severe inhalation hazards	Safe	—	Yes	Yes	—	Percent
Granules and pellets	G	Safe	Safe	—	No	No	—	Percent

[a]Some formulations, upon drying, will leave residues, which can be aesthetically unacceptable on ornamental plants.
[b]Active ingredient.

Table 13.2.
EPA pesticide label toxicity categories and associated toxicities

Signal Word	Toxicity (Oral LD$_{50}$)	Equivalent Toxic Quantity for 200 lb Human
Category I - Danger - Poison	0 - 50 mg/kg	0 - 0.16 oz
Category II - Warning	50 - 500 mg/kg	0.16 - 1.6 oz
Category III - Caution	500 - 5,000 mg/kg	1.6 oz - 6.4 oz
Category IV - Caution	> 5,000 mg/kg	> 6.4 oz

hend, multiply the LD$_{50}$ by (1.6 X 10^{-5}) to determine ounces of toxic substance per pound of body weight. For example, if a 200-pound individual ingested 1.6 ounces of a toxin with a LD$_{50}$ of 500 mg/kg, then the person would have a 50 percent chance of dying (500 x 1.6 x 10^{-5} x 200 pounds = 1.6 ounces).

Inhalation toxicity is expressed as milligrams toxin per liter of air (mg/liter) and represents a concentration of airborne toxin that would be lethal to 50 percent or more of a test population breathing that concentration.

All toxicity evaluation is done on surrogate animals, such as rats, mice, or guinea pigs, and represents an *estimate* of potential hazard to humans.

Categorization of pesticides based on their toxicity and associated signal words are shown in Table 13.2. This categorization also determines specific recommendations for equipment required by the applicator for safe handling, application, and possible medical treatment requirements for exposure victims. This information must also be included on the pesticide label.

Photo 13.2. Pesticide labels will indicate the protective gear required for application of the material.

Photo 13.3. Store pesticides properly and safely. Consult the label for storage precautions. Always store pesticides in their original container in a secure, ventilated area. Photograph by David Hensley.

9A. *Restricted use block* (*if applicable*). If the pesticide labeled is a *Restricted Use Pesticide* it must always designated as such in a block on the label.

7. *Front-panel precautionary statements*, 9B. *Environmental hazards*, 9C. *Misuse statement*, 10A. *Reentry statement*, 10B. *Category of applicator*, 10C. *Storage and disposal block*, 7D. *Statement of practical treatment*, 7E. *Referral statement*, 8. *Side or back-panel precautionary statements*, 8A. *Hazards to humans and domestic animals*, 8B. *Environmental hazards*, 8C. *Physical or chemical hazards*, 10D. *Directions for use.* These multiple information and requirement sections are normally the longest sections on the label and include the following minimal information: storage and disposal precautions; specific pests controlled; product rate and application carrier recommendations; application procedures; nontarget protection; compatibility with fertilizers or other pesticides; any additional information critical to proper use; and environmental protection. Additional information and directions can be listed.

Pesticide Adjuvants

Pesticide *adjuvants* are substances added to a pesticide formulation or spray solution to enhance effectiveness. Most pesticide formulations contain some sort of additive to improve its delivery or solubility. The landscape manager can also purchase adjuvants to add to a pesticide mixture to enhance pesticide performance.

While pesticides are formulated to be suitable over a wide variety of application conditions, they cannot be synthesized for all possible situations. The addition of a suitable adjuvant allows the applicator to customize the spray mixture for a specialized need or to compensate for different environmental conditions. Adjuvants are added to pesticide or spray solutions to:

- Improve the wetting ability of the spray solution.

- Control evaporation of spray droplets.

- Improve pesticide persistence.

- Increase foliar or insect uptake.

- Adjust the pH of the spray solution.

- Improve spray droplet coverage.

- Increase safety of the spray to nontarget plants or animals.

- Correct spray tank incompatibility problems.

- Reduce spray drift.

- Mark spray pattern (dyes, colorants).

Many spray applications benefit from the use of adjuvants; however, adjuvants should not be added haphazardly or without specific reasons. Check the pesticide *and* adjuvant labels to make sure these materials are suitable to the application site, target pest, and application equipment. Often a single product will accomplish two or more separate adjuvant functions, such as spreader-sticker, spreader-activator, or spreader-sticker-drift retardant. Some manufacturers also produce

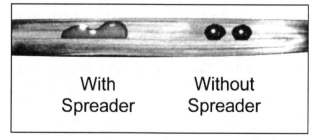

Photo 13.4. Spreaders are spray adjuvants that increase the spread or contact area of the pesticide on the target's surface. Photograph by Roch Gaussoin.

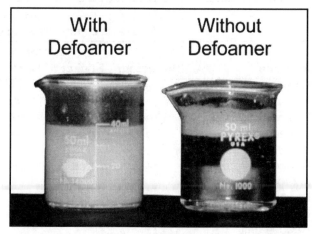

Photo 13.5. Defoamers can be added to the spray tank to limit foam to limit drift and improper application. Photograph by Roch Gaussoin.

299

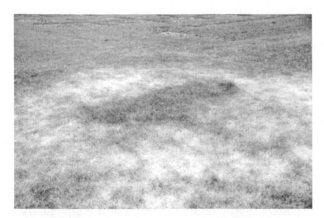

Photo 13.6. Even though spray adjuvants are listed as inert on the pesticide label, many possess biological activity. This damage on this Kentucky bluegrass turf was the result of a spreader-sticker applied at a very high rate. Photograph by Roch Gaussoin.

a blend of adjuvants to accomplish multiple functions.

Problems often result from the misuse of adjuvants. Using the wrong type or amount of additive can result in loss of selectivity or an increase in phytotoxicity of a spray material. For example, the addition of a surfactant to some 2,4-D formulations results in significant stand loss in Kentucky bluegrass. Once again, check *all labels* for proper use directions and adjuvant compatibility. A summary of adjuvants commonly used in landscape management and their functions are shown in Table 13.3.

Pesticide Application Equipment

Pesticides used in landscape management are normally applied either as a *liquid* through spray equipment, or as a *granular* formulation through dry application equipment. Each method or type of equipment has advantages and disadvantages. Selection of specific application equipment depends upon economics, availability, and suitability for the particular use attempted.

Liquid application equipment. Over 75 percent of all agricultural pesticide applications are made as liquid sprays. Spray equipment range from simple, hand-operated, non-powered applicators to complex, multi-nozzle, powered boom sprayers. Landscape managers must balance pesticide application needs, efficiency, and economics when selecting equipment. There is no single machine that provides for every specific need for a site manager. Several types and sizes of applicators will be necessary for safe, effective, and efficient application of the various landscape chemicals.

Hand-operated, non-powered sprayers. This equipment requires no power source to pressurize the unit. Most of the following are inexpensive, require minimal maintenance, and are simple to operate.

Hose-end sprayers. A small container containing pesticide is attached to a garden hose and pressurized from the water source. Hose-ends are

Table 13.3.
Adjuvants commonly used in landscape management

Purpose	Surfactant	Sticker	Spreader Sticker	Compatibility Agent	Buffer	Acidifier	Defoamer
Reduce surface tension	Yes		Yes				
Increase pesticide uptake	Yes		Yes			Yes	
Improve sticking	Yes	Yes	Yes				
Protect against wash-off/abrasion	Yes	Yes	Yes				
Reduce volatilization	Yes	Yes	Yes				
Improve mixing				Yes	Yes	Yes	
Lower pH					Yes	Yes	
Slow breakdown					Yes	Yes	
Reduce drift							Yes
Eliminate foam							Yes

suitable for application to landscape turf, shrubs, and small trees.

Hose-ends naturally require access to a water source. Hose-end sprayers are suitable for most formulations, but are most effective for soluble materials or those miscible in water. Formulations requiring agitation, such as wettable powders, must be frequently shaken. Hose-ends are not effective or suitable for large areas. They cannot be used on tall trees because the sprayer will not operate at or near vertical. Changes in water pressure can significantly alter output. Hose-end sprayers are difficult to calibrate.

Hose-ends are not the best choice for routine pesticide application, but are appropriate for some situations. Be aware that hose-end sprayers are not legal in some states without an anti-siphon device to eliminate the possibility of pesticide being inadvertently introduced into a public water system.

Compressed air sprayers consist of a small container (one to five gallons in volume) attached to a short hose and spray wand. The wand normally contains a single nozzle but multi-nozzle sprayers are available. Nozzles adjusting from a fine mist to a solid stream are common for small or homeowner oriented, compressed air sprayers.

The unit is pressurized with a hand-operated pump and is capable of developing fairly high pressures. Compressed air sprayers are suitable for

Photo 13.7. Hand-carried and back-pack compressed air sprayers are inexpensive and versatile in landscape management operations. Note the gauge on the back-pack sprayer allowing accurate calibration. Photograph by David Hensley.

small landscapes, shrubs, small trees, and spot spraying in turf. These sprayers are suitable for applying most formulations. Pesticides requiring agitation such as wettable powers need frequent shaking. Small units are useful for spot spraying and applications to areas inaccessible to larger equipment.

Compressed air sprayers require frequent pumping to maintain constant pressure. Pressure loss during spraying significantly alters output. Pressure limiting valves and pressure gauges increase accuracy and reduce pressure fluctuation during operation. Regular maintenance is required for continued operation and to prevent corrosion of metal parts. Compressed air sprayers are available as hand-held or backpack units.

Wick applicators are specialized applicators used to apply postemergence herbicides to weeds. The herbicide is gravity fed from a reservoir to a sponge or rope wick. The wick is wiped on the weed leaving a thin film of herbicide. Wick applicators are an excellent way to apply broadleaf herbicides around or under trees and shrubs because drift to nontarget plants is minimized. Wick applicators must be cleaned frequently and can only be used with water-soluble herbicides.

Powered sprayers. *Powered sprayers*, as per their name, require an auxiliary gas or electric power source to pressurize and deliver the liquid. Powered sprayers also require a pump. Most powered sprayers are equipped with tank agitators to constantly mix the spray solution and pressure regulation systems to eliminate pressure fluctuations. Many contain elaborate nozzle manifold systems. The expense and complexity of powered sprayers depend on their size, accessories, and ultimate use. They require periodic maintenance, but are necessary for applying pesticides to large areas.

Powered backpack sprayers are similar to non-powered backpack sprayers except that a small 2-cycle gas engine powers the sprayer. Powered backpack sprayers are suitable for all pesticide formulations. Their greatest disadvantage is the additional weight from the gas motor and fuel.

Mist blowers or *forced-aid sprayers* are specialized tree application equipment. With these sprayers, the spray droplets are propelled as a mist into the tree canopy. They are suitable for application of chemical that must penetrate a dense tree canopy or for spraying tall trees. Recent environmental concerns about drift potential of pesticides propelled at high velocity have caused greater scrutiny of this equipment.

Controlled droplet applicators (CDA). Liquid from a pesticide reservoir is precisely metered to a nozzle assembly that delivers it on to a spinning serrated disk. Centrifugal force throws the liquid out in a uniform pattern and droplet size. CDA's are best suited for herbicide and insecticide applications. The resulting tiny droplets are difficult to see. Controlled droplet applicators have a low output and are advantageous in areas where access to a water source is a problem. Improvements in CDA technology in the late 1980s increased interest, but the use of CDA applicators is still limited in landscape operations.

Low-pressure sprayers are the most common powered sprayer used in landscape management. Sprayers may be equipped with a single, hand-held nozzle or have a multi-nozzle boom for rapid application over a wide area. Low-pressure sprayers are versatile, applying material to turf or trees, and suitable for every pesticide formulation. They can also be adapted for liquid fertilizer applications.

High-pressure hydraulic sprayers generate high pressures, as the name implies. These units are equipped with a single nozzle and useful for all pesticide formulations. High-pressure sprayers are essential for pesticide application to tall trees and to penetrate dense foliage. They may be adapted for soil injection of fertilizers and other materials.

Granular Application Equipment

The selection of equipment to apply granular pesticides or fertilizers is less extensive and the machinery is less flexible than that available for liquid.

Granular spreaders can be used to apply fertilizers and for broadcasting grass seed. Granular formulations of pesticides are safer to use than their liquid counterparts. Application of granules sometimes results in less chemophobic resistance than spray applications. Granular formulations are usually formulated with a low percentage of active ingredients, reducing the possibility of serious damage resulting from over application.

Photo 13.8. CDA sprayers offer portability and low volume application. Photograph by Roch Gaussoin.

Photo 13.9. Low-pressure boom sprayers are ideal for large turfgrass areas such as golf courses, parks, and general grounds. Photograph by Roch Gaussoin.

Photo 13.10. High-pressure sprayers are essential for applying material to the canopy of trees. Photograph courtesy of Bestway Sprayers, Ritchie Industries, Conrad, Iowa.

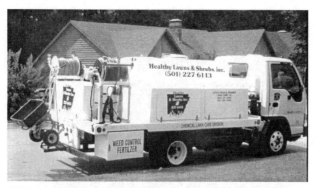

Photo 13.11. A commercial spray truck designed for efficient and profitable chemical application. The unit contains separate tanks and power hose reels so that two different materials can be carried and applied as appropriate on the route. Also note storage for small sprayers, a spreader, chemicals, MSDSs and other documents, and safety equipment. Photograph by James Robbins.

Photo 13.12. Drop spreaders contain a hopper mounted between two wheels. The width of drop spreaders used in landscape operations ranges from three to five feet.

Granular applicators also present several limitations. The volume of the carrier cannot be adjusted as with liquid materials, so each product must be calibrated individually. The actual product must be used during calibration resulting in potential exposure and pollution. Fewer products are available in granular form than in liquid formulations. Some granular products, especially postemergence foliar herbicides, are less effective than their liquid counterparts. Despite the disadvantages, however, many landscape firms use only granular applicators and have effectively used this as a marketing advantage to counter client phobia about spraying.

Hand operated granular applicators can be carried or strapped to the operator's chest. An adjustable opening at the bottom of the hopper meters the pesticide to a spinning disk operated by a hand crank. The speed at which the operator turns the crank determines the width of application. These spreaders are relatively inexpensive and easy to use. Machines constructed of stainless steel, heavy plastic, or other non-corrosive materials provide longer service. Walking and cranking speeds of the operator complicate calibration.

Drop spreaders contain a box or hopper mounted between two wheels. The width of the drop spreader hoppers used in landscape operations range from three to five feet. Larger models are used in agricultural operations. As the spreader is pushed, the wheels turn a baffled cylinder within the hopper that facilitates dispersion of the granules through adjustable openings at the base of the hopper.

The swath of the drop spreader equals the width of the hopper. Output is controlled by adjusting the size of the opening on the bottom of the hopper and, to a lesser extent, ground or walking speed. Some drop spreaders can be pulled behind a utility vehicle, but most are pushed by the applicator.

Drop spreaders are useful for applying granular materials in areas where the swath of a centrifugal spreader is too wide. Drop spreaders have a low coverage per unit time (they are slow) because of the narrow swath. They are also prone to skips and overlaps of applied materials. The problem of skips and overlaps is reduced by applying half-rates of the material in two, perpendicular applications. This, however, takes twice as long.

Centrifugal spreaders. The granular material is carried in a hopper that feeds a metered amount to a spinning disk. When the pesticide strikes the disk, it is thrown, via centrifugal force, in a relatively uniform pattern, around the spreader. The speed of the disk determines the effective spreader width. The disk speed is controlled by ground speed with ground-driven ap-

Photo 13.13. Small centrifugal spreaders can be used to apply granular pesticides and fertilizers. Photograph by James Robbins.

Photo 13.14. A motorized centrifugal spreader. Photograph by David Hensley.

plicators and by crank revolutions with hand-operated machines. Some spreaders utilize an external power source to drive the disk. These powered spreaders are mounted on utility vehicles or tractors and disk speed is independent of ground speed.

Calibration

Accurate calibration of application equipment is critical. Inaccurate or sloppy calibration has economic, legal, and environmental ramifications. Under-application results in poor pesticide efficacy, increased client callbacks for re-application, and affects profit margin. Over-application increases the possibility of damage to the site, irate customers, replaced landscapes, lawsuits, and is a breach of FIFRA. Over application of pesticides could result in civil and criminal penalties.

Calibration of liquid application equipment. Regardless of the type of equipment used, two pieces of information are necessary to calibrate liquid application equipment. These are *sprayer output* and *coverage*.

Sprayer output. The output of a sprayer must be determined. This is usually ascertained in *fluid ounces per minute* (OPM). A stopwatch, a container to catch the liquid, and an accurate liquid measuring device, calibrated in ounces, are needed to measure output.

Equip the sprayer with the nozzle or nozzles that will be used in the actual spraying operation.

Photo 13.15. A large centrifugal spreader powered by its wheels as they turn. Motorized units are also available. Photograph by David Hensley.

Photo 13.16. Improper pesticide application may result in client loss, negative public relations, and criminal and civil liabilities. Employees must be adequately trained to deal with the unexpected. Photograph by Roch Gaussoin.

Calibrate the sprayer at the same operating parameters (such as pressure, speeds, and terrain, if possible) that will be used on-site. For multi-nozzle boom sprayers, output should be measured for each nozzle. Replace worn and incorrect nozzles before final calibration.

Operate the sprayer in a stationary position for a predetermined amount of time (usually less than a minute) and collect the output in the collection containers. Measure the amount collected and record this number on a piece of paper or in a notebook. Repeat this output measurement a minimum of two more times to ensure an accurate reading. Use the *average* of the three readings to determine output in ounces per minute (OPM).

For example:

The output of each nozzle of a five-nozzle boom sprayer was collected for 10 seconds and the process repeated three times (Table 13.4). The average output of each nozzle was multiplied by five to obtain the individual nozzle *output per minute* (OPM). The average of the three collections, summed across all nozzles equals the *total output* of this sprayer in OPM.

It is sometimes more convenient to work with sprayer output in *gallons per minute* (GPM). Divide the output in OPM by *128 ounces per gallon* to produce the output in GPM. In this example the output was 364 OPM that, when divided by 128, results in an output of *2.84 GPM*.

This method for determining output can be used for most sprayers. One exception is high-pressure hydraulic sprayers used commonly for application of pesticides to tall trees. These sprayers deliver a large volume of material under very high pressures. Collection of the output in a container is impossible.

To determine the output of high-pressure sprayers, fill the spray tank with water to a predetermined level and operate the sprayer under actual spray conditions (minus pesticide) for a measured time. Record the amount of water needed to refill the tank back to the original level. Repeat this procedure at least two more times and determine output as outlined in the example of the multi-nozzle boom sprayer example.

Table 13.4.
Determination of output of the 5-nozzle boom sprayer in the calibration example.

Nozzle	OPM Ounces/10 seconds	(ounces per minute)	Average OPM
1	13	78	
	22	66	72
	12	72	
2	13	78	
	22	66	72
	12	72	
3	12	72	
	12	72	74
	13	78	
4	11	66	
	12	72	72
	13	78	
5	13	78	
	12	72	74
	12	72	
	Total output		**364 OPM**

305

Coverage. The second piece of information required for accurate calibration is *coverage* or the amount of time it takes to spray a given area. For most large-scale agricultural spraying operations this is expressed in *minutes per acre* (MIN/A). For landscape applications it is more convenient to express sprayer coverage in *minutes per 1,000 square feet* (MIN/M). *M* is the Roman numeral for 1,000.

Materials needed to determine coverage are a stopwatch and a tape measure. Measure a straight line between 25 and 100 feet in length and mark the beginning and end points. The calibration distance for self-propelled spreaders should be greater than that used for non-powered sprayers. Run the sprayer at the same speed to be used on site and record the time it takes to go the measured distance. Repeat this procedure a minimum of two more times to assure accuracy. Use the average of these three measurements to determine the coverage of the sprayer.

For example, to determine the speed of a five-nozzle boom sprayer used in the previous example:

Run	Seconds to travel 100 feet
1	89
2	90
3	91
Total	270

Total: 270 divided by 3 = 90 seconds per 100 feet

In this example the sprayer takes 90 seconds, or 1.5 minutes, to travel 100 linear feet.

Next, the *effective spray width* of the sprayer being calibrated must be determined. The effective spray width is determined by measuring the distance between the outermost nozzles on each side of the boom.

Let us assume that the five-nozzle boom in the example has an effective spray width of 10 feet. We already know that this sprayer takes 1.5 minutes to cover 100 linear feet. To determine coverage, multiply the linear feet traveled (100) by the effective spray width (10 feet) to determine the total area covered in the 1.5 minutes. For this example 100 feet X 10 feet = 1,000 square feet.

This sprayer, therefore, requires 1.5 minutes to cover 1,000 square feet. Its MIN/M coverage is 1.5. To determine *minutes per acre* (MIN/A) multiply MIN/M by 43.56 (1.5 X 43.56 = 65.34 MIN/A).

The output in OPM or GPM and the coverage in MIN/M or MIN/A are multiplied to obtain the amount of water applied per unit area. For our example, *ounces (oz.) per 1,000 square feet* (OZPM) = [364 OZPM X 1.5 MIN/M] = 546. Gallons per acre (GPA) = [2.84 GPM X 65.34 MIN/A] = 185.56. Simply put, this sprayer equipped and operated at the same conditions as calibrated, will deliver 546 OZPM or 185.56 GPA.

Some pesticide labels have specific OPM or GPA requirements. For example a label may read *apply this product in a minimum of 60 gallons of water per acre*. If the sprayer, as calibrated, results in an output that is higher or lower than required for a particular pesticide, adjustment will be needed. Sprayer output may be reduced by: 1) decreasing the nozzle orifice size; 2) decreasing the spray pressure; and/or 3) increasing the speed of the sprayer. Conversely, sprayer output may be increased by increasing nozzle orifice size and/or spray pressure, or by decreasing the speed of the sprayer.

Adding the Pesticide

Once a sprayer has been accurately calibrated the operator is ready to add pesticide to the tank. This is often the point at which many applicators make serious errors. Inaccurate measurement of the pesticide or miscalculation of the amount of product to add results in over or under application. As an example, assume that a turfgrass pesticide label requires the material be applied at the rate of *four ounces per 1,000 square feet*. Let us also assume that we are applying the material using the previously calibrated five-nozzle boom sprayer (delivering 4.25 gallons of water per 1,000 square feet).

It should be obvious that the addition of four ounces of product in each 4.25 gallons of water in the spray tank is required.

Errors are made when *dry ounces* are not distinguished from *liquid ounces*. Key points to remember to avoid confusion are that there are 16 dry ounces per pound and 128 liquid ounces per gallon. Further, dry ounces are a *weight* or mass measurement, whereas liquid or fluid ounces are a *volume* measurement. Containers used to measure liquid ounces are never appropriate for dry weight measurements. Keeping this simple, but often overlooked, point clear is paramount to accurate addition of pesticides to a spray tank.

Product labels normally list rates in the amount of *product* required for a given area or application. Universities and federal and state agencies, however, often express recommendations on an *active ingredient* (AI) basis. Because pesticides are very rarely formulated as 100 percent active ingredients, the amount of product and a recommendation based on AI are not synonymous.

For example, suppose the applicator has been using a product that is formulated as a 50 WP. The label rate is two pounds of product per acre. The label was misplaced and no one at the firm remembers the exact rate. An employee who had read this text suggests that the local County Extension Office is always more than willing to help. The agent informs him/her that the product should be applied at one pound AI per acre. The specific product is a *50 WP* indicating that the contents of the bag are 50 percent active ingredient or pesticide. The remainder is filler or adjuvant.

To apply the product at one pound AI per acre it is necessary to add two pounds of product per acre (1 lb. AI per acre ÷ 1 lb. product is 0.5 lb. AI). If the operator had added only one pound of the product per acre then he or she would have inadvertently under-applied the pesticide. Make sure when adding a pesticide to a spray tank that the desired rate, and what is added to the tank, are equivalent.

Calibration of Granular Application Equipment

Calibrating dry application equipment is similar to the process described for liquid applicators with a few subtle differences. The carrier (water) volume for liquid applicators can be increased or reduced depending upon the particular operation. Granular pesticides are formulated with an inert carrier so the pesticide concentration is fixed. It cannot be adjusted. This requires that calibration be performed for each and every granular product used. Also, the actual pesticide (or fertilizer)

must be used during calibration since the size and densities of granular products vary. Relative humidity also affects dispersion of granules. Calibration should be repeated under extremes of relative humidity if these vary considerably during the application season.

The first step in calibration of a granular applicator is to calculate the area to the covered (*coverage*) of a particular machine. For drop spreaders, coverage is simply the width of the hopper multiplied by a premeasured distance. For example, coverage of a drop spreader with a four-foot wide hopper traveling a distance of 25 feet is 100 square feet (4 ft. X 25 ft. = 100 sq. ft.).

The swath width of a centrifugal spreader is controlled by the speed of the centrifugal disk and is altered by changes in cranking speed of hand-cranked spreaders, ground speed of ground-driven spreaders, or motor speed for powered spreaders. Coverage by these spreaders, therefore, is variable and must be determined for the speed used in actual pesticide applications.

Determine the swath of centrifugal spreaders by placing a series of collection vessels on a one-foot spacing perpendicular to the spreader's line of travel. The containers can be cigar boxes, pie tins, or any similar receptacle. Each container used should have the same dimensions. Load the spreader with the pesticide and set the opening on a medium setting. Run the spreader, at the speed to be used in actual operation, over the collection vessels with the output open. This operation should be done at the shop or in an open or paved area, *not* on the client's lawn or driveway.

Check the collection containers for granules. By observing the amount and distribution of the material in the collection vessels, spreader swath can be reasonably estimated. If the material in each container is also weighed, distribution can be checked and adjusted.

Coverage of a centrifugal spreader is swath width multiplied by a premeasured distance. For example, a centrifugal spreader with a swath of 10 feet traveling a distance of 25 feet has coverage of 250 square feet (10 ft. X 25 ft. = 250 sq. ft.).

The next step is to determine the desired rate of the granular material. For example, the label rate of a pesticide is 180 pounds of *product* per acre. To facilitate calibration and avoid unnecessary waste of pesticide, this quantity is reduced to a much smaller area. In the previous drop and centrifugal spreader examples, coverage was determined to be 100 and 250 square feet, respectively. The amount of material to deliver 180 pounds per acre must be reduced to these smaller areas. This is done by setting up a *ratio* or *proportion* problem and solving for the unknown.

For the drop spreader:

$$\frac{180 \text{ pounds}}{43,560 \text{ sq. ft.}} = \frac{x \text{ pounds}}{100 \text{ sq. ft.}}$$

$$x = 0.41 \text{ pounds}$$

For the centrifugal spreader:

$$\frac{180 \text{ pounds}}{43,560 \text{ sq. ft.}} = \frac{x \text{ pounds}}{250 \text{ sq. ft.}}$$

$$x = 1.03 \text{ pounds}$$

When x is solved correctly, this amount of material should be applied to the calibration areas and is equivalent to the desired 180 pounds per acre.

The final step in calibration is to determine the spreader setting required to apply the desired amount of material, based on calibration, to equal the desired rate. Many granular applicators provide suggested settings for common landscape chemicals in their operations manual. To accurately apply pesticides or fertilizers, however, these settings should be used only as calibration guidelines, not as the accurate and absolute setting.

To determine the *correct* setting the spreader is to be operated at, the machine must be calibrated at the recommended setting, the output collected and weighed, and the setting adjusted as necessary.

Collection of the output from drop spreaders can be accomplished one of two ways. Many commercial drop spreaders come with a *calibration pan*. This is attached beneath the spreader so that when the spreader is pushed over the predetermined calibration course, the output is collected in the pan. If a calibration pan was not included with the spreader (many less expensive and homeowner models do not) one can be made.

Without a calibration pan, the spreader can be pushed over a clean surface, such as a shop floor or hard surface driveway, and the material swept up and weighed. A potential problem with this method is that the spreader is being pushed along a surface that will be very dissimilar to a landscape. Wide variations in speed result in inaccurate calibration. Use of a calibration pan is more efficient and the spreader can be calibrated on a surface similar to the actual operation.

It was determined that the drop spreader in our earlier example needed to drop 0.41 pounds of material in the calibration distance to apply the pesticide at the desired rate. This means that 0.41 pounds or 6.6 dry ounces of material must be delivered over a 25 foot course with a four-foot drop spreader. If the initial setting chosen does not deliver this amount then appropriate adjustment is needed. If the collected amount is less than the calculated requirement, then the setting can be increased or the applicator speed reduced.

Conversely, a decrease in the output setting, or an increase in speed, results in a lower output. Once a setting is found that delivers close to the desired amount, the output should be collected a minimum of two more times and the average calculated to ensure accuracy.

Use of a calibration pan for centrifugal spreaders has been impractical. I have read recommendations to tape a garbage bag over the bottom of the spreader to collect the output. The bag is removed and the contents weighed. This recommendation was probably made by someone who never tried it personally. It sounds much easier than it is in practice.

The PennPro Collector™ attaches to the bottom of several popular brands of rotary spreaders. The device collects the granules for weighing and direct calibration, according to the manufacturer. The apparatus may make rotary spreader calibration quicker and more accurate

The normal procedure for collecting output from a centrifugal application is to operate the spreader over a tarp or plastic sheet of known dimensions placed in the calibration path. The output is then weighed. If the tarp differs in dimensions from the previously determined calibration area, and it probably will, the operator must recalculate to expected volume for the size of the catch tarp. If the tarp is wider than the spreader swath then coverage is simply calculated as swath width multiplied by tarp length. The additional width has no bearing. If the tarp is narrower than the spreader swath, then coverage is equal to the catch tarp length multiplied by its width.

If the initial setting chosen does not deliver this amount then appropriate adjustments will be needed. If the amount collected is less than the calculated requirement, the setting can be increased.

Because the speed of travel of ground driven centrifugal spreaders affects spreader swath, increasing or decreasing speed affects coverage. Adjusting the speed of the spreading operations cannot, therefore, be used to alter output for a ground-driven spreader. For mounted centrifugal spreaders or any centrifugal spreaders whose disk speed is independent of ground speed, then adjusting vehicle speed can be used to alter output.

Applicators should remember that it is extremely difficult, if not impossible, to calibrate a spreader to deliver *exactly* the amount calculated. Granular pesticides contain low concentrations of the active ingredient to compensate for the inherent calibration inaccuracy. The applicator should adjust the settings so that the delivery is as close as reasonably possible to the recommended amount. The operator, however, should and must be willing to settle for close. If the calibrated amount is within 10 percent of the calculated amount, the applicator should proceed with the application confident that he/she is applying the material within a safe and effective range.

Determining Application Area

The area of an existing or proposed landscape must be determined to accurately calculate pesticide and fertilizer quantities. These calculations are used to determine job costs, material requirements, and inventory necessary. Determining the area of a landscape is not difficult and can be accomplished several ways.

A mechanical device that is sometimes used to measure areas of landscape drawings and maps is called a *compensating polar planimeter* or simply, a *planimeter*. A planimeter is an accurate measuring tool in the hands of an experienced operator, but it is limited to paper plans and maps.

Some larger firms use computer technology, including GPS and GIS, to calculate landscape dimensions.

Field and plan measurements of landscaped areas can be accomplished by the use of *geometric figures* or by the *line offset method*.

Geometric Figures

Any site can be divided into rectangles, trapezoids, circles, ovals and triangles of varying size. Calculating the areas of the various geometric figures and summing them, therefore, can determine the area of the entire or individual parts of the site.

Line Offset Method

If a particular area does not lend itself to the use of geometric figures, then the *line offset method* can be used. This method reduces large irregularly shaped areas to a series of smaller trapezoids spaced along a measured line. It is also useful for measuring areas of bodies of water. When done correctly, the line offset calculations will determine the area to within five percent. Determining the area of an irregularly shaped figure involves the following steps. Also, see Illustration 13.2 for an example.

1. Determine the *length line*. This is the longest axis of the figure. The endpoints are designated points A and B.

2. Mark the *offset lines* at right angles (90 degrees) to the length line. These lines should be equally spaced along the length line. The number of offset lines required or distance is somewhat arbitrary. If the shape of the area to be measured is relatively uniform, then fewer offsets are needed. The more irregular in shape the area to be measured, the more offset lines will be required. Additionally, the greater the number of offset lines used, then the greater the measurement accuracy.

Choose the number of offset lines to be used so that they divide the length line (line A-B) into equal segments and define areas amenable to calculation. For example, if line A-B equals 50 feet and the figure is reasonably uniform in shape, an appropriate distance between offset lines might be 10 feet. If the figure is irregular in shape, then 5-foot intervals between offset lines would better estimate the area. For very large areas, where the length line may exceed 300 feet, the offsets can be spaced 30 feet (10 yards) or further apart, to facilitate calculations.

Table 13.5.

Calculation of areas of various geometric shapes

A rectangle or square is a parallelogram with four right angles. The area is calculated by multiplying the length (L) by the width (W).

Area=(L)(W)

A trapezoid is a quadrilateral with only two parallel sides. The area is found by multiplying the average length of the parallel sides (A+B) by the height (H).

$$Area = \frac{A+B}{2}(H)$$

A triangle is a polygon with three sides. The area of a triangle is the base (B) multiplied by the height (H) divided by two.

$$Area = \frac{(B)\,(H)}{2}$$

A circle is closed curve with an equal perimeter radius from the center. The area of a circle is the radius squared (R2) multiplied by pi (3.14). The radius is equal to one-half the diameter.

Area= $(3.14)R^2$

An oval has an egg- like or elliptical shape. The area is the length (L) multiplied by the width (W), multiplied by 0.8.

Area=[(L)(W)] 0.8

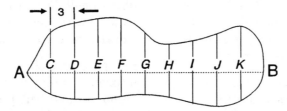

All measurements in feet

| 3 |

A C D E F G H I J K B

Length of Offset Lines

A = 0   I = 10
B = 0   J = 12
C = 10 K = 12
D = 12
E = 11
F = 10
G = 9
H = 7

Sum of offsets = 93

Area =
Sum of Offsets X Distance Between Offsets
=
93 ft X 3 ft = 279 square feet

Illustration 13-2. Line offset method.

3. Measure the length of each offset line. Make sure to measure every offset line from A-B, including the offset lines on each edge, if appropriate.

4. Add the lengths of all offset lines together and multiply by the distance between offset lines on the length line.

Public Relations and Pesticide Application

High visibility is one means used by landscape contractors to generate new business. One unfortunate aspect of this visibility is the perception by many consumers that the application of pesticides is a *life-threatening* and perilous operation. The application of pesticides to a landscape is necessarily a visible operation. Examples of employees who have had to stop applying pesticides because of queries from homeowners are commonplace. If the person applying pesticides can competently and politely respond to questions from the public, then downtime experienced can be minimized and public relations are vastly improved.

Much of the bad press pesticides and the green industry have received is not justified. Some of it is, however. The unscrupulous, unknowing, and uncaring actions of a few less-than-professionals in this industry have resulted in a black eye for all landscape professionals.

It is paramount that every landscape management firm presents a positive public image. This surpasses snappy uniforms and clean vehicles and includes people. Employees must be knowledgeable of what they are doing, why they are doing it, and the appropriate and honest answers to potential consumer or bystander questions. They must also have pride in their work and employer. Employee training is essential.

Additional steps that can facilitate a positive public image regarding pesticides include:

1. Join and become involved in local civic groups and neighborhood organizations. Area clean-ups and recycling campaigns can be especially appropriate.

2. Become proactive in local and state politics.

3. Develop fact sheets to be handed out to clients prior to a pesticide application explaining the product to be used and any associated hazards or instructions. Several professional societies have taken an early lead in providing information for use by local firms. Safety of the products and positive aspects should be promoted, but do not be overbearing. Print the information sheets on recycled paper.

4. Join and participate in non-extremist environmental and conservation groups such as

311

The Nature Conservancy, The Audubon Society, or Ducks Unlimited. Illustrate genuine concern for the environment and efforts to improve it. As someone once said, "We in the Green Industry are truly environmentalists; we just happen to be the calm ones".

5. Stay current with new pesticide regulations and products, and non-chemical alternatives. Select the least toxic alternative to effectively do the job. Investigate and try non-chemical controls where possible.

6. Join and support national, regional, and local professional societies.

7. Never become belligerent or argue with those with whom you want to make a point. Learn how to calmly and rationally express your views. Learn the facts; do not spout unsubstantiated claims or half-truths.

8. Recognize that some pesticides have resulted in problems and that not every operator is an honest and true professional. Most notorious past problems have been the result of applicator error.

9. Learn to respect the ideas and feeling of others. Everyone has the right to express an opinion in this country, even if it is wrong.

Bibliography

1. Anonymous. 1981. *Quick Calibration Guide for Spraying*. Spraying Guide 197. Spraying Systems Co., Wheaton, IL.

2. Anonymous. 1984. Which sprayer is right for you? *Landscape Contractor* 25(7):13.

3. Baxendale, F. and R. Gaussoin (ed.). 1997. *Integrated Turfgrass Management for the Northern Great Plains*. Coop. Ext. Pub. No. EC931557. Univ. of Nebraska, Lincoln, NE.

4. Bohmont, B. 1983. *The New Pesticide Users Guide*. Reston Publishing Co., Inc., Reston, VA.

5. Brandenburg, R. 1990. When 'Chemophobia' strikes. *Landscape Management* 29(3):66.

6. Buckingham, F. 1981. Choosing the right sprayer for the job. *Grounds Maintenance* 16(9):30.

7. Buckingham, F. 1982. Spreaders for granular material. *Grounds Maintenance* 17(11):26.

8. Christians, N. and M. Agnew. 2000. *The Mathematics of Turfgrass Maintenance*. 3rd Edition. Sleeping Bear Press, Ann Arbor, MI.

9. Evans, P. 1981. Calibrating hand sprayers. *Grounds Maintenance* 16:96.

10. Gaussoin, R. 1991. Water, pesticides and conservation. *Landscape Management* 30(10):8.

11. Gaussoin, R. 1992. Spray adjuvants. *Grounds Maintenance* 27(4):30.

12. Gaussoin, R. 1995. Pesticide formulations. *Golf Course Management* 63(3):26.

13. Gaussoin, R. and J. Fech. 1996. Effective tank mixing. *Grounds Maintenance* 31(2):70.

14. Boyd, J., R. Gaussoin and R. Duble. 1999. Pre-emergence herbicides: An early season weed cure. *Landscape & Irrigation* 23(2):22.

15. Gaussoin, R. 2000. A nonselective herbicide primer. *Golf Course Management* 68(2):56.

16. Fech, J. and R. Gaussoin. 2001. Post-emergence treatments: The war on weeds: Understanding postemergence products and application methods can help contractors destroy weeds. *Lawn and Landscape* 22(7):78.

17. Grisso, R. and R. Gaussoin. 1993. Spray application equipment. *Grounds Maintenance* 28(4):84.

18. Hoehm, C. 1993. Pesticides: Ruled by fact or fear? *Lawn and Landscape Maintenance* 14(3):32.

19. Marer, P. 1988. *The Safe and Effective use of Pesticides*. Univ. of California, Div. of Agriculture and Natural Resources. Publication 3324.

20. Pluenneke, R. 1982. Controlling hard-to-get-at weeds with wiper applicators. *Grounds Maintenance* 17(5):18.

21. Ware, G. 1994. *The Pesticide Book*. Thompson Publications. Fresno, CA.

22. Wilkinson, J. 1990. Be prepared for the next pesticide crisis. *Grounds Maintenance* 25(2):10.

Chapter 14
Leaf and Debris Removal

Removing leaves and debris during fall and spring clean ups can be very profitable. Nearly 80 percent of responding landscape management contractors in an industry survey offered fall cleanup services. Tree leaves can shade turf and bedding plants, robbing them of photosynthetic activity in autumn. Even a thin layer of tree leaves traps humidity at the grass surface increasing the opportunity for snow mold. Leaves also clog storm sewers, and can be unsightly. Removing interfering leaves increases the efficiency of late fall applications of nitrogen or broadleaf herbicides to turf.

Leaves and landscape debris, especially when wet, can also be hazardous to site users and expose owners to liability. Numerous lawsuits have resulted from people injured by slipping on wet leaves or grass clippings that were not cleaned up.

Disposal of leaves, clippings and other landscape debris is becoming a greater challenge for landscapers. Homeowners used to be able to pile leaves along the curb for municipal pickup (and still can in a few places). Today, burning leaves is banned or at least restricted in most municipalities. More than half of the states and many municipalities have laws against dumping green waste into landfills. If a disposal or composting site is available, there will likely be a charge.

To make leaf removal efficient, develop a leaf removal plan, acquire the necessary equipment,

Photo 14.1. Removing leaves each fall requires labor and planning. Seeds pods, spent flowers, pruning waste, leaves, grass clippings, and other debris require removal at various times during the year. In sub-tropical and tropical areas, leaves, seed pods, and spent flowers must be removed and disposed of year round.

and have a suitable disposal site. Consider the volume of leaves, the amount of time, labor, and equipment available or needed, and budget constraints.

Where there are many trees, especially a variety of species, leaf collection may start in early September and run into December. More leaves must often be gathered in the spring. Oaks, especially young trees, hold many of their leaves into winter and early spring, and accumulation of new leaves from other areas inevitably occurs. Pine needles are more difficult to pick up than leaves,

Table 14.1.
Reducing landscape debris

Turf

- Proper fertilization, irrigation, and mowing reduce excess clippings.
- *Grass cycling*, not bagging clippings, reduces time, debris and recycles nitrogen.

Trees and shrubs

- Proper selection eliminates pruning to maintain too-big plants in small spaces.
- Proper fertilization and management reduces excessive growth.
- Allowing plants to grow in their natural shape reduces pruning.
- Controlling weeds reduces competition and labor to remove them.
- Shredding/chipping debris on-site for mulch reduces handling and hauling.

according to managers in the Southeast. Some managers add a couple of additional mowings in the fall because leaves are easier to blow and remove with shorter grass. The mowers will also chop and dispose of many of the leaves.

Equipment

Providing lucky employees with hand rakes and push brooms to clean up leaves and other fall debris is inefficient and usually impractical on a commercial scale. Machines can do these tasks much faster and more economically, whether the area in question is a small flower bed or a large property. The goal is to select the right equipment for the sites and operation.

Several factors enter into equipment selection. Obviously, economics must be considered. To reduce equipment investment, select machines that can do more than one job. Grass catchers can collect clippings, remove thatch, and gather leaves in the fall. Hand-held and back-pack blowers are used for sweeping clippings and debris all year. Many turf vacuums also work on hard surfaces. Match equipment type and size to the area, volume of leaves and debris on site, and the time available. Consider the predominant weather during the leaf removal period and available labor.

For open lawn areas or those with relatively few trees, grass catchers mounted on lawn mowers may be the most efficient equipment. In addition to mower-mounted units, riding mowers can pull large independent catchers. Heavy accumulations are usually best handled by sweepers, blowers, or vacuums.

Blowers or vacuum units can clear high maintenance areas, such as courtyards, steps, flower

and shrub beds, fencerows, and others with limited equipment access. Hand raking remains an alternative for these areas. Leaves in areas adjoining wooded areas can be blown and scattered back among the trees.

Grass Catchers. Grass catchers for commercial mowers have changed during the past few years and there are dramatic differences among brands. The cutting action of the blades reduces leaf volume and packs them into the bag or hopper. There are immense differences in bag or hopper size for mowers that are essentially the same type and size. The effort required for bag removal and bag durability also varies. Look for bags that resist snagging, tearing, and mildew. Even though larger containers may reduce stops and save time, some personnel may have difficulty in handling extremely large bags or hoppers.

Photo 14.2. Vacuum collectors remove leaves and debris from turfgrass and paved areas.

316

To save time and reduce unproductive travel, keep a truck or trailer close to the mowing area to permit quick dumping of leaves and clippings.

Vacuum Collectors. Vacuum collectors on riding or small tractor mowers collect more material in the same time and with fewer stops. Pull-behind or rear-mounted units are powered by a separate engine or by the PTO. Engines range from four to eight horsepower. Vacuum capacity varies from eight to 45 bushels. The vacuum suction helps collect heavy clippings and thick or moist leaves better than mowers with grass catchers. The force of the air packs the material firmly.

The suction hose of many vacuum units can be disconnected and replaced with a flexible hose from eight to 20 feet long. This permits easy clean up of hard-to-reach window wells, flower and shrub beds, and areas next to fences and buildings.

Sweepers. Turf sweepers use stiff bristles to brush grass clippings, leaves, and debris into easily emptied baskets. Some sweepers are ground-driven; others are engine powered. Sweeping width varies from 30 to 72 inches, with larger units available.

Sweepers do not shred leaves or pack them as tightly as mowers or vacuum collectors. This means that sweepers with the same capacity as a grass catcher or vacuum must be emptied more frequently when covering the same size area. However, they are less expensive.

Blowers. Almost every landscape organization uses back-pack, hand-held and wheeled blowers. According to manufacturers, the sales of blowers for debris removal are growing faster than any other type of equipment.

Air speed (measured in miles per hour) and volume (measured in cubic feet per minute) of quality blowers can be adjusted to gently remove paper or fallen leaves from delicate flowers, or to remove empty bottles, rocks, and trash from bleachers or driveways. Blowers are also used to remove light snow and grass clippings from steps, sidewalks, and around parked cars, and to dry damp surfaces.

Leaves in beds are simply blown into adjoining turf areas for collection. In larger areas or for heavier leaf accumulation, blowers are used to windrow or pile leaves for later pickup. Pushed or self-propelled wheeled units are most effective for consolidating debris piles and moving piles or windrows.

Look for a unit designed for long hours of heavy use when considering a back-pack or hand-carried commercial blower. Most electric and small blowers built for intermittent home use are not constructed for commercial operations. Adjustable air speed and volume add flexibility.

Photo 14.3. Power sweepers make leaf and debris collection fast and efficient in open areas. Leaves along buildings and enclosed areas can be windrowed for collection with the power equipment.

Photo 14.4. Large turf vacuums collect, pulverize, and pack leaves and clippings. Large equipment is costly, but justified for leaf collection on large or heavily treed properties.

Photo 14.5. Hand-held power blowers and vacuums are very useful for windrowing leaves and debris and collecting them in areas inaccessible to larger equipment. Power blowers are standard equipment for removing grass clippings from surfaces. Photograph courtesy of Little Wonder®, Southampton, PA.

Unfortunately, leaf and debris blowers have become very unpopular and even illegal in some areas. Several municipalities, including the City of Los Angeles, have passed legislation to restrict or ban use of gasoline-fueled leaf blowers. Some of the claims by both sides have been extreme. At least one environmental group proposed that property owners and operators of leaf blowers might suffer qualitative and quantitative losses of soil, plant materials, structures, furnishings, personal well being, employee productivity, and customer satisfaction. Some Los Angeles landscapers initiated a hunger strike in response to the legislation. I wonder if they remember what we did before we had leaf blowers. Some landscape contractors claim the ban will result in their bankruptcy. An enrivonmental group argues that the disturbance of high-income clients outweighs the economic consideration of the contractor's increased cost in low paid labor. Talk about bourgeoisie.

Vacuums. Vacuums, available in various sizes, including truck-mounted units, dramatically speed leaf removal. Leaves are chopped by passing through the vacuum impellers so the volume is reduced. Some manufacturers offer blower/vacuum combinations.

Mulching Leaves into the Turf

Mulching mowers have made it possible to avoid separate leaf pick operations for some sites. The easiest and least expensive disposal method of leaves for many landscape sites is to mulch them into the turf. Shredding and mulching with mowers will reduce leaf bulk by 90 percent or more. Studies at Rutgers, Michigan State, and Purdue Universities have recently compiled enough data to show there are no long-term negative effects to healthy cool season turfgrasses. No studies have been reported on effects of mulching leaves into warm season lawns.

A Purdue study showed no turf discoloration or nitrogen tie up occurred as a result of mulching large volumes of leaves except where the grass received no fertilization. Fall applications of nitrogen to cool season turf compensated for any potential short-term nitrogen depletion. Mulching leaves into turf also did not affect soil nutrient availability, pH, disease incidence, or produce a buildup of leaf mat in the soil. On a positive side, mulching leaves increased microbial activity and improved soil quality.

Mulching leaves into turf saves crew time and minimizes expenses for large vacuums or other spe-

Photo 14.6. Back-pack power blowers remove leaves and debris from paved areas. Select units with adequate power and with adjustable air stream. Photograph courtesy of James Robbins.

Photo 14.7. Powerful wheel-mounted blowers clear and consolidate large amounts of leaves quickly. Photographs courtesy of Little Wonder®, Southampton, PA.

Photo 14.8. A power blower mounted on a mower concentrating leaves for easy pickup. Photograph courtesy of James Robbins.

Photos 14.9 and 14.10. A vacuum truck. The vacuum unit is mounted on the rear of a pickup or larger truck. A flexible hose allows removal of leaves from plant beds and many other difficult areas of the landscape. Photographs courtesy of Little Wonder®, Southampton, PA.

cialized equipment. It also reduces compaction by reducing the number of large pieces of equipment used on the site and produces an insulating layer of organic material.

Leaf mulching is not for every landscape manager or site. Eliminating leaf pick up can also eliminate a source of revenue. It may not be acceptable for some extreme quality sites. Heavily wooded lawns, already thinned by shade, may not be able to withstand the extra abuse of mulching the tree leaves.

Disposal Sites

Most municipalities banned burning of leaves several years ago. Suitable disposal sites are becoming difficult to find in some areas. According to some estimates, landscape waste accounts for 18 to 20 percent of all municipal solid wastes. Surveys have shown that yard waste composed 30 percent of landfill material in Alabama and 47 percent of Arizona landfill waste. Approximately 75 percent of landscape waste is comprised of grass clippings. The remaining 25 percent is fall-collected leaves. State and local restrictions on disposal of landscape wastes are developing rapidly. In 1989 there were seven, primarily East Coast states, with such restrictions in place or in the process of implementation. By 2000, nearly half of the states and many municipalities had passed legislation banning green waste from landfills and/or requiring yard waste to be recycled. Other localities are contemplating similar legislation or have established percentage goals for recycling to reduce the waste stream.

Table 14.2.

Effective mulching of leaves into turf

- Break leaves into the smallest pieces possible.
  - Greater surface area hastens microbial breakdown.
- Mow/mulch as frequently as feasible during fall leaf drop.
  - Mulching thin layers of tree leaves into turf is more efficient and effective.
- Mulching dry leaves is more efficient and effective.
- Mulching mowers are more efficient at macerating leaves.
  - Non-mulching mowers still chop and disperse leaves well enough to be practical, and can windrow leaves for easier pickup
  - Non-mulching machines vastly reduce volume.
- Fall fertilization programs for cool season turf assure no discoloration or nitrogen depletion.

Photo 14.11. Industrial trash disposal services are used by many resorts, golf courses, and other in-house managed sites to dispose of landscape debris collected by the grounds crew. Photograph courtesy of James Robbins.

Photo 14.12. Composting green waste and landscape debris is an environmentally sound method of disposal producing a product that can be used in landscape operations or sold.

Composting

Many landscape companies and municipalities have found composting to be an ecologically and profitable means of leaf and yard waste disposal. Leaf and yard trimmings are also desirable for bulking agents in municipal and animal biosolids composting operations. Quality compost is a valuable and relatively inexpensive soil amendment and mulch for landscape contractors and homeowners. The landscape market is the most popular and largest market for commercial compost producers.

From a composting point of few, leaves and other yard wastes are a special class of feedstock because of their seasonal availability (except in subtropical and tropical areas), high C:N ratio (except grass clippings), and the relatively few environmental risks they pose.

If a landscape firm or community is going to undertake composting leaves, the composting operation must be well sited and designed. Requirements for compost operations vary with state and community. Consider the adjoining residential areas, prevailing winds, topography, and drainage. Most localities require some type of permits or licenses for compost operations, and the requirements vary. Leaf and yard waste composting facilities need to be properly operated and maintained to ensure minimal impact on the surrounding environment and community, and to produce a quality product that can be used or marketed.

Composting methods. In most situations, leaves and other yard wastes are composted using minimal (passive) or low technology. More intense management reduces the time to a finished product.

Table 14.3.
Composting for landscape management contractors

PLUS

- Eliminates green waste from landfill stream.
- Provides valuable green resource as mulch and soil amendment.
- Fosters good public relations.

MINUS

- Requires space.
- Requires equipment for turning.
- Requires commitment and time.
- Can be unsightly.
- Can produce odors, especially if not monitored or done haphazardly.

Photo 14.13. Several different types of equipment are available to mechanize composted and bark mulch. These machines make mulch application quick and profitable. Photograph courtesy of James Robbins.

Minimal or passive technology composting is not usually recommended unless the company or community has a relatively large and well-buffered composting area. The time required for complete composting is longer (usually 2 to 3 years) and the potential for odor with this method is greater. Passive composting has the least operational or maintenance requirements. It is generally applicable to small operations with plenty of remote space, but little or no additional resources.

Leaves and yard waste are formed into piles no more than 12 feet high with a front-end loader. Once or twice a year the piles are turned for aeration and reformed. Since the piles are not turned frequently, anaerobic conditions will occur, resulting in odors being released when the piles are turned. Passive compost operations should be sited in remote areas with significant buffers from residential or sensitive areas. Turning piles during periods of precipitation minimizes odors and may provide the material with needed moisture. A minimum of two to three years should be anticipated to achieve proper stabilization.

The composting area should be large enough to hold up to three years of material. Allow about an acre per 2,000 cubic yards. Leaves and landscape waste must be free of contaminants. Each year's leaves should be segregated and finished

compost removed regularly so that the site remains viable and does not become a dump.

Low-Level Technology composting is the choice for most landscape firms and communities for leaf composting operations. Operation, maintenance and equipment requirements are modest. Leaves and yard waste are formed into long narrow piles (windrows) and periodically turned by a front-end loader based on temperature and time (an average of every three to four weeks). Turning, mixes and breaks up material, aerates the windrow, and releases excess moisture. Proper periodic turning insures uniform decomposition and a quality product. The time requirements to decompose the material vary, but when done effectively, this method allows leaves and yard waste to compost and be moved into curing piles in 10 to 12 months. The following year's leaves and greenwaste can be composted in the same area. The low technology approach balances time, space, and fiscal considerations, and can produce a useable, stabilized product in one year.

More intensive compost operations can be used to speed decomposition, but these methods require additional equipment and management. An *Intermediate-Level technology* composting operation uses sophisticated and expensive windrow turning machines instead of front-end loaders for aerating and turning. A windrow turning machine shreds, turns, and aerates the material, resulting in a more thorough and efficient blending and aerating than a front-end loader can achieve. Windrow turners powered by a tractor PTO are less expensive and work well.

Decomposition of the organic material is more rapid requiring turning every week or two to maintain sufficient oxygen in the windrows. Leaves can be composted in four to six months, approximately half the time of the low-level technology approach. This intermediate technology method is more appropriate for large-scale operations (4,000 tons or more), where it can be more cost effective given the greater efficiency of the windrow turning machines.

Nitrogen is sometimes added to nitrogen-poor organic materials such as leaves or wood chips to increase the rate of decomposition. Sources of nitrogen are typically animal manure or high-nitrogen fertilizers, such as urea.

Photos 14.14. and 14.15. High tech and large scale composting operations require specialized and large equipment. Photograph 14.14. Courtesy of James Robbins.

There are several different *High-Level technology* composting systems requiring less space, greater operational control, but significant capital input. These methods result in shorter composting time than other methods described earlier. Given the large capital investment in equipment and higher operation and maintenance requirements, however, this technology is appropriate only for large operations, where leaf and yard waste are used as bulking agents for sludge or manure composting.

Static Aerated Piles are a high technology approach widely used in sludge composting. In static aerated piles, or forced aeration composting, blowers aerate piles of organic material from below. Turning is only required periodically to exchange inner and outer material. This process maintains near optimal levels of oxygen and temperature to maximize the rate of decomposition. The composting process can be completed in two to four months, depending on aeration and the concentration of high nitrogen waste being composted.

Equipment and staffing needs. Most landscape firms and communities already own the basic equipment needed for low-tech composting method. A *front-end loader* is the key piece of equipment needed for low-technology leaf and yard waste composting. The front-end loader is used for forming, combining and turning windrows, as well as forming curing piles. Loaders that have buckets of at least two cubic yards with a vertical reach of 12 feet or more are most effective. The front-end loader should be available one day (or a portion thereof) per week during the collection season (mid-October to mid-

December, for leaves) for small operations, and up to five days a week for larger operations. The loader must be available to accommodate turning and pile reconstruction when needed, an average of every three to four weeks during the remainder of the year.

Water equipment (water trucks or hydrants and hoses) is required for wetting organic material and for fire fighting purposes.

A 3-foot stem *thermometer* is recommended for monitoring windrow or pile temperature, the prime indicator of active composting.

Facilities accepting tree limbs or other woody materials need a *chipper* to prepare them for composting or mulch. Woody materials break down slowly increasing the composting time. Wood chips are not recommended for composting by themselves or with leaves because of their long decomposition time, but they make a good bulking agent for composting green waste or other high nitrogen materials.

Shredders or *tub grinders* are optional, but useful equipment for leaf and yard waste composting. They reduce the size of the material before windrowing, thereby accelerating decomposition by increasing the surface area exposed to air. Shredding leaves, however, also causes greater compaction limiting oxygen within the pile and results in a need for more frequent turning. Shredding after composting creates a uniformly fine product.

Screens or *sieves* can be used in the final step of the composting production to remove any contaminants, improving compost quality Screening is also useful for blending sand or loam with finished compost, and for production of a uniform product.

A municipal or large-scale landscape composting operation (more than 4,000 tons) requires dedicated staff. Staff availability, training, and performance make the difference between a successful operation and a series of potential nuisance or environmental problems. Training helps employees understand the material and the composting process. On-site staff responsibilities include: monitoring the deposition of leaves and yard waste; wetting, forming, combining and turn-ing windrows; monitoring and record keeping; quality control; and any final processing and storage of the compost. Small operations need only part time staffing.

The compost can be used or sold as mulch or soil amendment. Shredded and screened composted material is salable to nurseries, contractors, or to the public. Some cities allowing citizens to pick up free compost have discovered it to be a good public relations effort. Sales to landscape contractors or nurseries may pay for the cost of handling and composting the green waste.

Table 14.4.
Comparison of a yard trimmings/biosolids compost
and common horticultural organic materials

	Compost	Muck soil	Reed sedge peat	Sphagnum peat	Aged poultry manure
Organic matter (%)	46	12	74	97	43
pH	7.0	7.5	5.2	4.2	—
Soluble salts (mmhos/cm)	2.23	0.64	0.31	0.07	15.10
Bulk density (lbs/cu ft)	32.2	70.2	14.3	7.0	39.3
Moisture holding capacity (%)	227	53	428	1307	166
Cation exchange capacity (me/100g)	17.3	13.6	4.0	3.1	—

Adapted from: Field Guide to Compost Use. (The Composting Council, 1996. Alexandria, VA.)

BIBLIOGRAPHY

1. Alexander R. and R. Tyler. 1992. Using compost successfully. *Lawn & Landscape Maintenance* 13(11):23.

2. Anonymous. 1991. Recycling, compost efforts gaining nationwide. *Lawn & Landscape Maintenance* 12(4):24.

3. Anonymous. 1996. *Field Guide to Compost Use.* The Composting Council, Alexandria, VA.

4. Anonymous. 1998. Woman slips on landscape debris. *Law Reporter* 41(4):140.

5. Anonymous. 2000. Leaf season. *Turf* Oct:20.

6. Anonymous, 2000. Landscaping at top of compost market charts. *Lawn & Landscape* 21(11):16.

7. Augsdorfer, B. 1994. Picking up profits for fall. *Arbor Age* 14(8):16.

8. Augsdorfer, B. 1995. Given the opportunity, "wood" you recycle? *Arbor Age* 15(11):20.

9. Barkdoll, A. and R. Nordstedt. 1994. Comparison of composting systems. In: *Composting Source Separated Organics.* JG Press, Emmaus, PA.

10. Bilderbeck, T. and M. Powell. 1996. *Using Compost in Landscape Beds and Nursery Substrates.* North Carolina Coop. Ext. Ser. Pub. AG473-14.

11. Buckingham, F. 1984. Leaves and debris: Have a blast and give'em a clean sweep. *Grounds Maintenance* 19(8):22.

12. Buckingham, F. 1985. Leaves-after they fall. *Grounds Maintenance* 20(10):18.

13. Comery, W. 1989. Leaves - from trash to cash. *Grounds Maintenance* 24(9):20.

14. Evans, J. 1992. Turning autumn leaves into cold hard cash. *Lawn & Landscape Maintenance* 13(7):32.

15. Fletcher, R. 1992. Composting landscape waste. *Journal of Arboriculture* 18(3):112.

16. Gibson, H. 1989. Leaf removal. *Grounds Maintenance* 24(9):12.

17. Gibson, H. 1991. Tree debris; alternatives for disposal. *Arbor Age* 11(11):6.

18. Gibson, H. 1992. Leaf removal strategies. *Landscape and Irrigation* 16(10):8.

19. Hall, J. 1994. *Texas Municipal Compost Marketing Manual*. Texas Natural Resource Conservation Commission, Austin, TX.

20. Hensley, D. 1996. The keys to efficient leaf cleanup. *T&O Service Tech* 1(4):15.

21. Hollyer, J. *et al.* 1996. *Recycle Organics from Wastes to Resources*. University of Hawaii College of Tropical Agriculture and Human Resources, Honolulu, HI.

22. Knoop, W. 1995. Leaves fall as problem or opportunity. *Turf & Landscape Press* 6(11):5.

23. Massachusetts Department of Environmental Protection. *Leaf Composting Guidance Document*. Division of Solid Waste Management, Boston, MA.

24. Mecklenburg, R. 1993. Compost cues. *American Nurseryman* 177(4):63.

25. Reicher, Z. and G. Hardebeck. 2000. Mulching tree leaves; an alternative to disposal. *Grounds Maintenance* 35(8):10.

26. Renkow, M., C. Safley, and J. Chaffin. 1994. Cost analysis of yard trimmings composting. In: *Composting Source Separated Organics*. JG Press, Emmaus, PA.

27. Rynk, R. *et al.* 1992. *On-farm Composting Handbook*. NRAES-54 Northeast Regional Agricultural Engineering Service, Ithaca, NY.

28. Storm, P. and M. Finstein. *Leaf Composting Manual for New Jersey Municipalities*. NJ Department of Environmental Protection, Division of Solid Waste Management, Trenton, NJ.

29. Tyler, R. 1995. Who's composting? *Lawn & Landscape Maintenance* 16(4):44.

30. Wilkinson, J. 1989. Composting yard waste. *Grounds Maintenance* 24(9):10.

31. Zahirsky, K. 1992. Landfill ban alternative-composting. *Davey Technical Journal* 9.

Chapter 15
Snow Removal

Snow removal is an important part of many landscape management and lawn service businesses, especially in the North and Northeast. Interest in removing snow as a sideline has increased from the Snow Belt to Dixie. One arborist in Honolulu, *The Tree People*, offers snow removal free to all of his clients. Clients frequently mandate snow removal as part of a full-service management program. The work extends the use of key employees and equipment and provides cash flow during the off-season. Plowing snow also keeps the company visible in the winter months. Concerns about safety and liability implications, however, provide grounds managers and contractors additional challenges.

Some companies service only their general maintenance clients, while others actively seek new business. Snow removal is a profitable part of many enterprises. Successful snow removal contractors in the US and Canada indicate gross profit margins in excess of 60 percent are normal, and gross profit margins for ice control services in excess of 70 percent are achievable. A former student told me that snow removal was the most profitable part of his very successful landscape management business. Some large sites in the Snow Belt budget several million dollars annually for snow and ice management.

However, many experienced contractors still caution that snow removal should not always be counted on as a significant portion of the company's profit base. Snow removal contracts may only pay the overhead for some, at best.

While it may seem that everyone is plowing snow, the number of companies actually doing the work is limited. Successful and profitable snow removal requires specialized equipment, a system to address the mechanics of snow removal, an effective pricing system, knowledge, and dedication to customers and from employees.

Marketing and pricing strategies

The two biggest months for marketing and pursuing snow removal contracts are July and August. Focus marketing to the firm's market niche and client base. Personal contact and direct mail seem to be the most effective marketing tactics. Some contractors report success with talk radio ads. Increasing numbers of municipal and state governments are privatizing snow removal to protect their shrinking budgets. Target new business strategically. Cluster new accounts around existing clients, reducing time between jobs.

Part of estimating and pricing is properly ascertaining what the customer is seeking. Understand his/her needs and priorities and explain the type of equipment that will be used on site. Snow services are significantly different than other exterior landscape services. Mowing or pruning can be postponed for a few days without adverse effect. However, contractors must respond immediately when it snows and remain on the job until it is completed.

Competition establishes the price environment. If the firm chooses to work outside the traditional environment, the firm must be able to distinguish itself and sell the client on the cost difference. Premier service on a timely basis reduces price resistance and develops a standard that clients will expect.

The price structure and profit should compensate for especially risky and stressful work. Snow removal operations occur in inclement weather, often at inconvenient times such as holidays or weekends, and at all times of the day and night. Work is done over extended periods involving overtime and premium pay. The work is stressful due to fatigue, unrealistic expectations, clients' demands, and working conditions. Wet, heavy snow and bitterly cold weather are additional burdens that are hard on equipment, vehicles, and people. Chances for accidents due to weather and weariness increase many-fold.

Quoting prices, especially for large sites, requires good knowledge of production rates for equipment and personnel, including subcontractors, and the type of snowfalls that might occur. There are several alternatives for pricing and bidding snow removal services, but all are complicated by nature. Contractors charge per hour, per plowing, per inch of snow, per incident, or per season as part of a larger contract. A mixture of these types is desirable as the contractor can take advantage of the best of all worlds. He/She makes money during mild or snowy seasons. Salting and clearing sidewalks are usually established as separate additional charges regardless of the price for snow plowing.

Per hour charges (time and materials) are effective if special equipment such as front-end loaders or power brooms are required. Per hour pricing is the easiest, but the profit margins are usually lower because of the tendency to compete directly with the competitors' prices by the hour. Establish rates for each class of vehicle or piece of equipment, including driver or operator. Contractors sometimes negotiate slightly lower hourly rates if clients agree to pay minimums. Make sure

to determine if the hourly rates are charged from portal to portal or for on-the-job-site times only.

Plowing snow *on a per inch basis* is usually, but not always, reserved for very large accounts in areas of the country where snowfall totals can vary from zero to 60 or more inches per year. Universities, airports, and very large industrial or shopping centers are examples of where per inch contracts are normally used. Contractors charging by the inch normally establish brackets and charge for each snow occurrence based upon the total accumulation during any one incident.

Common brackets are zero to three inches, three to six inches, and in excess of six inches. Some establish maximum allowable accumulation for the season and either add a surcharge or invoice at a predetermined rate when accumulations exceed this maximum. Salting or hauling operations are typically not included in a per-inch price.

Per-push charges are a pre-determined amount per plowing. Per plowing contracts are often the most profitable with good equipment and expertise. Each time the contractor appears on site, there is a separate charge. For small storms, the operator will wait until the snowfall is finished. For larger storms, there will probably be more than one plowing operation necessary to clean the site.

Per season pricing contracts are frequently tied into other landscape management services. Condominium and homeowner associations prefer a guaranteed price for the season. However, they are reluctant to grant multi-year contracts and expect the contractor to assume the bulk of the risk. This type of contract is easy for the client to budget but the unpredictability of nature makes it risky for the contractor. For instance, three to five, greater than two-inch depth snows occur annually in the Kansas City area. If the contractor plans and bids for five such snows and there are only two, then he/she has made relatively easy money. However, what if there are eight such snows and three are over a foot in depth? The contractor may well lose money on the endeavor.

Request a multi-year contract with a liquidated damages clause for early cancellation, ex-

Photo 15.1. Determine where snow will be piled before the storm, and have a clear understanding with the client about removal procedures. Too often, snow is piled on planting beds, crushing the plants below.

cept for non-performance. This will average out mild and heavier years. If only a single year contract is available establish a surcharge for total accumulations exceeding an average year.

Regardless of the pricing method, the condition of the site and obstacles must be considered. Ideally two people should estimate the same site and compare notes to insure accuracy.

Adjustments to normal hourly charges for labor and equipment are in order when removing snow. Maintenance and fuel costs of trucks, tractors, and other vehicles are greater during snow removal. Vehicles are operated for long periods in lower gear ranges. Trucks used for extensive winter operations frequently require heavier front axles and sometimes double batteries. Consider the cost and maintenance of blades and other equipment specific for winter use. Two-way radios are a necessity for efficiency and safety.

Most employees removing snow require premium pay. A number of contractors pay premium shifts for pre-6:00 a.m. and post-6:00 p.m., or for weekend snow removal.

Good records determine actual cost per unit or per hour. Records of the time required to service each client during certain conditions enable the manager to prepare an accurate bid for next year's contract. Similar records of mileage, fuel, and maintenance costs will provide a true picture of operating costs.

Retainers

Some clients prefer to engage the contractor on a non-refundable retainer or minimum billing. A *retainer* guarantees the client exclusive use of certain pieces of equipment on his/her property until the snow is cleared. Customers are billed against retainage for services provided. In most situations the customer is invoiced for additional service at an agreed upon rate when the retainage is exceeded because of above average snowfalls. Shopping malls frequently place contractors on retainer to ensure the parking lots are cleared. Equipment is sometimes parked on-site so it can be rapidly mobilized.

It is essential not to sell 100 percent of the firm's capability. Good management dictates a reserve of employees and equipment to cover breakdowns, absenteeism, illness, and unforeseen difficulties. Most contractors try to schedule at around 80 percent of their capacity.

Contracts

Expectations and needs of clients differ. Some clients anticipate that the contractor will be there to catch each snowflake as it falls. Determine the site's requirements *with* the client. Develop a very clear understanding and include everything discussed in the final contract.

Specify the terms of the contract and beginning and ending dates for service. Address the specific responsibilities of each party and other pertinent issues. Establish where and when salt or sand will be used and moving and removal of snow if accumulations are large. Will the contractor be responsible for removing sand or grit from the parking area after the snow season? Establish property boundaries, priority expectations, and starting times.

Make sure the schedule of payment is suitable to both parties. Are minimums or retainers required? Establish insurance and limits on liability. The conditions for termination and liquidated damages available to the contractor upon cancellation without cause should be established and clear to the customer.

Make sure that the list of contacts is in proper sequence and that the home and cell phone numbers are included.

What determines a snowfall and when plowing will begin? A usual contractual starting point is one-inch of snow on the ground with more falling. Some clients are not concerned with snows less than two inches in depth. Several contractors break down fees according to the depth of snow, such as one to two inches, two to four inches, four to six inches, and over six inches. Each is billed accordingly.

Determine where the snow will be piled or whether it will be removed from the site. Is space available to pile snow until it melts? Long-term snow piles in parking lots eliminate parking spaces and are unsightly. Melting snow running across traffic areas may re-freeze at night, creating hazardous walking and driving conditions. This may increase the client's and the contractor's liability. Removing snow from the site adds labor and equipment costs if peripheral areas or road ditches are unavailable. A plan for removal, if required, and a place to dump the snow are prerequisites.

Avoid gravel parking lots unless the additional time necessary to plow them correctly can be recovered. Include a disclaimer in contracts for gravel lots allowing an additional charge for redistribution in the spring or making it the client's responsibility.

As with any contract, the specifics must be agreed upon and written so both parties understand and remember them. Communication with the client includes explaining the time and equipment necessary for the services, before an agreement is signed. Try to list the necessary equipment. Customers better appreciate the cost of services when they fully understand what is involved.

Other facets to address in the contract are removal of ice and snow from walks, sanding and salting streets, and snow removal from or protection of trees and shrubs. Who determines how frequently salt or deicer is applied? Is the property automatically salted? Clarify the difference in results, activity, and cost of different deicers. Verify the client's preference of deicers. Also note any costs for extra equipment like front-end loaders and dump trucks. Include a disclaimer holding the firm harmless for injuries on the property. *"The client agrees to hold the firm harmless for any and all liability due to slips and falls on the contracted property."*

Establish a reasonable payment schedule. A few companies require an initial payment as a start-up fee or Autumn Retainer. This provides cash flow in late fall.

Insurance

The contracting firm is liable for much or all of the damage to the site and plants due to removal operations. Advise the company's insurance carrier of snow removal operations. Snow removal contractors and operators should have two main types of insurance – automobile or vehicle liability and general liability.

Commercial vehicle liability insurance protects the truck or vehicle. Insuring equipment can be complicated. If an item, such as a snow blade, is scheduled on the vehicle policy then it is covered only when it is physically attached to the truck. Removable equipment should be insured on the contractor's equipment schedule to protect it during the summer.

General liability insurance includes two parts: premises and operations, and completed operations coverage. The premises and operations portion protects *"you doing what you do, when you are doing it."* If a contactor is cleaning a walk and someone is injured or flying debris or ice damages property, the injuries or damages are covered under this type of policy. They would not be under typical automobile or vehicle insurance. Com-

Photo 15.2. The most common snow blade is designed so that snow rolls off of the blade and away from the line of motion.

pleted operations coverage protects the contractor once the job is finished and the crew has left the site. The contractor would be covered if someone slipped and fell after the job has been properly competed.

Carry a minimum of $1 million liability insurance and more in high traffic areas. Discuss limitations of the firm's liability with the client and include these in the contract. Encourage employees to report damage immediately, regardless of the cause.

Consider the additional liabilities created by snow removal. Snowplowing is typically accomplished during the worst possible weather in the middle of the night. It is conducted by employees who may have worked all day or by sub-contractors over whom there is little control.

Hiring *sub-contractors* to plow means relinquishing a degree of control. Subcontractors may be included under the firm's insurance coverage with a proportional increase in premiums. A better plan is to require sub-contractors to carry sufficient liability coverage. This protects the firm. Keep a current certificate of insurance of all sub-contractors on file. Some snow removal contractors require subcontractors to list them as an additional insured on at least the subcontractor's general liability policy. This requires the insurance company to notify the contractor should the insurance become expired or if it is cancelled. Also, make sure the subcontractors pay worker's compensation insurance; otherwise you may be required to pay the premiums for his/her employees.

Equipment

Most firms adapt summer vehicles, commonly trucks, tractors, skip loaders, and front-end loaders, for winter use to avoid additional equipment costs and to stretch their investment. Some contractors prefer two-wheel drive trucks. Others prefer four-wheel drive vehicles. Load the bed with at least 500 pounds of ballast to increase traction. Be sure a set of chains is available for four-by-two trucks. Four-wheel drive vehicles are frequently recommended and useful for problem areas, such as ramps or steep drives. They seldom require chains.

When purchasing a general-duty truck that will also see snow duty, consider opting for an automatic transmission cooler or heavy-duty clutch. Heavy-duty front suspensions are recommended for improved plowing and dry-road handling. For winter starting and night work, use a heavy-duty battery and alternator; some trucks are equipped with double batteries for plowing. For high-speed, straight-line plowing, choose a long wheelbase. Shorter wheelbases, however, aid maneuverability. Select all-season radial or bias-ply tires.

Two-way radios serve as communication between the operators and the base. The driver can report problems, breakdowns, or anything else that impedes progress. The manager can monitor progress and redirect crews as necessary. A full-time dispatcher ensures special requests are addressed in a timely fashion and can direct crews to call-in business.

Many types, styles, and brands of blades are available. The most efficient snow blade is curved so the snow continually rolls over the blade surface instead of being pushed into a large pile ahead of the blade. High-density polyethylene liners for snow blades save fuel, according to their manufacturers. Coat snow blades with light oil during the summer and between snows to prevent rust. Lights and hydraulics are also needed. Purchase the toughest, most durable equipment and accessories possible.

Snow blowers are expensive but offer advantages. They disperse snow over a greater distance or onto grassed areas. Blowers, blades, and power broom attachments are available for many utility vehicles, lawn and garden tractors, small tractors, skip loaders, and mowers. Adapting existing equipment saves capital and provides greater return on investment. Plastic or plastic-and-canvas cabs or enclosures protect operators from the cold and blowing snow. They can be installed on small riding and walk-behind units.

Keep snow blower chutes well oiled to permit easier rotation and prevent water from freezing in the joints. Special paints or sprays, if desired, can improve snow flow. Farm supply stores stock extra-slick paint used by farmers to improve the flow of wet grain from wagon boxes. These paints may improve performance of older snow removal equipment.

Comparison shop before investing in specialized snow removal equipment and make sure the equipment fits the needs. Match equipment to the

Photo 15.3/15.4. Power brushes or brooms efficiently remove light or dry snow from walks or drives. Equipment photograph courtesy of Ariens® Company.

area; don't send a six-foot blade to clear a four-foot walk or twenty four-foot street.

There is incredible variety of snow blowers, snow throwers, and other equipment available. Power brooms, for instance, do a nice job removing light or dry snows from walks and enclosed areas. They can be adapted to summer cleaning operations. Power brooms have trouble, however, removing heavy or packed snows; students on college campuses refer to them as ice polishers. Think safety. Avoid the temptation to remove safety equipment and deadman controls.

Sand and deicer spreaders add to the scope of services a contractor can deliver. Units that mount in a pickup bed make salting and sanding of private streets and parking lots realistically efficient for the smaller operator. Spreaders are especially useful in regions that receive ice with/or instead of snow.

Subcontractors

Many landscape contractors involved in snow removal rely heavily on subcontractors. The amount of equipment that must be put on the street at one time to meet a growing demand may exceed availability. The proliferation of 4-wheel drive vehicles and other smaller contractors with a few pieces of equipment make this a viable source of help to a growing company.

One contractor told me that he relies almost entirely on subcontractors for snow removal in the Midwest. Some pay a bonus to subcontrac-

Photo 15.5. Snow blowers are versatile tools moving large amount of heavy or wet snow in a short time. Snow blowers are available in various sizes, from units handling walks to streets, to meet the needs of any operation. Photograph courtesy of Ariens® Company.

tors for recommending new plowers to the firm. Subcontractors are personally accountable for their equipment and have a strong motivation to produce. Check referrals and references for prospective contractors. Be sure they are reliable, and have the proper licenses and insurance before engaging them. Training for subcontractors is as important as for regular employees.

Pay rates for subcontractors differ with contractors. Typically, the driver is paid by the hour for his/her time and equipment. Hourly rates usually increase with previous experience and the number of years the driver has worked for the company. The type of equipment furnished is also paid at different rates depending on efficiency and size. Verify equipment. Require subcontractors to have a cellular phone during each call out.

Scheduling

Preparation for snow removal must begin in advance of the first predicted snowfall. Equipment should be tuned and winterized. Check batteries and replace if necessary; be sure to have gasoline antifreeze available.

Snow stakes are seldom seen in the Midwest and Midsouth but are part of the winter landscape in the Snow Belt. Snow stakes mark boundaries and objects that could damage equipment or impede the operation, such as fire hydrants, planting beds, irrigation heads, and curbs. They may be worth considering for some removal operations, especially on first-time sites.

Determine in advance which employees will handle which accounts. Assigning a worker to handle the same account year after year increases efficiency and reduces callbacks.

Schedule a dry run on a rainy day before the snow season. A practice run allows employees and subcontractors to become familiar with the sites and routes and to iron out problems. Develop maps of each property showing the section to be plowed first, locations for piling snow, obstacles, breaks in the pavement, manhole covers, curbs, and other points of caution.

Indicate areas that are to be shoveled and which will be plowed. Include any special instructions from the client or supervisor. Keep copies in the vehicles and on file in the office. Should an operator be delayed or become ill, another crewmember can take his/her place with enough information about the site to avoid unnecessary trouble.

When a snowfall is expected, listen to the late weather report and check local conditions periodically during the night. This unenviable duty can be shared among the supervisors and managers and may require more than one night owl if contracts are spread over a wide area. An awareness of the actual conditions means that crews and equipment can be dispatched accordingly.

Because of engine starting problems in cold weather, keep snow equipment inside heated buildings, if possible. Some equipment representatives caution that moving snow with warm equipment causes some of the snow to melt and freeze on the surface. This increases plugging of blowers and pileup on blades. A compromise is to keep equipment inside for easier starting but allow the machines to cool outdoors several minutes before clearing snow. Metal surfaces cool rapidly and the melting/freezing problem is eliminated.

Understand the client's needs and priorities. Factories will need to be plowed before 8:00 a.m. Retail store lots have to be cleared before 9:00 a.m. Apartment and residential plowing usually remains more flexible. After clearing lots before cars are parked, parking lot aisles may need to be pushed several times during the business day. The lot is often replowed after it empties. Areas with weekend or infrequent use, such as churches, may be plowed last. Obviously, areas such as fire lanes must be identified and kept open. Try to diversify the size and type of accounts serviced, according to starting times of the client.

Many snow removal contractors indicate that efficiency increases when snow can be removed at night. From 7:00 pm to 6:00 am there are fewer interruptions, less traffic problems, and reduced chances of personnel and equipment damage according to proponents. An early start on night-time snow removal also increases customer satisfaction. The night work is hard on crews, however, especially hand removal workers. Fatigue is a problem for drivers and shovelers. Visibility is often reduced dramatically and breakdowns can also be harder to deal with in the wee hours.

Many contractors prefer to remove snow several times during heavy storms, instead of waiting for the storm to abate. Smaller amounts are easier to remove and the workload is spread over a longer period. Piling snow on the windward side of parking lots or use area increases later drifting and multiplies removal efforts and costs.

Back-up crews are essential. They provide efficiency and maintain job quality. It is also a good idea to have a mechanic on-call or available. He/she can make on-site repairs and serve as a back-up driver, if necessary. Several contractors keep relief drivers on-call; however, remember to include the cost of this on-call person when calculating overhead.

Table 15.1.
Reducing the risk of frostbite or exposure

Frostbite can occur whenever the temperature is below 32° F, but is more likely during strong winds, at higher elevations, and when the skin is wet. Even the less serious early stages of frostbite are extremely painful. Simply rewarming the affected areas can prevent true frostbite. Contact medical help if exposure has been prolonged or severe.

Other factors contributing to chances of low temperature injuries or actual frostbite include:
- Consumption of drugs or alcohol lower body temperature and impact decision-making.
- Exposed skin or wet clothing drastically increases risk.
- Fever can result in below-normal oxygenation of arterial blood.
- Previous injury from exposure to cold increases risk.
- Overexertion drains calories and heat.
- Tight clothing, even tight footwear or gloves can diminish the flow of blood.
- Blood-vessel diseases can diminish blood flow.
- Fatigue and dehydration diminish the body's protection against cold.
- Neuromuscular diseases and injuries resulting in sensory loss reduce ability to recognize extreme cold.
- Psychosis can diminish ability to take protective measures against the cold.

Deicing Materials

Using a deicer product lowers the freezing point of water thus facilitating removal of snow and ice and reducing re-freezing. Use of deicers is increasing as customers demand higher levels of service and clean surfaces at all times. Deicing products are tools, not panaceas. They can make the job easier and less costly to achieve the desired results when the right project is used correctly. They can also cause damage and be ineffective and expensive when not used correctly.

Typically the choice of product is made on price. There are, however, several other questions that the user needs to consider:

- Where will the material be used?

- What is the application rate required to be effective?

- What is the impact on surrounding plants?

- What is the impact on concrete?

- Are there any hazards to users or pets?

- What about tracking of the material indoors?

- Will it be used frequently or only a few times during the season?

- What is the temperature at the time of application?

- Is it readily available?

Table 15.2.
Price comparison of some de-icing materials

The following are per bag pallet prices (FOB Baltimore and New Jersey) from a large mid-Atlantic wholesale distributor of ice melting materials to the professional industry. Additional discounts were available for truckload orders.

Material	Per 50 pound bag (pallet price)
Rock salt	$3.95
Calcium chloride	$12.90
Blended product	$7.95
(sodium, calcium and magnesium chlorides)	

The most common material used to thaw ice on walks and roadways is *rock salt* (sodium chloride [NaCl]), alone, or mixed with sand or cinders. Salt has been used as a road deicer since the 1940s and remains a very effective tool. Unfortunately, it damages some surfaces and plants. At 30°F (pavement temperature) one pound of salt will melt more than 40 pounds of ice. At 20°F, however, the same one-pound of salt melts only about eight pounds of ice. Salt can still be effective at lower temperatures, but significantly higher rates are required to accomplish the same effect. Salt will continue to melt ice down to about –5°F. Continued use of salt over a long period can contaminate ground water and destroy the structure of the soil.

Calcium chloride and other non-sodium based deicing chemicals are preferable but more expensive. Because of their price, non-sodium deicers are often blended with rock salt to increase low temperature effectiveness at a more reasonable price. Calcium chloride and *magnesium chloride*

Photo 15.6. Sand and salt spreaders expand the winter services that a landscape management firm may offer. Spreaders are essential if the contract calls for caring for streets or large parking lots. Smaller spreaders are adaptable to pickups.

melt ice faster than rock salt and are effective at much lower temperatures. Early application of these deicing materials at warmer temperatures allows efficient removal of snow during clean up. Calcium and magnesium chlorides are less damaging to plants, but there are no deicers that are totally safe for plants.

Table 15.3.
Characteristics of some deicing materials used in landscape management

Deicing material	Damage to concrete	Effect on plants	Effect on metals	Relative cost	Approximate lowest practical temperature (°F)[1]	Comments
Ammonium nitrate	Moderate	Slight to moderate	Slight	Moderate	~ 20 to 25	Fertilizer material, seldom used as deicer.
Calcium chloride	Slight	Some	Corrosive	Moderate	-25	Often used in blended products.
Calcium magnesium acetate	None	None	Non corrosive	Very high	20	Very expensive, used at airports and where corrosion is critical.
Magnesium chloride	Slight	Slight	Corrosive	Moderate	5	Often used in blended products.
Potassium chloride	None to slight	Slight	None to slight	Moderate	~ 20 to 25	Mutate of potash fertilizer.
Sodium chloride	Moderate	Damaging	Corrosive	Low	20	Most common and least expensive material.
Urea	None	Slight	Slight	Moderate	~ 20 to 25	Fertilizer material, used primarily at airports.

[1]Minimum effective temperatures for most materials depend on concentration.

Pre-wetting rock salt with liquid chemicals is becoming a popular practice. Salt must first be dissolved into brine before it can melt ice. Pre-wetting gives salt a jump and wetted salt is less likely to bounce off a pavement service. A range of liquid materials, including dissolved salt, calcium or magnesium chloride, and blended materials are used at a rate of eight to 10 gallons per ton of rock salt. Salt piles are wetted and mixed with front-end loaders before loading and spreading. Pre-wetting salt as it is applied is the most effective method, but requires specialized tanks and spray equipment on the spreader trucks.

Calcium magnesium acetate (CMA) is a specialized deicer material identified by the Federal Highway Administration in the 1970s as the only effective deicer to meet a standard of low corrosion and environmental safety. It is no more corrosive than tap water and is biodegradable. CMA is effective to 20°F and is used at the same rates as rock salt. If CMA is applied to road surfaces early in a storm, it reduces snow packing and bonding of ice to the pavement. The downside for CMA is economics. It is about 30 times more expensive than rock salt. CMA is finding a market for critical areas where corrosion from salt or other deicers cannot be tolerated.

Ethylene glycol is an expensive, non-corrosive liquid deicer commonly mixed with liquid urea and used primarily at airports. *Potassium acetate* is a biodegradable liquid deicer effective in cold temperatures. It is usually mixed with a corrosion inhibitor and used primarily around airports. Corrosion-inhibiting additives are also available for liquid calcium and magnesium chlorides.

Urea is used for deicing at airports because it is non-corrosive to metals. Urea and other fertilizer materials (such as ammonium nitrate) are not effective at temperatures below 20°F. Urea, alone or mixed with sand, is sometimes used on sidewalks and can substitute for salt around plants. Greater amounts of urea are required to obtain melting equal to sodium or calcium chlorides. Excessive amounts of urea or other fertilizers will damage plants and turfgrass.

Abrasives

Mixing deicing agents with abrasives such as sand, cinders, or ash, increases their effectiveness. Tests have shown that 50 to 100 pounds of salt per cubic yard of sand is normally effective. The mixture reduces the amount of salt or melting material needed and adds the grittiness of the abrasive for traction and increased melting. When pavements reach temperatures at which salt is no longer effective, abrasives can help to deal with slippery conditions. Abrasives do not melt ice and eventually plowing and chemical applications will be required for final snow removal.

Apply deicing materials carefully. Do not use them to melt snow. Spread the mixture of abrasive and deicer after plowing or shoveling, and after the threat of more snow is past.

Anti-icing materials

Anti-icing materials are applied before a storm to prevent ice from forming. It is a relatively new technique being used in areas where a higher level of service is desired. Anti-icing materials are applied as a liquid in the range of 25 to 50 gallons per lane-mile. The small amount of chemical residue remains in place for several hours or even days. When the storm arrives, the chemical prevents the initial bonding of the snow or ice with the pavement. When properly applied, anti-icing keeps snow in a softer slush-like state, making it easier to drive through or remove for a longer period. The up-front cost for anti-icing equipment and material has prevented wider adaptation.

Salt damage to plants

Damage to plants occurs from splashing or drift of salt spray from traffic, or from contamination of the soil. Salt spray results in death of buds and twigs of deciduous plants and browning of needles of evergreens. Excessive salt in the soil acts more slowly, and damage may not show up for several years. Symptoms include an initial bluish-green cast to the foliage, marginal burn of leaves or needles, and reduction of growth and vigor. Symptoms are more evident in late summer or during drought stress. They can be confused with symptoms resulting from damage due to insects, diseases, nutrient imbalance, or chemical misapplication.

Salt injury to plants increases with the amount of vehicle traffic, the amount and number of salt applications, proximity to the roadway or application area, speed of the traffic, location of plants downwind or in drainage patterns away from the source, and with plant species.

Photo 15.7. Planting beds too often serve as snow storage areas. Serious injury can result if the snow is laden with salt or from the weight of the snow. Salt can build up in the soil over several years without proper management.

Injury can be avoided or reduced by using non-salt deicing materials. Apply deicers only when needed and at label rates. Do not pile or store snow on plant beds or turf. Anti-desiccants and anti-tranpirants have been recommended for protecting foliage and reducing drying of plant tissue. These materials have been shown to be ineffective, however, and in some cases resulted in increased plant damage. Plants or trees that are subject to injury can be protected from salt injury with barriers of plastic or burlap. Avoid planting in high salt drift zones along highways and use resistant plants in problem areas.

Soil additives, such as organic matter, activated charcoal, and gypsum, have been used to improve the structure of soils damaged by salt application. Incorporation is necessary for organic material and activated charcoal, and greatly improves the effectiveness of gypsum.

Municipal snow removal

Removing snow from the streets of large cities or small towns requires even more planning and preparation than contract plowing. A snow response plan must be developed to accommodate emergency services, citizen needs and expectations, equipment, personnel, budget, and contract services available. Every citizen or user will judge the plan, the services, and the personnel during each and every snowfall. Failure to remove snow expeditiously has cost many politicos and department directors their jobs.

An individual must make the decision to mobilize the troops. Responsibility for work in different areas is assigned long before the storm. Equipment must be serviced and ready to respond, and an adequate number of blades, spreaders, and other equipment must be ready to go. Many cities adapt non-traditional vehicles, such as trash trucks, to winter storm use by having blades available. Road graders and front-end loaders are also effective snow fighters.

Sand or other girt and deicers supplies have to be ready and adequate. This is not a time for as-needed ordering. Many cities and towns are woefully under equipped and unprepared to remove any snow that does not melt in 24-hours.

Employees are to be trained and ready to respond upon notification. Some organizations require employees to carry pagers for alert. Each employee and supervisor must know what he/she is expected to do. Communication during the storm via radio or cell phone is essential to respond to emergencies and changing situations. Remember, mechanics are as important as drivers.

Establish priorities for removal. Major roads and streets and emergency services (hospitals, fire stations, police stations, and emergency medical services) are first response sites. Lives are at stake if they cannot be cleared and kept clear.

Secondary streets and residential areas are usually secondary response. Typical first attack in secondary areas is to plow a single lane down

Photo 15.8. Landscape managers are sometimes called upon to deal with things other than plants, such as removing the snow from this roof.

the center of each side street so emergency services vehicles can get through. Residents and businesses must usually assume responsibility for their drives, walks and parking lots. Deep snows may necessitate loading and hauling snow from downtown areas and narrow streets. Parks, stadium lots, and other nonessential areas are typically the third or last priority.

Snow removal in large cities, small towns, or in-house operations requires planning, communication, and teamwork.

Bibliography

1. Allin, J. 1999. A snow operation system. *Lawn & Landscape* 20(9):S1.

2. Allin, J. 1999. Snow-response plans. Are they important? *Ice & Snow Manager* 2(3):14.

3. Allin, J. 1999. Soliciting new business. *Ice & Snow Manager* 2(4):12.

4. Allin, J. 2000. Pricing snow plowing services for maximum profits. *Tree Care Industry* 11(9):24.

5. Allin, J. 2000. Productivity in sidewalk snow-removal operations. *Tree Care Industry* 11(11):58.

6. Allin, J. 2000. The quest for growth in the snowplowing industry. *Tree Care Industry* 11(12):38.

7. Anonymous. 1979. Snow removal. *Landscape Contractor* 20(11):17.

8. Anonymous. 1980. Calcium chloride controls dust, melts ice. *Grounds Maintenance* 15(9):54.

9. Anonymous. 1983. Snow removal: is it for you? *Landscape Contractor* 24(11):8.

10. Anonymous. 1986. Is snow removal a necessary service for landscape contractors? *Landscape Contractor* 27(1):40.

11. Anonymous. 1991. Deicing agents can reduce time, effort of snow removal. *Landscape Contractor* 32(9):16.

12. Anonymous. 1991. Good contracts a requirement for snow removal. *Landscape Contractor* 32(12):14.

13. Anonymous. 1992. Chemical deicer comparison chart. *Landscape Contractor* 33(1):42.

14. Anonymous. 1999. Smart snowplow selection. *Lawn & Landscape* 20(9):S14.

15. Anonymous. 1999. Jack Frost's nip can be serious. *Ice & Snow Manager* 2(4):22.

16. Anonymous. 1999. *Chemical Deicers and Their Effect on Vegetation.* Dow Chemical Co., Midland, MI.

17. Anonymous. 2000. *Conservative Use of Chemical Deicers Saves Plants and Concrete.* Dow Chemical Co., Midland, MI.

18. Bartlley, J. 1999. Nighttime snow removal: good news and bad news. *Ice & Snow Manager* 2(4):7.

19. Buckingham, F. 1983. Streamlining snow removal. *Grounds Maintenance* 18(10):10.

20. Buckingham, F. 1986. Plan now for a better snow-removal season. *Grounds Maintenance* 21(7):48.

21. Davis, B. 1994. There's no business like snow business. *Landscape Contractor* 35(9):10.

22. Dyer, A. 1999. Snow service specifics. *Lawn & Landscape* 20(9):S8.

23. Dyer, A. 1999. Policy protocol. *Lawn & Landscape* 20(9):S27.

24. Dirr, M. and J. Biedermann. 1980. Amelioration of salt damage to cotoneaster by gypsum. *Journal of Arboriculture* 6(4):108.

25. Evans, J.A. 1991. The cold war. *Lawn and Landscape Maintenance* 12(10):42.

26. Fitzgerald, J. and D. Janssen. 1992. *Winter Deicing Agents for the Homeowner*. Univ. of Nebraska Coop. Ext. Serv. Nebguide G92-1121-A.

27. Gibson, H. 1989. Tactics for snow removal. *Grounds Maintenance* 24(11):10.

28. Gibson, H. 1990. Deicing agents. *Grounds Maintenance* 25(11):42.

29. Greenstein, S. 1990. Snow removal: Proper planning can lead to a successful venture. *Landscape Contractor* 31(9):12.

30. Hall, R. 1993. Snow removal. *Landscape Management* 32(8):8.

31. Hasselkus, E. and R. Rideout. 1979. *Salt Injury to Plants*. Univ. of Wisconsin Coop. Ext. Ser. Bul. A2970.

32. Hayhurst, H. 1993. Marketing your snow removal services. *Landscape Contractor* 34(9):10.

33. Hayhurst, H. 1993. Contracting snow removal. *Landscape Contractor* 34(9):15.

34. Henretty, D. 1993. Snow removal: Making your winter more profitable. *Landscape Contractor* 34(9):22.

35. Hensley, D. 1982. Snow removal contracts. *Kansas Nursery Notes* (3):9.

36. Heydorn, A. 1999. Advise customers on the right deicer. *Snow Pro* 12(1):S7.

37. Ingham, D. and N. Sappington. 1995. Snow removal made easy. *Landscape & Irrigation* 19(12):18.

38. Keep, D. 1998. How to use liquid anti-icers. *Lawn & Landscape* 19(9):4.

39. Keep, D. 1999. Detouring deicing dilemmas. *Lawn & Landscape* 20(9):S22.

40. King, J. 1989. Snow removal requires professionalism and the right equipment. *Landscape Contractor* 30(12):8.

41. Kujawa, R. 2000. Bidding effectively. *Ice & Snow Manager* 3(3):7.

42. Leatzow, J. 1983. Insurance for snow removal contracting. *Landscape Contractor* 24(11):13.

43. Levin, T. 1999. Chicago department of streets and sanitation. *Ice & Snow Manager* 2(3):22.

44. McIver, T. 1999. Success with subcontractors. *Landscape Management* 38(9):SR3.

45. Nilsson, P. 1999. Snow removal-finding the best work. *Snow Pro* 12(1):S3.

46. Smith, S. 2000. Ice IQ: Ice control strategies. *Landscape Management* 39(11):64.

47. Steele, B. 1992. To plow or not to plow. *Landscape Contractor* 32(9):12.

48. Steele, B. 1992. Avoid plowing pitfalls with sufficient insurance. *Landscape Contractor* 32(9):12.

49. Walker, D. 2000. Snow removal challenges and solutions. *Ice & Snow Manager* 3(3):14.

50. Stevens, R.H. 1993. New snow removal technology. *Landscape Contractor* 34(9):17.

51. Wandtke, E. 1992. To plow or not to plow. *Landscape Management* 31(210):38.

52. Wenzel, C. 1979. How to turn snowflakes into cold cash. *Landscape Contractor* 20(10:)6.

Index